PRACTICAL GUNSMITHING

EDWARD A. MATUNAS

SEDGEWOOD® PRESS, New York

Published by OUTDOOR LIFE BOOKS

Published by
Popular Science Books
Sedgewood® Press
750 Third Avenue
New York, New York 10017

Distributed by Meredith Corporation, Des Moines, Iowa.

Designed by Jeff Fitschen

Library of Congress Cataloging-in-Publication Data

Matunas, Edward.
  Practical gunsmithing / Edward A. Matunas.
    p. cm.
  Includes index.
  ISBN 1-55654-048-5
  1. Gunsmithing. I. Title.
TS535.M348 1989
683.4—dc19   88-34331
                         CIP

Manufactured in the United States of America

10 9 8 7 6 5 4 3

Contents

Introduction

Cars are tuned by master craftsmen, but they are also tuned by average owners. Part of the enjoyment of a car can be knowing that you, the owner, made it run its very best, having improved acceleration, smoothness, even fuel economy. And so it is with gunsmithing.

You can have your favorite rifle repaired or tuned by the very finest artisan. Indeed, as with auto repairs, there are gunsmithing jobs that should never be attempted by the average owner. But, there are also many repair and maintenance jobs that can be completed in a limited home workshop. Doing these can provide a great deal of pleasure.

It's a source of pride to know it was your work that transformed your rifle's accuracy from mediocre to near minute-of-angle accuracy. And you can save considerable money when you add some custom feature or make some needed repair with your own labor. These savings can be converted into more ammunition, firearms, or accessories, which are always worthwhile goals.

Not everyone should attempt even minor gunsmithing, but if you have patience, a steady hand, good eyesight, and a bit of mechanical ability, you can accomplish a great deal of home gunsmithing. It is hoped that this volume will help you accomplish those tasks while avoiding the disappointments or damage that accompany many well-meaning, but uninformed attempts at gunsmithing.

Gun maintenance or repair always requires top-grade precision tools as well as the needed parts. Since these are not always readily available, an Appendix lists the sources of a great many tools and parts discussed in the text. If you need an item not available, contact the sources shown. Patience in this area will help insure that the job goes smoothly and without disappointment.

By the very nature of the topic, no gunsmithing book can be truly complete. The best gunsmiths, even after 50 or more years at their trade, will admit they are still learning. However, it is hoped that this effort will enhance each reader's knowledge and make a number of specific jobs go easily.

ACKNOWLEDGMENTS

A book of this kind demands a great deal of assistance from a large number of people and companies—far too many to mention. The author acknowledges such help and thanks all for their valuable assistance.

Very special thanks for extensive assistance go to Dick Dietz of Remington Arms, to John Realmuto for his guidance in my earliest attempts at gun repair, and to those countless persons who brought me their cherished firearms for repair, alteration, or customizing during my 12 years of commercial gunsmithing. It was that experience which laid the foundation for this work.

PART 1

AN APPROACH TO GUNSMITHING IN THE HOME WORKSHOP

1

Does That Firearm Need Work?

Needless repair can do more harm than good. Too many firearms are reduced in value by well-meaning gun owners who were unable to determine that their guns really did not need the extensive work undertaken.

For example, Joe Huntzmuch takes a spill and his .30-30 carbine lands among some less than smooth forest-floor debris. He finds a few minor scratches on the blued surface and several similar marks on the buttstock, plus one rather serious dent. Instead of judiciously touching up the metal with a bluing pencil and applying a steam pad to the stock dent followed by an overall application of stock polish, Joe disassembles the rifle and sands down the metal and wood. Heavy doses of cold blue and stock finish leave it looking like a rifle that has been so battered as to require complete refinishing. The value of Joe's carbine is now about half what it was worth before all of his attention. There's wisdom in the old advice that if it works, don't fix it.

Another example of misdirected effort is Eddie Goodshot's discovery that his rifle is not smartly ejecting fired cases. This "problem" is common when a bolt is worked too slowly—which is what Eddie had done at the range when

he discovered his "trouble." Unaware that nothing needs fixing, he grinds, files, and polishes the extractor and ejector until they are so altered that they truly refuse to work and must be replaced. What Eddie needs isn't gunsmithing but firearms-manipulation instruction.

A similar situation occurs when the owner of a pump shotgun manipulates the action timidly instead of pumping it fully and vigorously—the gun fails to kick out fired cases. The gun isn't malfunctioning—the shooter is. Another example is a semiautomatic rifle that fails to feed smoothly when the bolt is eased forward on the first round from the magazine. Chances are, nothing is wrong with the rifle. The shooter simply doesn't realize that to function properly, a semiauto needs to have its bolt snapped shut on the first round, just as it would in a normal firing cycling.

In other instances, shooters have replaced sights, reamed chambers, or performed other unneeded work simply due to lack of understanding the basics of manipulation, use, or care of their firearms.

When a condition other than normal is present, some remedial effort is in order, but as shown in the examples, the remedy needs to be in keeping with the degree of abnormality. It is important, therefore, to know what is normal and what is abnormal.

With respect to firearm manipulation, proper operation should be fully understood. To avoid

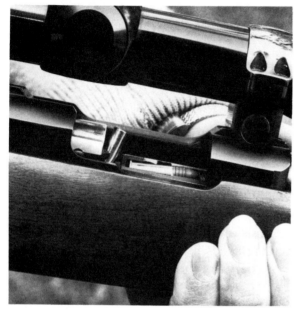

Improper ejection may be the fault of improper manipulation rather than a defective gun.

any malfunctions due to improper gun handling, simply operate all firearms as you might under field conditions. This is to say, work a rifle's bolt as if you had just missed a shot at a big buck and were hurrying for a follow-up shot. Ditto for the proper handling of a pump or lever-action. Apply the same principle of vigorous manipulation to rimfire rifles and shotguns.

Remember that all semiautomatics require the full compression of the bolt-return spring (recoil spring) and the rapid release of that compression to achieve full forward bolt velocity and energy. Thus, when chambering the first round from the magazine be sure the bolt is fully drawn to the rear before releasing it smartly for its forward travel. Avoid any tendency to ease the bolt forward.

In addition, ammunition must be properly loaded into the firearm. For most tubular magazines this means being certain the cartridge is fully pressed into the magazine, allowing any retainers or cartridge stops to snap into place behind the cartridge head. With clips or box magazines, the cartridges must be positioned with their heads fully to the rear and snapped into place so that they correctly seat below any retaining ears or receiver protrusions. Thumb pressure should always be applied to push the cartridge rearward and downward, after each is inserted into the magazine.

Poor accuracy versus good accuracy may merely suggest that a good bore cleaning is needed, or perhaps that a screw or two is loose in the scope mount.

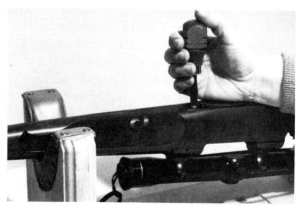

Keeping guard screws tight on the rifle's fore-end will correct many so-called accuracy problems.

A great many assumed feeding problems are caused by the use of incorrect ammunition. Not every repeating rifle chambered for the .22 LR will feed properly if loaded with .22 Short or .22 Long ammunition. And some .22 semi-automatics were designed to function only with either standard-velocity or high-velocity Long Rifle ammo, but not both types. Nor will every rifle chambered for the .357 Magnum properly feed .38 Special ammo. Ditto for rifles chambered for the .44 Magnum and their functioning with .44 Special ammo. In short, you need to be sure the correct ammunition is being used.

Sometimes the correct ammunition selection becomes subtle. Almost all semiautomatic rifles chambered for non-handgun cartridges should be used only with ammunition that has the case mouth crimped into a bullet cannelure. Many handloaders forget this important detail. As another example, many semiautomatic pistols require the use of round-nose ammunition, simply not being designed to function with pointed or flat-nose bullets.

Also, light powder charges, sometimes employed in target ammunition, will often fail to function semiautomatics. This varies with firearm design. For instance, the Marlin semi-automatic Camp Carbine, when chambered for the .45 Auto cartridge, will completely cycle its bolt, ejecting the case and feeding a live round,

Tight pattern of ejected shells is a good indication of consistent ammo ballistics. If the cases were widely dispersed it might mean faulty ammo.

Torn cartridge rims were caused by using this ammo in a semiauto rifle. The problem was traced to the ammo, not the firearm.

even if the fired cartridge contains no powder. The pressure created by the primer alone is sufficient to drive the bolt fully rearward while forcing the bullet into the barrel throat.

Interpreting the need for maintenance or repairs is not difficult, but it requires mature thinking and a common-sense approach to avoid "overkill." Recognizing the signals of trouble or impending trouble is the beginning of the necessary approach.

Should a gun fail to feed, fire, or extract, most often the problem is dirt and/or congealed lubricants. The mechanism needs to be kept meticulously clean for reliability. Cotton swabs, pressurized cans of gun cleaner, and very tiny

Look to the firearm as cause of difficult only after the shooter and ammo have been eliminated.

course, assist in determining what may be wrong. Indeed, reading through material presented later in this work, such as specific information on the Browning A-5 and other firearms, will help familiarize the reader with where to look for problem corrections.

In general, problems are often the result of certain recurring defects. A firearm that is not feeding properly—when manipulated as intended with the correct ammunition—will often be found to have bent clip ears; a broken cartridge guide; worn, damaged, or improper receiver dimensions on feeding surfaces; a weak magazine spring or a faulty follower (depending, of course, on the type of firearm).

Each problem with a specific firearm must be approached in an orderly fashion to prevent needless effort, which, if misguided, could make matters worse. It is important to be absolutely certain what kind of work is required before moving ahead. It is the bad guess at what's needed that lies behind the ruin of so many guns.

amounts of high-grade lubricant are needed to maintain positive functioning. This is especially true with gas-operated semiautomatics.

When using a bolt-action rifle, knowing that a two-inch group is a good one with run-of-the-mill ammo is an important aspect of analyzing a problem. It usually takes good reloads to get the 1½-inch or smaller groups we often hear about. Naturally, rare exceptions can occur. More on this later.

Once you are certain that inaccuracy or malfunction is not caused by lack of routine maintenance, limited shooter capability, or poor ammo quality, you can reasonably assume something is wrong with the firearm. You can then begin to look for problems of a specific nature.

Being familiar with cause and effect will, of

Basic Inspections

Headspace Checks

Some basic inspections should be routine for the home gunsmith. The first of these, an important one for safety (especially if reloads are used), is a headspace check. Using the appropriate gauge, headspace should be checked every 1,000 rounds for centerfire rifles. The same frequency would apply to handguns using magnum cartridges. Shotguns and standard-caliber handguns should be checked every 5,000 rounds. Quality rimfire rifles and handguns can be checked every 10,000 rounds.

Headspace gauges must be used delicately, and the action should never be forced against the gauge. If a stripped bolt is used (no internal

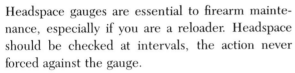

Headspace gauges are essential to firearm maintenance, especially if you are a reloader. Headspace should be checked at intervals, the action never forced against the gauge.

Dummy cartridges are useful for routine firearm inspection as well as testing repairs. But to insure that no mixup with live ammo occurs, they should be clearly identified.

springs, firing pin, ejector, or extractor), it will be much easier to feel the action closing on the gauge and insure that the action is fully seated without the forcing of parts. Naturally, if headspace should prove excessive, the gun should be taken out of service until properly repaired.

Dummy Cartridges

Another important inspection is the functioning of the action with dummy cartridges (no primer or powder). If you do not reload, have a reloading friend or a local gunshop make up enough dummy rounds to fill the magazine and chamber of your firearm. Then, with crisp motions, function your firearm's action to insure that the dummy cartridges feed smoothly from the magazine and that the action closes fully on them. Check that proper extraction and ejection occur on the opening stroke of the action. Also check for any excessive damage that may occur to the case or bullet during the feeding cycle.

The same dummy cartridges used for routine inspection can later be used when doing repair work. Be certain not to mix live and dummy cartridges together! Dummy cartridges should

have a hole drilled through the case for easy identification—or you can paint them black. And remember that the use of dummy cartridges should never lead to careless firearm handling. Always handle firearms and dummy cartridges as if loaded ammo were being used. In this way, a mix-up will never cause a disaster.

Firing-Pin Indent

Another routine inspection should be a visual review of the firing-pin indent on the fired primer—or on the case if rimfire ammo is used. Shallow indentations are a warning of future problems. They can be caused by dirty or gummed actions, frozen lubricant, a weak mainspring, and sometimes even a broken firing pin. Shallow indents can also be caused by excessive headspace or reloaded cartridges that have been resized in a too-small sizing die.

Unique Features

Other inspections include the scrutiny of all unique firearm features. Check the safety for proper functioning, after making sure the chamber and magazine are empty. If the firearm has a half-cock hammer safety, check it by applying pressure to the trigger with the hammer located in the safe position. Also check such things as magazine releases, cartridge cut-offs, and any other movable parts required in the proper operation of the firearm.

Stocks

Inspect all wooden and synthetic materials used for stocks and handguards. Look for splits, cracks, or dents. Any such defects need prompt repair, as delay may cause complete failure.

Barrel Crown

Also carefully check the crown at the muzzle end of the barrel. Nicks or any damage at the crown, which can influence the bullet as it leaves the barrel, will reduce accuracy. Happily, such damage is easy to repair.

Generally, any firearm that functions in a less than perfect manner or displays any appreciable finish wear is a candidate for appropriate home gunsmithing. Simply keep in mind that it is self-defeating to attempt major repairs when only minor ones are needed. And always be sure you know exactly what is needed before beginning a repair.

Specific details for many popular firearms will be provided further along. For now, it is important only to realize that firearm knowledge, in-

Finding problems before they become major can keep gunsmithing requirements to a minimum. This small stock crack has not yet caused any accuracy problems. A bit of epoxy now will keep it from becoming a major split.

spection, and maintenance are important aspects of any gunsmithing program. And the extent of any repair undertaken should be in keeping with the magnitude of the problem.

2

Can I Fix It?

A great many repairs can be made by the firearm owner, but a number of others should be undertaken only by a qualified gunsmith. In fact, some repairs are best left to trained personnel at the factory of the firearm's origin.

Each owner should carefully assess his capability before beginning any repair. It's also vital to determine if all the necessary tools and parts are on hand. Nothing can make a job go sour quicker than improvising when a special tool or part is not available.

Headspace correction is one area that, in most instances, should be left to professionals. Often, the correction of a headspace problem involves the removal of the barrel from the action, the removal of a portion of the chamber end of the barrel, the contouring and re-threading of the chamber end of the barrel, reinstallation of the barrel, and, finally, rechambering. Such an undertaking requires, at a minimum, a very exacting barrel vise with appropriate jaws, an action wrench, a really good lathe, chamber reamers, and headspace gauges. All but the last two are not apt to be among the equipment of the average firearm owner. In addition, the rethreading of the barrel will require a first-class toolmaker's knowledge. Obviously, headspace problems are not normally in the domain of the serious firearm hobbyist gunsmith.

Rechambering any firearm to accommodate a different cartridge should be approached care-

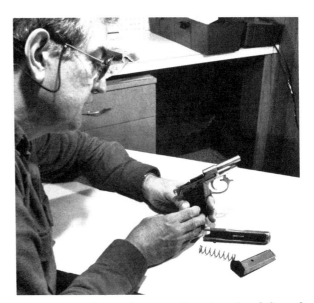

Most gunsmithing jobs are well within the ability of the careful firearm owner. But it is important to recognize those that are not.

fully. The thinning of barrel walls can be dangerous if the person doing the rechambering is not thoroughly familiar with the requirements for maintaining adequate chamber-wall strength.

Any work requiring welding, brazing, or heat treating is best avoided by the amateur. If not properly applied, the use of heat on any firearm part can be disastrous. Total knowledge of what can happen if the job is done incorrectly is essential. The heating of a very hard receiver to anneal a spot for drilling and tapping can be ruinous to the receiver's strength. Furthermore, softening a spot on the receiver to start a drill is, for most folks, the first step in breaking a tap off in that receiver. Very hard receivers should be drilled and tapped only by someone with very extensive experience. When taps break off in a receiver or barrel, they are very, very tough to remove without causing extensive damage.

Heating a bolt handle so it can be bent for scope clearance, or welding on a replacement handle, requires very special care and knowledge if the strength of the bolt's locking lugs is not to be adversely affected.

Barrels heated for the brazing of sight bases can wind up too soft or excessively brittle if the job is not handled correctly. I saw one revolver blow up after it had been converted for the exclusive use of blanks. The cause was improper heating of the cylinder when it was pinned to prevent the chambering of cartridges with bullets.

Even soft-soldering jobs can lead to problems if the person doing the work is not familiar with all the pitfalls. Heating any firearm part is potentially dangerous if you are unfamiliar with all of the problems. Besides, any amount of heat, even from a soft-soldering job, will discolor the metal surrounding the work area. Unless you are fully experienced and have the proper facilities for refinishing, the use of heat in repairs should be avoided.

In general, any repair that might compromise the strength of a firearm should not be undertaken by the amateur. Even the drilling of holes in a barrel or receiver, while often a practical undertaking for the cautious and skillful individual, needs to be very carefully done if the firearm is to remain safe.

Needless to say, scope sights should be repaired only by the manufacturer. Even if the owner could accomplish a satisfactory scope repair, the ability to replace the inert waterproofing gas in a scope is beyond the capability of most of us.

The making of firearm parts often is not practical due to requirements for heat treating in order to obtain the correct degree of part hardness. Few home gunsmiths have the necessary equipment to bring a part to the required temperature, to hold that temperature for the required time, or to allow for the necessary controlled cooling or quenching, let alone have the proper equipment to measure the results of the hardening process.

But most other gunsmithing chores can be handled by a careful person who is able to use ordinary tools with the appropriate skill. For example, the firearm owner can replace almost any part of a firearm except the barrel or receiver if he has the correct part, necessary tools, and the know-how. Some factories restrict the sales of certain parts to gunsmiths only. And a few

Parts replacements most often go quickly and easily, and are well within the scope of a home gunsmith.

parts are available solely for factory installation. Those restrictions are to protect the consumer from potential physical harm and the factory from liability for that harm. Such parts often include barrels, receivers, bolts, and trigger parts.

The restricted parts may require special tools and/or knowledge for correct, safe installation. Trigger parts, while easily installed, are likely to be restricted to prevent a too-light trigger pull from causing an accident. Besides unintentional discharge by finger pressure, too-light trigger pulls often prove to be the cause of a dropped firearm discharging. However, we will discuss trigger adjustment and replacement later.

Easily replaced parts include sights, stocks, firing pins, extractors, ejectors, and various springs. Other easy-to-install parts include cartridge guides, cartridge followers, magazine boxes, swivels, replacement clip magazines (to convert box-magazine firearms), replacement floorplates and trigger guards, and similar items. The careful workman can also replace such items as buttplates and custom-style triggers or can

Without much effort a box-magazine rifle, with or without a floorplate, can be converted at home to a convenient clip model using only simple tools.

Some parts, such as this Remington bolt and trigger, are restricted to factory installation. Such restrictions are for the protection of the firearm owner.

add recoil pads, special scopes, and personal touches.

While the refinishing of blued or anodized metal surfaces is best left to properly equipped professionals, or the factory of origin, wood refinishing is always in the domain of a handy firearm owner. And the simple touch-up of metal finishes, even plating touch-up on small parts, can be a practical undertaking. But remember that any refinishing, no matter how well done, does detract from the value of most commercial firearms.

One possible exception is that sometimes careful refinishing of a custom firearm will not detract from its value. Another exception is a firearm so badly worn and/or abused as to have little value. In this case, proper refinishing can add value to the firearm, as well as extend its useful life.

More often than not, poor accuracy can be corrected by the firearm owner. Recrowning of a barrel, rebedding of an action or barrel, and the glass bedding of the action and barrel are all practical home gunsmithing efforts that can greatly enhance a rifle's accuracy. Many shotgun barrels can be altered to accept screw-in chokes. Complex firearms can be disassembled for needed cleanings, and careful owners can adjust the trigger pulls on some makes and models to suit their needs for accuracy. The list could be

Accuracy got you over a barrel? Chances are you can correct the problem yourself.

lengthened, so it is obvious that you don't always require the services of a gunsmith to get the maximum potential from your firearm, or to repair it if it breaks down.

Safety Precautions

Deciding whether you have the skill, experience, and tools to handle a job, keep in mind that seemingly routine repairs sometimes have safety aspects that need to be considered. For exam-

ple, a firing-pin replacement can cause problems if the new pin protrudes excessively from the bolt or standing breech. Such a condition could lead to a pierced primer and allow hot gases to be dumped into the gun's action, possibly with disastrous results. Yet many firing pins are made to very exacting dimensions and employ positive stops to forward motion. These are readily replaced.

Another consideration is the need of a firearm to be absolutely reliable after repair. Suppose the work is done on a handgun used for personal protection. The improper installation or alteration of something as simple as a trigger-return spring or mainspring could bring about a malfunction at the worst possible moment.

3

Hand Tools

Gunsmithing, like many other undertakings, demands a good supply of appropriate, high-quality hand tools. Carpenter's screwdrivers and a few chisels will not suffice, nor will a department-store cleaning kit allow you to restore accuracy to an often-fired rifle.

Even a tool as simple as a cleaning rod is worthy of careful selection, because a poor one can damage a bore. Since proper cleaning is basic to maintenance, I'll begin this discussion of hand tools with a review of cleaning implements.

Cleaning Rods and Tips

Most shooters purchase an aluminum cleaning rod, either separately or in a kit. But an aluminum rod is soft, bends easily, and if used with the essential snug-fitting patches and bore brushes, is soon apt to be bent and warped. As the rod continues to be used, sections of it bear firmly against the bore, and bits of aluminum are shaved from it. The roughened rod surface then begins to pick up particles of grit, which become firmly embedded in the soft rod. These rub against the bore's surface and the cleaning process begins to do more damage than good.

So why are there aluminum rods? Well, they are inexpensive, and for a once-a-year shooter they could, perhaps, with good care, be used for a number of cleanings, thereby lasting that many years. But such rods are not really suitable for the serious shooter—and brass rods are not a heck of a lot better.

The minimum acceptable rod is a good, hard steel one that is properly selected for size and correctly maintained. Because of its hardness, a steel rod is not easily bent, nor will it be easily roughened and abraded. It will not become a host for embedded particles of grit that could ruin a bore. If a steel rod is disfigured, however, it can readily hold undesirable material picked up in cleaning or, worse, a hard rod's damaged portion can rub and cause bore damage.

A rod should be significantly smaller than bore size. Bore-sized rods are a serious hazard. Should a patch fall off the jag and get between rod and bore, a very serious jamming of the rod will occur. Often, the bore's surface will be damaged before the rod is freed. On the other hand, if a rod is excessively small in diameter, it can be bent too easily. The rod should be from 0.03-

inch below bore diameter to perhaps as much as 0.10-inch below, the larger amount being practical for the larger bore diameters.

I once used a very nice stainless-steel rod for cleaning a favored .22-250 rifle. However, the rod had a fair amount of flex when pushing a snug patch through the bore. If a cleaning-rod guide was not used, it would bend considerably. One day, while in a hurry, I could not find the appropriate cleaning-rod guide and I commenced cleaning the rifle anyway. The rod buckled enough to contact a sharp corner on the action, which simply began shaving the steel rod with each forward stroke. The rod also took a slight set. Then I began to feel the grating of the rod on the bore's surface. Luckily I stopped in time, when I felt the first tinge of something wrong. But if I had not been paying careful attention to the feel of the rod's passage through the bore, I might have ruined a $200 barrel rather than an $18 cleaning rod. Going slow and only with the right equipment is the moral of the story.

The best cleaning rods are, in my opinion, made of spring steel and are nylon-coated. Because of the strength of the spring steel, such rods do not easily take on a set. And if one somehow acquires a slight bow, the plastic cover-

ing will prevent barrel damage as the rod rubs the bore.

Naturally, the soft plastic covering of a coated rod is more easily damaged than the hard surface of a solid steel rod, but I would rather risk damage to the rod than damage to a barrel which might cost ten times as much. The soft plastic surface is very easily cleaned, so you don't have to worry that it will hold abrasive grit.

Regardless of the type of rod selected, it is important to wipe it clean every time it is removed from the bore. Wipe away any foreign material with a patch lightly moistened with solvent. Then run a dry patch along the rod, carefully drying it and feeling for any abrasions.

Sometimes a damaged steel rod can be repaired by a careful application of crocus-cloth. But keep in mind the relative value of the rod versus the barrel if tempted to use a rod that's not just right. Using too long a rod will help cause the bowing that can eventually ruin it. A too-short rod will see you banging knuckles against the end of the all-important cleaning-rod guide.

Ideally, several rods are required. If you attempt to use one rod for a number of calibers, its diameter will probably be too small or too large for some barrels. One rod is required for .17

Nothing can replace a quality cleaning rod. These Parker Hales feature a spring-steel core with an outer covering of bore-protecting acetate.

caliber, another can do for .22 through .26 caliber, and another for .27 on up to perhaps .40. Larger bores will require a hefty rod.

The tip used on the rod is important. One

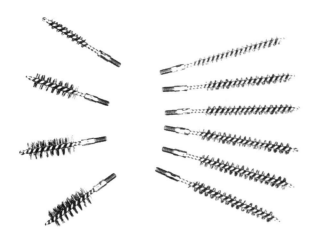

Properly fitting bore brushes of top quality are necessary for maintaining accuracy.

good style is the pointed jag that allows the impaling of a patch, to hold it in place, and also lets the patch fall free at the muzzle when the rod is withdrawn from the breech end.

The diameter of the enlarged section of the tip immediately behind the point is critical. If it is not of the correct diameter, the patch will not be snug in the bore. The user then will try to compensate by using multiple patches. This is wasteful and indicates that the right tool is not being used. A tip for every caliber is essential to insure proper patch tightness, although patches do come in varying sizes and need to be matched to the tip.

When using a cleaning rod it is important to protect scope lenses with caps to prevent the tip from piercing a lens during a careless moment. A cleaning-rod guide is also essential to prevent damage to the action, chamber, or throat that could be caused by the sharp tip.

A useful alternative to pointed tips is the blunt jag, which has the ability to hold a patch that is carefully placed over its end and wrapped

Scope caps are an important cleaning "tool." They protect the lens coating from harmful cleaning solvents as well as other damage.

Cleaning-rod guides, which fit into the action, are basic and essential gun-maintenance tools.

around it. However, even when care is used, patches can fall off before the rod enters the bore, especially if a cleaning-rod guide is not used.

The slotted tip is the worst choice as it invariably does not allow uniform patch contact with the bore. In some instances, the metal of a slotted tip can directly contact the bore as the rod is pushed through.

Rod tips must have threads that fit the rod with exactness. Sloppy threads may allow the tip to work loose and cause incorrect alignment in the bore.

Ideally, I prefer rod tips made of brass to prevent damage to the gun if the tip inadvertently hits or is forced against the bore, chamber, or action surfaces. If a tip becomes damaged, due to the softness of the brass, you can easily replace it and will have the satisfaction of knowing that more expensive damage to the firearm has been prevented.

Soft plastic tips are nearly useless as they buckle one way and then another as they are used to push a snug patch through the bore.

Finally, any good rod used for rifled arms needs free swiveling of its handle to insure that the patch can rotate in the rifling. Without a rotating rod, the patch would be forced to ride over the rifling and thereby be unable to do a good job of wiping in the grooves. Ditto for any use of a brush.

A swiveling *tip* is fine in theory, but in practice you have no way of knowing if it's working or if the load placed on it is causing it to bind up. A good many swiveling handles do not rotate properly, either. A quality rod is needed.

The most satisfactory rods I have used are the spring-steel, nylon-coated, one-piece rods manufactured by J. Dewey Manufacturing Company, and the Parker-Hale rods. Indeed, I own one Parker-Hale rifle rod that I purchased in the early 1950s, and it's still going strong. The handle has been partially broken off, but it still swivels perfectly and its acetate coating is in almost perfect condition. It has outlasted what would have been seven to twelve slightly more or less expensive rods. And by the way, that particular rod is *not* expensive.

Screwdrivers

After cleaning equipment, the hand tools most often used are screwdrivers. They are also the most often misused and abused tools. Improperly selected and/or misapplied screwdrivers can cause extensive damage to screw heads and surrounding metal and wood. All this can be avoided merely by knowing what a screwdriver is able to accomplish and how to obtain the desired results.

Screwdriver bits are tough—if a quality tool is purchased and the right size is used. For example, a screwdriver blade that is $\frac{1}{8}$-inch wide and approximately $\frac{1}{40}$-inch thick has an average working strength equal to about 15 inch-pounds of torque and an average breaking point of about 17 inch-pounds. This means the maximum working strength of this tiny bit will be easily reached by applying pressure only with the thumb and first two fingers. If you use a screwdriver with a bit of this size and attempt to turn up a screw with a closed fist, something is going to give. Either the blade will bend, twist or break, or the screw head will be damaged or broken.

A full hand grip on a screwdriver will develop 50 inch-pounds of torque. That's enough to break a bit with a width of $\frac{1}{5}$-inch and a thickness of $\frac{1}{25}$-inch. The use of a T-shaped handle or a ratchet handle with a leverage length of $3\frac{1}{2}$ inches will allow a force of more than 200 inch-pounds to be applied. This is enough to damage screw bits with heads measuring up to $\frac{3}{8}$-inch wide and $\frac{1}{20}$-inch thick.

Obviously, the craftsman must keep in mind the working strength of the screws and the bits used to turn them into place. The table on page 304 shows the average working torque and breaking torque for screwdriver bits, and these also apply to screws with corresponding slot sizes. Note that there is only a small difference in working torque and destructive torque—usually about 10 percent.

Obviously, the larger the screw, the more torque can be applied to a proper-fitting bit. Generally speaking, use only the thumb and first two

These poorly sharpened, bent, and broken screwdrivers are signs that the owner is not properly equipped for even routine tasks.

Screwdrivers are the premier gunsmithing tools. A few sets of good ones are essential.

This Chapman gunsmith's screwdriver set allows ample torque to be applied without running the risk of breaking screws.

Accessory hex-head drivers are also available from Chapman. These reduce the chances of mangling hex-head screws when applying high torque.

fingers to tighten screws that have fine-width slots and/or shallow slots. Hand pressure can be used on larger screws such as those used for scope mounts. Normal hand pressure, or even a 3½-inch T-handle or a ratchet handle can be used for tightening large action screws.

All the foregoing assumes that the screwdriver handle is not more than an inch in diameter. When a screwdriver with a large handle is used, special care must be taken or you can over-torque the bit or the screw.

When purchasing screwdrivers or bits, keep in mind that extremely hard tips break abruptly and can cause severe damage to metal and wood surfaces when this occurs. A tool with some spring is preferable. If you should ever over-stress a bit, its spring might give you ample warning to ease up immediately.

It is imperative to use a screwdriver with a bit that exactly fits the screw head, both in width and thickness. Parallel sides on the bit are essential to insure full contact with the walls and the bottom of the screw slot.

A bit that is too narrow will bear only on opposite ends at the outer edges of the slot. And it will not afford sufficient purchase to loosen or fully tighten the fastener. A tapered bit will bear only at the top edge of the slot and, because of its wedge shape, will cam out of the slot when maximum torque is applied. All of these ill-fitting variations can damage the screw and/or bit.

When using a bit with the correct shape and diameter, it is essential to position it correctly in the slot. If it does not bottom properly or if it is not held plumb, damage to the screw or bit is sure to occur.

Brownells Magna-tip Super-Set will supply a screwdriver bit for almost any gunsmithing need, along with two different-sized handles.

Short-shanked and ratchet-handled, this Lyman stubby screwdriver kit can prove handy for some jobs.

Using screwdrivers without damaging fasteners and nearby surfaces demands care, and a knowledge of how to apply torque.

means using an easy-out. Other times it means drilling and tapping for a larger screw and thread size. On occasion, a broken screw can mean a ruined or greatly devalued action, barrel, frame, etc. So if you don't have a perfectly-fitting screwdriver, wait until you can purchase one. Or you can grind an existing bit to fit. Take your time and be sure it's a *perfect* fit.

When grinding a bit, be sure it *remains cool.* A bit can quickly reach temperatures of 400°F. or more while it is being ground. Such a temperature will remove all its hardness making further use impractical. Keep in mind the very small surface area and thickness of the bit when grinding a screwdriver. It takes only a few seconds against a grinding wheel to make the temperature of the work area rise to 250° or even 350°. A few more seconds and temperatures of over 400° will be generated. Keep work on the grinder for only three seconds and then quench in cold water. The quenching water should be at least a quart can. Small volumes of water can be quickly heated as quenching is repeated.

Screwdrivers should be segregated by the thickness of the blade. Keeping all your blades and/or bits of a given thickness in one drawer or rack will enable you to quickly find a blade of the correct width once you have determined the proper thickness. By keeping blades segregated by thickness, you will prevent an accidental use of the wrong thickness.

Burred screws detract from a firearm's appearance and indicate that its owner is a tinkerer who doesn't know what he is doing. Such screws should be replaced, carefully, with proper-fitting screwdrivers.

Broken screws can be a major problem. Sometimes a screw with a broken head can be removed by carefully rotating it with a pointed punch on the outer edge of the slot of the remaining half of the screw head. But a less than careful approach can mean further disfigurement of the surrounding wood or metal.

Often there is no way to remove a broken screw other than drilling it out. Sometimes this

Hex Wrenches and Screws

Originally, hex-head screws were introduced to prevent the mangling of slot-head screws by poor-fitting screwdriver bits. That was a good idea since many gun owners used the wrong bits. But the idea was not put into fully effective application.

In my experience, most of the hex-head screws used in the firearms industry are more easily damaged than the slotted types. This is due to a number of factors—too small a hex, too shallow a hex, too soft a screw, or simply poor dimensional tolerances on the hex or the hex wrench. The result is a hex cavity that quickly has its shoulders wiped away, leaving a generally rounded hole. When this happens, the screw can neither be tightened sufficiently nor removed for replacement.

The offending hex screws are most commonly found with scope mounts and rings. Indeed, the only truly satisfactory hex screws I have encountered are those supplied with Redfield scope rings and bases. These hex screws have an adequately large hex, made to minimal tolerances and punched amply deep. When used with an adequately dimensioned and hardened hex wrench, these screws can be repeatedly torqued up very tight, and removed without damage.

But most of the hex screws encountered on firearms and scope mounts are so unsatisfactory that I go out of my way to find replacement slotted screws.

Caution is needed when using hex wrenches and screws. Use a pressurized degreaser/solvent to clean out hex holes and wipe any grease from wrench surfaces to insure a dry, slip-free surface. Be absolutely certain the hex wrench fits the screw snugly and is bottomed in the screw hex before turning it. Finally, use the hex wrench as intended. The long end goes into the screw and the short end is used for leverage. Using the long end for leverage guarantees that a hex hole will be quickly ruined. It's difficult to tighten a screw adequately against recoil-induced movement when the wrench is used properly. That's another reason to vote against hex-head screws. I have had many shooter bring a ruined receiver to me after attempting to remove a damaged hex screw.

The fit, hardness, and spring of a hex wrench are just as important to damage-free turning of hex screws as the same qualities of a standard bit used on slotted screws. Even the best hex wrenches will wear out. When the sharp corners of your hex wrench become shiny and round, get a new one. Even a large hex wrench can be purchased for less than a few dollars. The smaller sizes seldom cost a dollar.

Hex-head bits to fit standard, interchangeable-bit screwdrivers are available. When combined with a one-inch-diameter handle, these make the best possible tools for avoiding the hex-destroying excess torque that can be applied when the long end of a hex wrench is used as a handle. Such hex-head bits are available for fine screwdriver sets such as the one designed for gunsmithing and made by the Chapman Manufacturing Company. Brownells also offers hex-head wrenches in its Super-Set screwdriver kit.

Phillips Screwdrivers

One other type of screwdriver needed for firearms work is the Phillips-head style. Phillips-head screws are often used on recoil pads and sometimes on buttplates. One of their advantages lies in the usual shape of the matching screwdriver shank—rounded. A round-shanked screwdriver placed into a recoil pad will not chew up the pad while the screw is being turned. If used properly, such screwdrivers can be placed into a recoil pad and removed leaving little evidence of their passage. Only three or perhaps four sizes of Phillips-head screwdrivers are required for most gunsmithing chores.

Phillips-head bits have a tendency to "walk" out of the screw slots, so it is important to maintain adequate bit-to-screw pressure. And make no attempt to overtighten!

Many gunsmithing screwdrivers are manufactured with round shanks and parallel-side bits. However, some fully acceptable ones are still made with flattened side shanks and semi-chisel points that have been "hollow" ground to produce the necessary parallel sides. Synthetic handles stand up best when multiple mallet taps must be applied, but wood handles give a better no-slip grip. Some of both styles are appropriate.

Tight Screws

While the torque that can be applied to a screwdriver is limited, it is often possible to loosen an extremely tight screw that has slightly rusted in place or has been set with Loc-Tite thread cement—without damaging screw or bit. When a screw refuses to turn loose with the appropriate torque applied, a slight tapping on the screwdriver may be the answer.

First, be absolutely sure the screwdriver is bottomed in the slot and is not binding on the slot sides. If it binds or is not held plumb, a broken screw may result. Now, with the firearm securely held and properly padded, tap the screwdriver handle squarely on top, with a few smart but lightly applied blows of a small hammer or mallet. This will often drive the screw threads downward into the mating threads sufficiently to create the "play" necessary to start the screw out. Do not overdo the tapping, as a split screw or stripped threads could result. Do not use wood-handle screwdrivers for this purpose as they occasionally split when tapped.

This tapping procedure is also used to tighten a screw an extra tad to insure that a scope mount or sight will not work loose. Simply snug up the screw in the normal fashion with the appropriate torque. Then, being sure the screwdriver is of the proper size and held plumb, give the top of its handle two or three smart but light blows with a small brass hammer. Again apply the normal amount of torque to the screwdriver and you will often gain an extra fraction of a turn. This procedure should be used only if you don't expect to remove the screw at some future time, because the screw may set up so tightly that later extraction is extremely difficult.

Many gunsmiths place a *single drop* of thread-locking compound such as Loc-Tite on the screw before turning it into place—if it is intended never to be removed. This can be useful when installing scope-mount bases or iron-sight bases. Yet tomorrow's needs are usually unknown. I have changed many a scope base or sight system for owners who decided to use a different one or bought a newer scope requiring a different base or removal of the iron sights. Thread-locking compounds should be used judiciously, since one drop will insure that a screw will stay tight. Removal will then be difficult, although there is a 50–50 chance of satisfactory removal if the screw is lightly tapped with a small hammer as mentioned earlier.

Bench Vises

A vise is often essential, and because it frequently needs to be turned to position the work correctly, one that swivels is desirable. If the jaws can be pivoted to horizontal and vertical positions, all the better. Any swiveling vise needs to lock positively, without excessive jaw pressure, in whatever work position is selected.

There are a great many suitable vises, but perhaps the most popular in the firearms trade is the Versa-Vise, made by Gaydash Industries of Kent, Ohio. It swivels 360 degrees in either a

A good bench vise is an indispensable gunsmithing tool. This one is the very popular Versa-Vise.

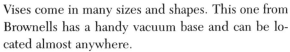

Vises come in many sizes and shapes. This one from Brownells has a handy vacuum base and can be located almost anywhere.

A small vise, like this one from Forster, is often needed when working on small parts or subassemblies. The swiveling feature is a plus.

vertical or horizontal jaw position, and it has a screw adjustment that allows automatic swivel locking when the jaws are closed to variable levels of pressure. This vise seems to be the ideal size for most gunsmithing chores. I have used the same one for more than 30 years and for 90 percent of my gunsmithing. It's still going strong.

Too large a vise is not practical. A gun is too easily damaged by a vise capable of delivering excessive pressure with modest tightening. Occasionally, there will be a need for a larger or smaller vise if you do a wide range of gunsmithing. The need for a larger vise has been limited to less than half a percent of all my work, whereas a small vise has been used for perhaps 10 percent of my gunsmithing time.

Small vises are irreplaceable for stoning or filing small parts, working on small sub-assemblies, or trying to hold anything tiny. A swiveling feature is also mighty handy, as well as jaws that allow for vertical or horizontal positioning. One perfect solution is the Forster Products Swiv-O-

Ling vise. Others can be found, often in hobby shops or specialty tool houses.

The normal working vise should have a jaw opening of at least 3½ inches, with a four- to five-inch opening about perfect. The jaws should be three to four inches long. A ⅞- to one-inch opening is adequate for the small vise, while ¾-inch seems appropriate for jaw length. For a heavy-duty vise, accept no less than a six-inch opening, with jaws of equal length.

Obviously, you cannot place a firearm (or some part thereof) in a vise and tighten the jaws without causing damage to the firearm. It is necessary to protect the gun or part from the bare vise jaws. A bunch of old rags wrapped around the gun won't be a satisfactory solution. Wooden vise-jaw pads are essential, and at times you may require a set of commercial felt jaw pads, especially for the small vise. For rough works, a set of lead jaws for the medium and large vises are in order. A vise without the necessary protective jaws is not a suitable gunsmithing tool.

Hammers and Mallets

Small hammers and mallets are used for setting or freeing screws (in conjunction with the appropriate screwdriver), installing sights in dovetails, and removing drift pins (with appropriate punches), as well as a great many other chores. The key to selecting hammers and mallets lies in their intended use.

For use with very fine drift-pin punches, only very small, light hammers are appropriate or you may soon break the punch. When driving sights in or out of dovetails with a heavy brass punch, use a series of light taps rather than a few heavy blows which can cause an improperly aligned or ill-fitting sight to destroy the barrel's dovetail. For most work, half-pound, one-pound, and two-pound hammers should be all you require.

For the one-half- and one-pound size, a brass, flat-faced (both ends) hammer is appropriate. Purchase only solid-head hammers affixed to the handles in such a way that the head cannot rotate on it. Do not make the mistake of purchasing a hammer whose head is threaded onto the handle. These invariably work loose after a few

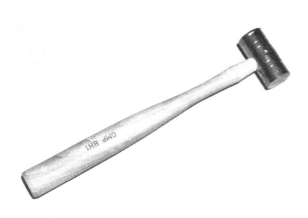

A few hammers are needed in the shop for setting or freeing screws, installing sights, removing drift pins, etc. This mallet is useful in delivering blows to delicate parts of a gun, such as a trigger assembly, without harming them.

blows, and severe part damage can occur when the head suddenly turns and ricochets away from its intended application point. Screw-on plastic or brass hammer faces do not seem to work well, either, as they frequently break off at the thread, again creating the potential of damage to a gun.

It is safest to have brass heads on your two smallest hammers. This will prevent undue damage to any metal surface accidentally struck. For the heavier hammer, one rounded head and one flat head will prove most useful. The heavier hammer need not be brass; in fact, ideally, it should be steel, as a rounded steel head can be used for peening dovetails and similar work.

Avoid a handle made of two or more sections that are threaded together. These threaded sections, when they become loose, can cause the head to rotate. To avoid hammer heads that will eventually rotate on handles that are press-fitted, be sure the section of the handle entering the head is not of a rounded shape. A positive, non-round shape is necessary to prevent eventual head-turning.

A good, solid leather mallet can be very useful. An alternative would be a nylon or other plastic mallet. Such tools let you deliver blows to delicate parts without harming them, as when you tap a very tight shotgun magazine cap to free it for removal, or tap a trigger assembly that is frozen in place.

Be sure never to use brass or steel hammers on any aluminum part. Always use a leather or plastic mallet for such purposes. And use *gentle* blows only. Aluminum bends or collapses easily.

Punches

Punches are essential for removing drift pins. When used to remove solid pins, they can range in size from two-thirds to about nine-tenths the diameter of the pin. A tight pin requires as large a punch as possible to prevent bending or breaking of the punch. When used to remove hollow or rolled pins, the punch should very nearly, but not quite, equal the pin's diameter. If a punch that is too small in diameter slips inside a hollow (rolled) pin, it can freeze solidly in position, which can mean a major problem. There are punches with raised centers on the end, designed specifically for hollow pins.

Always begin by applying only hand pressure when punches are used to remove pins. Many pins, especially in some Ruger models, are so loose as to need only a very slight pressure to free them. When driving pins out of an aluminum housing, great care must be taken not to damage the soft metal.

The punch sizes needed will depend on the firearm to be worked upon. Generally speaking, if you have one each of ⅟₃₂-inch, ⅟₁₆-inch, ⅛-inch, and ¼-inch, you will be able to handle most jobs. But there are a few assignments, just a few, that require a smaller or perhaps in-between punch.

Always be certain the punch is held plumb to the pin to prevent damage to punch, pin, or surrounding areas. Use only light taps. A heavy blow can cause a punch to slip from the rounded head of a pin and damage surrounding surfaces. Once a pin has been started sufficiently to let you hold the punch below the surface, there's a temptation to use more forceful blows. Resist it. The punch still can do damage on internal parts that could well be unprotected due to an interrupted pin hole.

Most punches should, of course, have flat heads—that is, with the exception of center punches, which will be used for starting a drill bit, peening metal, and locating swivels, holes, and similar work. Ideally, the center punch should be on a ⅜-inch-diameter shaft and should be quite hard. A shallow point is preferable to a long, skinny one which will deform easily.

Like screwdrivers, punches need to be kept cool if you regrind them to repair a broken tip. Overheat them and they will soften. And a soft

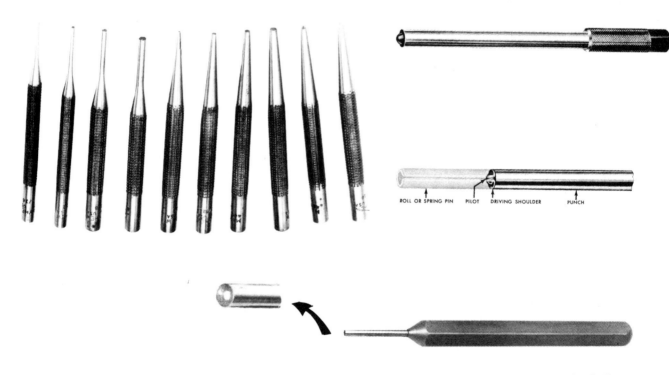

A wide variety of punches is required. Shown are a universal set (*upper left*), a cup-tip punch for removing rounded-head pins (*upper right*), and a hollow-pin punch.

punch will peen outward, getting larger at the tip and head with each hammer tap. This can cause a difficult situation or a ruined parts housing, so be careful to keep punch temperatures well below 400° when regrinding.

Chisels

A good set of woodworking chisels will be required for rebedding a barrel and/or action to improve accuracy. Chisel shanks need to be long enough so you can keep your hands a comfortable distance from the work, and the handles should be large enough for a comfortable grip. However, handles that are too large can absorb some of the feel of the cutting, which can lead to a poor job.

Chisel blades must be very sharp. All the cutting must be accomplished by the keen edge rather than the strength of your hand. If a chisel will not cut with a light steering pressure, it is too dull to do a proper job. Dull chisels lead to split wood or excessively large peels and gouges, which can easily ruin a stock.

You will need round, V, and flat shapes, and you will need angled blades, to the left and right. Also, each shape must be available in a variety of sizes, up to perhaps a ½-inch width.

You can give a chisel a preliminary sharpening with a belt sander and then finish it with stones of the correct shape. Use the belt sander sparingly to avoid ruining the temper of the very thin cutting edge. If you have no belt sander, the job can be done entirely with stones. If the sharpening is done before the chisel becomes excessively dull, a stone alone will quickly return the needed sharpness.

When selecting chisels, I strongly recommend buying those offered specifically for gunsmithing. Many carpenter chisels are not up to the task. However, for rough work with a mallet for preliminary stock shaping, standard carpenter's chisels will do quite nicely.

Rasps and Files

Some rasps are needed to do work that chisels alone can't easily accomplish. The basic shape of

A basic set of chisels is needed. More elaborate sets will be useful for extensive stockmaking and checkering.

An assortment of gunsmith files is useful. This set from Brownells is suitable for almost any gunsmithing task you're likely to encounter.

to wear rapidly in use, perhaps creating a potentially dangerous situation. However, files can be practical for the fitting of parts that have a uniform hardness throughout.

Files in triangular and flat shapes will prove useful. For most efforts, small sizes are appropriate. Files with flats ⅛-, 3/16-, ¼-, and ⅜-inch wide will be the most useful. Occasional requirements for 1/16- or ½-inch files may occur.

Files need care of the same sort as rasps. Don't store them in piles, as bumping together will quickly dull them. Store files and rasps so that they cannot come in contact with one another or any metallic object.

Coarse files are satisfactory for rough and preliminary work, but fine-cut files should always be used for finishing steps. And soft aluminum will require a more open file than hard steel. Perhaps the best way to judge whether you are using an appropriate file is the ease or difficulty of removing metal.

a stock, for instance, is best roughed out with a coarse wood rasp. Barrel-channel rasps are quicker and easier to use than chisels. Finally, bottoming rasps allow the amateur to get good, flat surfaces and sharp angles that might otherwise be beyond his capabilities.

Like chisels, rasps must be very sharp. Protecting their cutting surfaces is all that can be done to keep them in good shape. Don't throw a bunch of rasps in a drawer where they can be bumped and banged together. Properly cared for, a good rasp lasts a long time, but once it becomes dull you should throw it out rather than risk the ruin of a job.

For most home gunsmithing, only a very few files are needed. Their use is limited, as any application will remove metal finish and often surface hardness. Of course, if you must make a metal part, you will need a good selection of files.

Routinely, files are mostly used for shortening screws, fitting scope bases, removing burrs, and perhaps cutting sight dovetails.

Files should never be used for trigger or sear work, because that would remove all or most of the surface hardness of the parts and allow them

Files for gunsmithing should be sharp to insure clean, well-executed work.

Polishing stones are effective ways of smoothing out rough spots without undue danger of taking away too much material. When stoning, always maintain original part lines and angles. Stones are the proper tools for shaping or sharpening screwdrivers and chisels.

Files should not be applied in a strong-arm attack. Let the file do the cutting. If it will not cut easily, it is either the wrong file for the job or is dull and should be discarded.

In some instances you may encounter parts so hard as to defy effective filing. Consider this a good indication that the part should not be altered in any manner other than perhaps smoothing it out a bit with some hard stones.

Polishing Stones

Stones are needed primarily for trigger work. They are essential for tuning many triggers. Trigger-assembly parts should never be attacked with a file, as the removal of metal can cause a trigger to fail (that is, to fire) when the gun is bumped or handled roughly. Also, the surface hardness of trigger-assembly parts should never be jeopardized. Any change to triggers, sears, firing-pin surfaces that mate with sears, bolt stops, ejectors, extractors, safeties, hammers,

locking surfaces, and similar parts, must be in smoothness or in dimensional changes measured in 0.0001-inch. Work on these parts should, therefore, always be done with appropriate stones.

Stones are also useful for the final smoothing of work accomplished with files. For example, after cutting a ⅜-inch dovetail into a barrel for front or rear sight installation, it is always wise to smooth up the whole work surface with a triangular stone. This will allow the new sights to be driven into place without undue binding and the distortion of the parts that may follow if excessive force is applied.

Stones are extremely fragile and will shatter if dropped or hit by a heavy part. Because they are delicate and because the size, shape, and hardness of a stone needed for a specific job varies extensively, it is suggested that stones be purchased as needed. The only stones that are routinely required are those used for chisel sharpening and screwdriver-bit finishing after grinding.

The foregoing are all of the basic hand tools needed for routine maintenance. Power tools and specialized gunsmithing tools and jigs will be required for any work beyond routine maintenance and will be discussed in later chapters.

4

Power Tools

Commercial gunsmiths could not survive for long without power tools, including an elaborate (and expensive) lathe, a floor-model drill press, power grinder, belt sander, flexible-shaft grinder (for hard-to-reach places), and an electric checkering tool. But for basic repairs undertaken at home, none of these is essential. Indeed, some hobbyists have no power tools at all. Whether you need them—and which ones you need—will depend on the types of jobs you're prepared to tackle.

For the home enthusiast, I would rank the most important power tools as follows, rating the most frequently used tool No. 1, the next most often needed No. 2, and so on:

1 Disc Sander and/or Belt Sander (tie for first place)
2 Drill Press—bench or floor model
3 Grinder
4 Lathe
5 Flexible-Shaft Grinder/Polisher
6 Polishing Wheel/Fixture/Motor
7 Electric Checkering Tool
8 Hand Drill
9 Miscellaneous (milling attachment for lathe, etc.)

Of course, in addition to the power tools listed, many others are found in the shops of some gunsmiths. But they won't be used often unless the gunsmith specializes in some particular job that is best accomplished or most quickly completed with the aid of an additional tool. You may already have a partially equipped, more or less completely equipped, or even extremely well equipped workshop. But if you don't there's no need to spend your life's savings to tool up extravagantly. You'll be well advised to acquire the first five items on the list, and get the others later on, one at a time, as the need arises.

Disc or Belt Sander

A disc sander and/or belt sander will see a great deal of service for the installation and trimming of recoil pads. Indeed, once the operator learns how to carefully install a recoil pad, he may be surprised at how many pads he will find himself installing on personal firearms as well as on those belonging to acquaintances. Because recoil pads are a great asset on many shotguns and on any rifle of .27 caliber or larger, and because of virtually unserviced market potential, these sand-

This sander will do most jobs, as it combines a disc and belt in one unit, making it a natural for recoil-pad installation and other gunsmithing chores. This one is a Jet, available from Brownells.

ers may be the best possible initial area of investment in power tools.

Drill Press

A drill press is among the minimum essentials for such jobs as drilling and tapping barrels and receivers for the installation of sights. A drill press is also useful for such basic jobs as swivel installation, skeletonizing magazines, and many other tasks.

The drill bit must be held in an absolutely precise position when drilling sight-mounting holes. This is not possible with a hand-held drill. Even with the best of jigs used for drill-bit alignment, a hand-held power drill will lead to grief. It's just too easy to have a bit "walk" off its intended location or be bent and broken.

Most gunsmiths use free-standing floor-model drill presses. But a good bench-mounted drill with a base that is perpendicular to its chuck can be entirely satisfactory.

Naturally, any drill press used will need positive and accurate adjustments to stop the downward movement of the drill at a precise, predetermined depth. This prevents barrels from being drilled more than halfway through and prevents drill break-through on irregular inside receiver surfaces. The prevention of drill break-through is important whenever the drilled hole is located over any contoured or stepped inside receiver surface. A drill that breaks through on such a surface can "walk" away from its original axis and elongate holes. Oval holes cannot take a full thread.

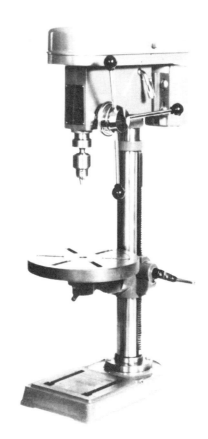

A precision drill press is one of the most often used power tools in the gunsmith's shop. This is a bench-mounted Jet, from Brownells.

A portable grinder is handy and relatively inexpensive. It is useful for regrinding screwdrivers and rough-shaping chisels.

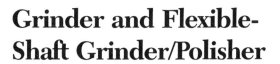

Grinder and Flexible-Shaft Grinder/Polisher

Of all the power tools in a home workshop, a small grinder is one of the most useful. It can be used for regrinding screwdrivers, rough-shaping chisels, and shortening screws (though a lathe is preferable for this last task).

A flexible-shaft polishing/grinding tool can be used for slicking up feeding ramps and similar chores. However, for the most part, its application will be limited to military-surplus firearms.

Lathe

A small lathe can also be a useful home tool. The only sure way to obtain a proper barrel cut (when shortening) and accurately recrown the cut barrel is with a lathe.

Small, flexible-shaft grinders can speed some otherwise impossible grinding jobs. This is a Chicago Wheel and Manufacturing tool.

A small precision lathe, like this Emco Compact 5, is useful in a gunsmith's shop, especially for cutting or recrowning a barrel.

Milling attachments are available for drill press and lathe. They sometimes can make easy work of an otherwise difficult task.

A good lathe will also enable you to turn smooth contours on stepped military barrels. However, no barrel turning should be attempted without also having the ability to straighten the barrel. Barrels that escape bending (which occurs because of the release of internal stresses during a turning operation) are very rare indeed.

A lathe is also useful for making some small parts, such as certain firing pins. It is essential to any rebarreling effort and is almost a must for any rechambering effort.

Polishing Wheel

Polishing wheels need to be sturdy, large, and driven by very powerful motors if they are to be practical for polishing firearms in preparation for bluing or plating. Polishing is as much an art as checkering, and few folks ever learn how to get a firearm as shiny as a new mirror without causing value-destroying rounded edges, pulled holes, and the like. Thus, polishing wheels and their motors and fixtures have limited application for the home hobbyist. Moreover, the ventilation necessary for safe polishing requires a carefully engineered exhaust system. Best not to get deep into this area without first talking to a number of commercial refinishers.

Electric Checkering Tool

Almost all custom stockmakers these days use an electric checkering tool. It speeds up the work enormously and makes it far easier—in a physical sense. In terms of concentration, steadiness, and the need to be meticulously careful, it actually seems to make the work harder for some people, at least until they've gained a bit of experience in this delicate art. And an art it most certainly is. A mistake in design, a miscalculation, or the slightest slip of the hand, and a stock that might have been an object of beauty as well as a functional gem can instantly become a "junker."

All the same, checkering, like any other stock work, is fun, useful, extremely gratifying when you turn out a good job—and potentially profitable if you become really adept. My advice is to read all you can on the subject, and begin by trying your hand on a cheap or battered old stock (preferably several such stocks) that you won't mind sacrificing if things go wrong. I also suggest that you start by copying or slightly varying simple patterns before creating your own or graduating to more complex designs or cutting very fine patterns that require difficult curves, borderless, no-runover edges, 20-lines-to-the-inch delicacy, and the like.

Portable power drills have little value to the gunsmith except for cleaning heavily leaded bores when fitted with a rod and wire brush.

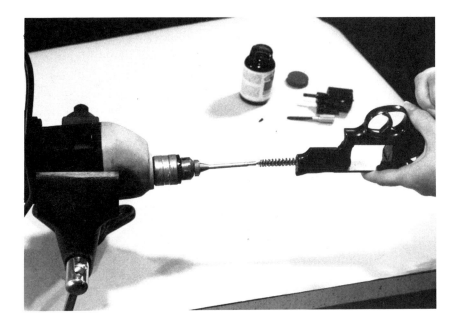

Hand Drill

The use of a hand-held electric drill is limited in gunsmithing. When clamped to a bench, this tool is useful for power-scrubbing lead-fouled bores. But beyond this, the use of a manually directed drill demands a very steady hand and an exacting eye. Even a slightly misdirected bit can bring grief. It's best to consider a small benchtop drill press for drilling needs, as a hand-held drill is an accident about to happen.

Work-Area Safety and Efficiency

The installation of any power tool should be based on considerations of safety, lighting, and work space. Except for the operator, there should be no traffic in and around the work area. Adequate shielding is necessary. For example, all grinding wheels (which can explode) should have adequate covers over them and adequate means of vacuuming away the by-products of grinding. Eye protection and hand protection should be kept at the work station and used at all times.

Except for hand drills and such, your power tools must be permanently and securely mounted. A drill press or lathe that can shift is dangerous and can ruin a job or a part of your anatomy. Each power tool also requires special operating knowledge (and practice before it's used on any valued gun part). While drill-press operation may seem fairly straightforward and is mastered rather quickly, running a lathe at times requires very special knowledge. Home-study (correspondence) courses are available, but it's even better to attend a high-school or trade-school evening course in machine-shop practices. And even after that, you want to keep a good machinist's handbook in the work area.

5

Work Area and Special Tools

Every craft has its own requirements with regard to work space and special equipment. Fortunately, the home gunsmith's requirements are modest. Perhaps the most important consideration in locating and setting up your shop is that it be free of all distraction at the times when it will be used. It makes good sense to select an area remote from normal household traffic. If you live alone, this is no problem. If there are children, young adults, or a spouse at home when you will be working, it's best to select an area well out of the way. A corner in the basement or attic, or a small unused room can be a perfect place to set up shop.

Work and Storage Area

The space selected must be well lighted; this point cannot be overstressed. Sometimes the ability to find out what's wrong with a firearm boils down to being able to see a part that is rubbing or binding against some other part. The only clue might be a very small, hard-to-see spot that has been rubbed bright by friction.

Other efforts, especially the assembly or disassembly of intricate parts groups, require plenty of light reaching down into the mechanism. Many folks simply hang a good battery of fluorescent lighting above the workbench, and often this can be a satisfactory solution.

However, if the ceiling above the work space is low, the normal moving about of a 50-inch-long firearm can create the hazard of broken glass should a barrel or buttstock bump a long fluorescent tube. This is especially true when bringing a gun to the shoulder to check a scope's eye relief, when disassembling barreled actions from stocks, or even when using a cleaning rod. Where low ceilings are present, I prefer standard bulbs mounted in out-of-the-way places. Two, or perhaps three, bulbs of 150 to 200 watts, teamed with a spot lamp that can be swiveled to direct its beam where most needed, often make an ideal lighting combination for the work area.

Avoid placing any bulb where it will be within three feet of the critical work space. Of course, if bulbs are adequately shielded from accidental breakage with clear, unbreakable covers, then the placing of lights or the style selected becomes less critical. It may be best to install lighting after the bench has been built, unless you are absolutely certain of your requirements.

Any work area selected will have specific lighting needs, and sufficient light will vary with the age and eyesight of the gunsmith. Most of us require ten times more light at age 50 to see equally well, under a specific set of conditions, as we did when we were 10 years old. Plenty of light for a 25-year-old will prove entirely inadequate for a typical 55-year-old.

The bench itself is equally important. Through the years, I've found that most folks err by building a bench too low to work with guns comfortably. You need to get a bit closer to your work than other hobbyists. A benchtop 36 inches from the floor is an absolute minimum, and one between 38 and 42 inches is usually preferable, depending on the user's height. This range will be ideal for vise-mounting, too, with the extra height of the vise bringing work even closer to the eyes. A stool with the seat 12 inches lower than the benchtop works well for most of us. The important criteria of bench and stool height are that you be comfortable and the work be easy to manipulate.

It is important to have sufficient space to lay out disassembled firearms in an area not directly in use as a work station. Tools and maintenance equipment should also fit on the bench without encroaching on the area actually used for working. A cluttered bench can result in firearms or parts being put down on top of tools, other parts, or what have you. When this happens, needless marring of the gun's finish can result.

I find an L-shaped bench most convenient, using one section for laying out the disassembled firearm and the other for actual work and tools. I keep the section where the disassembled gun is to be placed free from all other items in order to prevent any possible damage. The L shape keeps the firearm and its various parts a lot handier than if they were placed at the far end of

a long, straight bench—and that can save a lot of time.

The dimensions of a benchtop, regardless of its shape, should give you the equivalent work area of a 12-foot length and at least a two-foot width. Any additional space on a longer bench generally will not be used except as a junk accumulator. A wider bench, up to perhaps three feet, is a nice plus, but any additional width will be unused as it will be awkward to reach farther back. I prefer an L-shaped bench to have a seven-foot section (the longer leg of the L) with a shorter five-foot section.

I use the short section for storing the firearm and subassemblies not needed at the work station. I like my medium vise to be mounted at the right front corner of the long section. The small vise is mounted just to the right side of the bend in the bench. I mount my large vise on a separate, sturdy, three-by-three-foot bench.

Allow plenty of room under the short length of the workbench for storage bins and drawers in which you will keep tools and parts. I do not like any shelving under the long bench section, unless it is well recessed so that I can sit comfortably with my legs under the work station.

While many folks store tools, materials, parts, or cleaning equipment on shelves above the back edge of the bench, I do not. It's too easy to drop an item as it's taken from or placed on such shelving, or to knock another item off the shelf. Falling items always seem to land on top of a stock or scope, damaging or disrupting work in progress.

The top of any gunsmithing bench must be level. Small parts that roll off to vanish on the floor can be a real cause of lost time. The top of the bench must be free from protruding bolts, lugs, or nail heads that can damage a firearm's finish. And it's extremely important that the bench top be solid. Any cracks, spaces, or holes will swallow up small parts.

Some gunsmiths assure themselves of a solid surface by covering the bench with a sheet of Formica. This takes care of the problem of losing parts in spaces between top planks, but it creates another problem—a too-smooth surface that allows small parts to roll about, and sometimes off, the bench. A piece of slightly textured Masonite is a fine compromise, though it may need occasional replacing.

Any bench used for gunsmithing must be sturdy. There can be no movement when vise-mounted work is filed or rasped, or when a rear sight is driven into a barrel dovetail. If you are reaming a shotgun barrel for interchangeable choke tubes, or recutting a rifle's chamber, the holding vise and the bench must be rock-solid. It follows that the bench must be solidly constructed and firmly bolted to the wall behind it and/or the flooring.

Certain special-purpose tools belong on every bench, while others are needed only occasionally. Included are such items as a front-sight pusher, drill-and-tap fixture, scope leveler, slave pins, bit brace, cleaning vise, headspace gauges, broken-shell extractors for chambers and for reloading dies, collimator, various types of stock-making screws, bore lights, plating kits, etc. Some of these merit discussion, as nothing makes a job go easier than the correct tool or fixture.

Cleaning Vise

The most common maintenance chore, bore cleaning, can be accomplished with the usual vise and properly padded jaws to hold the gun. But the use of a bench vise for this purpose can sooner or later result in needless damage to a firearm. The padded jaws will slip, the gun will be bumped against the vise or slip in it, or the vise will be overtightened.

Bore cleaning can be accomplished after a fashion without a vise, simply by holding the firearm in the hand. But this can lead to other problems. It takes two hands to start a cleaning rod straight, to guide it while brushing and swabbing, and to prevent it from damaging surfaces while being placed into use. There may be times when several weeks of swabbing and soaking are needed to get a high-velocity rifle bore clean, and leaving the gun in a bench vise or simply laying it aside can lead to nicks and dings

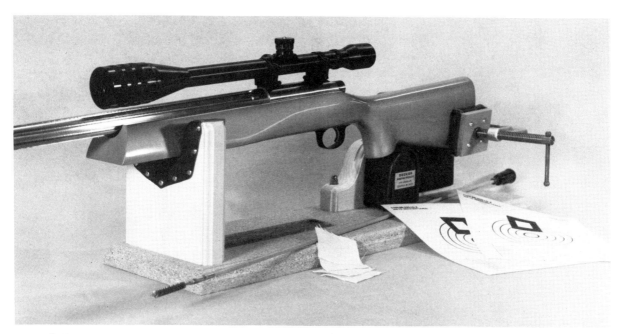

A good cleaning vise (shown is a Decker) is essential for the frequent shooter. It will also serve as a work station for scope installation and many other jobs.

Left-handed cleaning vises are also available for guns with cheekpieces positioned for left-handed shooters.

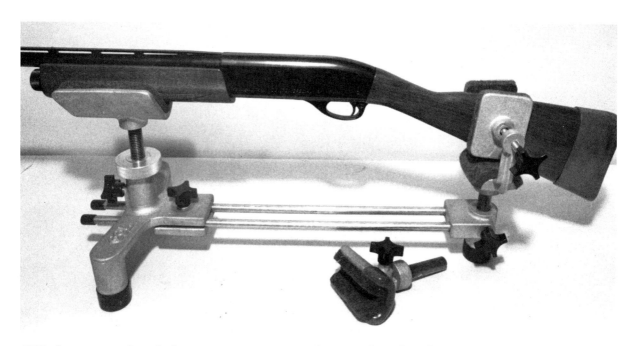

CCL shooting stand, with the appropriate accessory clamp, is also a fine cleaning vise.

when the firearm sooner or later gets in the way of other efforts.

A better solution, an absolute necessity to my way of thinking, is a cleaning vise, a cradle properly padded at the forearm support and at the butt clamping area. A cleaning vise makes bore cleaning easier and almost eliminates any poten-

tial for damage. One good cleaning vise is made by Fred Decker. Others are available.

The Decker vise is nicely designed for a good many uses. For example, it is a far better gun cradle for scope-mounting than a standard vise. It completely eliminates the need to remove a rifle's stock to solidly mount the action for screw tightening during scope-mount installation. It is also an ideal vise for inletting chores, bore sighting, and other jobs for which the butt stock does not need to be removed. Such vises soon earn the gunsmith's regard as indispensable equipment, and they are relatively inexpensive. The Decker vise's milled-away base section is very handy for holding the small screws and parts often used during sight installation and other chores.

Collimator

A collimator, while not essential, can be an extremely important tool for bore-sighting or changing sights for different loads, and it is useful for verifying that a sight is still adjusted properly—for example, when arriving at a hunt-

ing camp after a long trip, during which your gun case may have seen some vigorous handling by airline personnel.

Basically, a collimator allows highly accurate bore-sighting (the alignment of bore and sights on a target) without the errors that can occur due to limited visual acuity or a less than rock-solid rest. The collimator is used with spuds that fit the bore exactly. These are slipped into the muzzle and protrude sufficiently to allow the collimator to be mounted to them. The spuds must fit the bore perfectly, as any canting will induce substantial error. For this reason, I favor spuds of the type made for the Redfield collimator. They feature a hollow shaft with a raised and ever-so-slightly-larger-than-bore-diameter bearing surface. They are split at the end, allowing the over-bore diameter to compress slightly in order to fit the bore exactly. The user, however, should not expect the spuds to work in grossly under- or oversized bores. And care must be taken to prevent misalignment when inserting them. A tolerance range of plus or minus

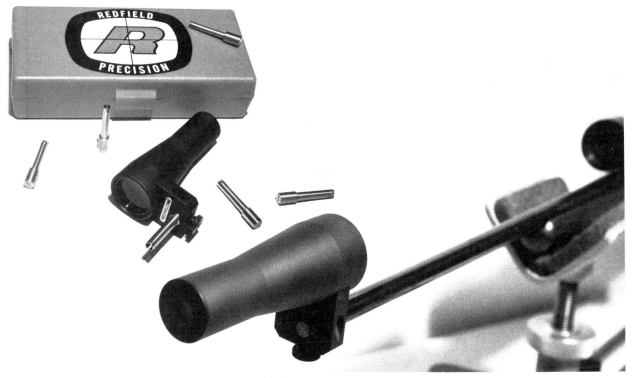

A good collimator and a set of spuds are needed for first-class sight installations as well as for sight-adjustment.

0.001-inch from nominal is quite satisfactory with respect to bore diameter and the proper fitting of Redfield spuds.

When mounted over the muzzle, many collimators show an X-type reticle on the collimating lens as viewed from the shooter's position. The scope's crosshairs are then aligned to intersect the center of the X, and adjusted so that the aiming point coincides with the collimator's reticle center. The firearm is then correctly boresighted. That description covers the use of a collimator equipped only with a center reticle, but if you have a unit such as the Redfield collimator, which is equipped with a grid, its usefulness will be greatly extended.

Because different rifles, even of the same make and model, and even when using the same lot of ammo, will have different points of impact, each rifle's sights will align with its bore in a somewhat different manner. By placing a grid-equipped collimator back into position after actual sighting-in at the range, and making a careful observation of where the sights now align on the grid, you have a reference that will enable you to readjust the sights at a later date if they are moved accidentally or perhaps readjusted for a different load. Simply keep an exact record of the sight's intersection on the grid after actual range firing and adjustment with a specific load.

Also double-check the "repeatability" by removing the bore spud and checking collimator alignment several times. With some bore/spud/collimator combinations, repeatable bore-sightings are not possible.

The point at which sights align on the grid can vary notably with any change in the lot of ammo used. One of my .30-06s has the sight reticle aligned 2½ graduations low and three graduations right when a Nosler 180-grain Partition bullet is used. Sighted with a load using the Speer 150-grain bullet, the scope's reticle is on the grid at ½ graduation high and ¾ graduation left. When the scope is properly adjusted for a Sierra 125-grain bullet, the vertical crosshair aligns perfectly in the center of the collimator's grid, while the horizontal crosshair is three graduations high. When switching loads, I install the collimator and adjust the crosshairs to coincide

with these previously recorded positions, and then I verify the settings by firing at a target, making any necessary minor adjustments.

You may be unable to bring the sights back to an exact adjustment owing to changes in stock bedding or the ability to see the sights with reference to a very exact position on the grid. You should, however, be able to adjust the sights to bring the actual point of impact within an inch or two of where it was when you last sighted-in the firearm with a specific load.

The grid-equipped collimator's usefulness can be further extended. When I travel to some distant place to hunt, I always sight-in my rifle carefully on my home range. When I'm satisfied that the setting is perfect, I install the collimator in the muzzle (always making sure its grid is not canted with reference to the rifle's scope). Then I make a very exact observation as to where the scope's reticle appears on the grid. I make a written note of this observation and stick it in the collimator's box, which then goes into my camera bag. When I arrive at my hunting camp, I can check whether my sight has been knocked out of alignment during the trip; I merely install the collimator and verify the scope's reticle position on the grid against my written notes.

When necessary, I readjust the reticle back to its original position and fire a few rounds to verify the adjustment. A grid-equipped collimator used in this manner can prevent a hunt from being spoiled by a missed shot. My grid-equipped collimator came in a well-padded plastic box that protects it from damage and it has been a welcome piece of equipment on more than just a few hunts.

Crosshair Square

Another tool that is super-handy is the B-Square Cross Hair Square. Normally, shooters who want the crosshairs of a scope to be absolutely aligned with the rifle mount the barreled action in a vise and use a level on the bottom of the action. Then the level is placed on the top of the scope turret, rotating the scope until it also appears level. All this requires removal of the stock and is dependent on a suitable flat on the action and another on top of the scope-adjustment cap. In short, it's a lot of work and the system is less than perfect.

All this can be avoided with bolt-action rifles by removing the bolt, inserting the B-Square Cross Hair Square in its place, and adjusting the scope's vertical crosswire (by turning the scope tube in its rings) to be parallel to the scribed mark on the Cross Hair Square—simple, quick, and quite precise.

Of course, the crosshair level's scribed line is not on the same optical plane as the scope's reticle, so it takes a bit of initial trial and error to determine just where to place your eye in respect to the distance from the level's surface. At best, both vertical lines (level scribe and reticle) will not be simultaneously sharp. Nonetheless, a very accurate leveling of the scope is possible. Be sure to hold the B-Square Cross Hair Square level against the flat bottom surface of the bolt raceway when aligning the scope or the accuracy of the installation will be compromised.

B-Square scope leveler is a simple tool—but a mighty handy one for installing scopes.

Drill Jigs

If you mount a scope on a non-commercial sporter, you may need to drill and tap the receiver. These operations are critical, and many a receiver has been ruined by less than careful procedures.

At the very least, you should use a simple drill jig, such as the B-Square Pro-Jig, for the drilling operation. A jig of this type will guarantee that all the holes are exactly positioned and truly perpendicular, that the recoil shoulder (if there is one) on the mount base will properly align with the mating receiver edge, and that each hole will be the proper distance from the next hole. You must make certain the jig's flat base plate is at a true right angle to the drill bit. This is a passive step if a drill press with a level bed is used.

The Pro-Jig, however, cannot be used for drilling of scope-base holes in a barrel, or holes for open-sight bases, or holes in a receiver's side for a peep sight. Nor can it guarantee that the holes aligned centrally on the receiver will align with the bore's axis. If the barrel is not square in the receiver, a problem could be encountered. But the Pro-Jig is a giant step ahead of any attempt to drill a receiver without some mechanical aid for positive alignment. The Pro-Jig cannot be used as a tap guide, but a separate tap guide can be purchased from B-Square.

In my 12 years of commercial gunsmithing, I found only one system 100 percent satisfactory for installing scope bases, open-sight bases, front ramps, and receiver sights—and if the holes to be drilled were on line with the bore's axis, even side-mount scope bases could be installed easily with it. This system employs the superb Forster Universal Sight Mounting Fixture and a drill press.

Because the Forster Universal Sight Mounting Fixture uses built-in V-blocks to align all holes with the barrel, the drilling and tapping is always accurate, even if the barrel is badly aligned within the receiver. This jig will work with most rifles. The stock, naturally, needs to

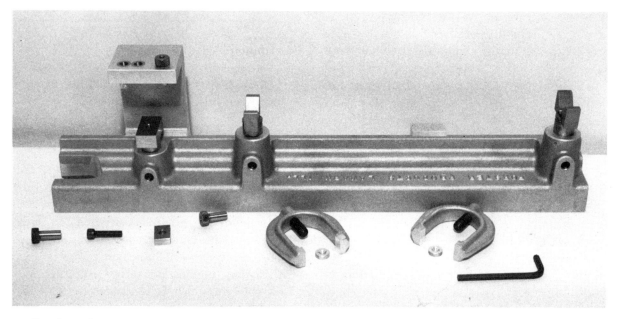

Drill and tap fixture, such as the Forster, is required for advanced gun repair.

be removed. In the case of a rifle with a two-piece stock, only the fore-end need be removed. A rifle with a tubular magazine or with a gas or slide-action system below the barrel will require the removal of these appendages before using the Forster fixture.

The V-blocks are adjustable for height, as is the jig's action-support pillar. To eliminate unnecessary disassembly, there is a clearance cut in its base for the trigger group. Aluminum pads are supplied to protect the barrel from the mounting clamps. The leveling of the action, accomplished by the action-support post, is easy and quick. Hardened steel bushing inserts can accept interchangeable guides for the drill or tap sizes normally used (6–48, 8–40, and 10–32 thread sizes). A tapered point-locator pin insures that each hole drilled will correctly align with the base or sight to be installed.

There is no sight-drilling or tapping job that the Forster jig won't handle. It can be used even when holes are not to be located along the bore's axis. If you anticipate sufficient need to justify the cost, this jig is one of the best investments you can make.

Front-Sight Pusher

A front sight can be difficult to install. The dovetail of the sight and the ramp must mate very snugly. But the usual pounding on the sight, even when a brass punch is used, can

Williams Front Sight Pusher allows you to install or remove a front or rear sight without pounding with a hammer and marring the gun.

distort it, or the ramp screws can shear or strip when the sight is pounded into place. Such problems are not always encountered, but once is enough to make you wish for a better way. The solution is a front-sight pusher such as that sold by Williams. This ingenious little unit will allow you to install or remove a front or rear sight from any ramp or base without marring the sight, ramp, or base, or compromising the ramp-to-barrel integrity. This tool is, in my opinion, a must for the gunsmithing bench.

Headspace Gauges

Headspace in a rifle, shotgun, or handgun is critical. From minimum to maximum, this dimension may have a total spread of only 0.006-inch. Headspace can increase with the use of ammunition that causes slightly too much pressure, or because of faulty gun parts, etc. It should be checked with routine frequency just as you check the oil level in an auto. Unfortunately, few shooters ever perform this task. Headspace gauges are not easily located, but the folks at Forster provide them, as perhaps can others.

Headspace gauges most often are available in three sizes, called "go", "no-go," and "field," (old military nomenclature). The go size is a minimum over which the action should always fully lock. The no-go size is the equivalent of a maximum gauge over which the action should *not* fully close.

The field gauge is best described as a gauge to avoid. It has no real application for the serious hobbyist. In military use, if a gun in the field will close on the no-go, but not on the field gauge, it can, if required, continue to see service. However, the firearm's performance will be far from ideal. Reloading cases fired in a chamber that is beyond the no-go gauge is always hazardous.

Broken-Case Remover

Most of us who do our own gunsmithing are also handloaders. And if you make enough of your own ammunition, sooner or later you will tear the rim off of a case during resizing, leaving the case firmly stuck in the sizing die. There are many products that will allow the stuck case to be removed after drilling and tapping the case head. However, there is a far more practical,

Headspace gauges are available for rimmed, rimless, and belted cases.

efficient way. The E-Z Way stuck-case remover, sold by Superior Products Development Co., is exactly what its name implies. This is the very best tool for the purpose, and the only one of its type. It's very inexpensive, too.

Broken-shell extractors for use in firearm chambers—such as those made by Marbles years ago and those currently made by Alex Inc.—can be invaluable. They allow the removal of a broken shell from a rifle's chamber without much more effort than pushing a cleaning rod into the bore. These broken-shell extractors can also be used if the entire head pulls away from the case body in a loading die.

Broken-shell extractors can make the very difficult, time-consuming task of removing a broken shell a simple two-minute effort. It's advisable to keep a broken-shell extractor on hand for each of the popular bore sizes—.22, .24(6mm), .25, .26(6.5mm), .28(7mm), and .30 caliber.

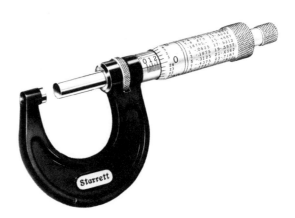

A good micrometer is often needed for gunsmithing chores. This Starrett is an industry standard.

plify common tasks, making them go quicker at an increased level of workmanship.

A good bit brace, some round steel stock for making slave pins, a bore light, and similar items have varying degrees of usefulness. You can purchase such things on an as-needed basis or, if having a well equipped shop gives you pleasure, they can be purchased when you set up a shop area. The use of many of the tools and jigs I've mentioned will be covered in detail in appropriate chapters.

A good micrometer and/or vernier can prove essential for some types of work. These instruments are available at Sears stores and various other outlets that sell tools and machinist's equipment, as well as from gunsmithing-trade suppliers.

Plating Kits

A small, inexpensive plating kit, such as the one supplied by Texas Plating Supply Co., can be very useful. Plated screws or small parts can easily be refinished with gold, silver, nickel, brass, chrome, and so on, at a cost best described as surprisingly low. And firearms can be given special esthetic treatment by gold-plating all exposed screws and so on.

Other Tools

Convenience tools such as swivel drill jigs, recoil-pad trimming jigs, and bolt-jeweling jigs are available from B-Square and other firms that cater to gunsmiths. Each of these jigs helps sim-

The Appendix lists suppliers of special as well as common gunsmithing tools. Write these companies and compare their products before purchasing too many of your needs. And be sure to obtain a catalog from Brownells, the industry specialist in supplying gunsmithing needs of all types.

As the need arises, look over the gunsmith trade catalogs for other special tools and jigs that are designed to make work go faster, more accurately, and without the cussing that usually accompanies certain nettlesome tasks.

6

Parts and Supplies

Having the right part on hand when it is needed is a gunsmithing joy. The need to order one can be complicated by minimum-order requirements, long delays (up to four months of waiting for some), or even total frustration if no one currently has what you need.

The solution is to keep a supply of parts on hand. You do not need to have a spare bolt or stock in the parts bin, but some items such as firing pins, firing pin springs, extractors (with springs and plungers), ejectors (with springs), cartridge guides, and similar parts are all frequently needed. If you are gunsmithing for your own pleasure, one spare part of each type for your personal firearms should be kept on hand.

Some discretion can be used, of course, depending on how much money you wish to convert into spare parts for an anticipated need that

A wide range of parts will be needed as the scope of gunsmithing broadens. Having a variety of parts on hand keeps the job moving.

43

may or may not arise. If you have several Model 70 Winchester Featherweights in the long-action variety, you would reasonably need to keep on hand only one firing pin (and related firing-pin assembly parts). If you have Ruger 77s in .30-06, .280, .270, .25-06, and .35 Whelan (a custom chambering), you will need only one spare extractor because all of them use the same part. But, you will need another extractor to fit any belted magnum, one for any of the .257 Roberts, 7mm Mauser, 6mm Remington, or similar size, and one for the short family of .243, 7mm-08, .308 or .358.

Obviously, it pays big dividends to learn which guns use identical parts. Interchangeable parts can include (but not always) extractors (along with springs and plunger), ejectors, firing pins, sears, cocking pieces, cartridge guides, magazines (with followers and springs), shell carriers, and a host of other items. Referring to the manufacturer's parts list will sometimes help in determining part interchangeability. But you will need to develop the knowledge of which cartridges have identical head dimensions (hence, usually interchangeable extractors and ejectors) or identical length and basic shape (hence, usually interchangeable magazines, magazine springs, magazine follower, and cartridge guide).

It's useful, of course, to know which parts are most often needed. During my dozen years of gunsmithing, I replaced many Marlin Model 336 firing pins for every Winchester Model 94 firing pin. Yet you may need several Model 94 cartridge lifters and never need one for a Marlin Model 336. And folks seem to have a real knack for breaking off cartridge guides on Marlin .22 rimfire bolt-action rifles. Very few Remington Model 870 firing pins ever need replacing, but a fair inventory on Remington Model 1100 O-ring barrel seals might prove handy.

The firearms you own will govern which parts need to be kept on hand for your own use. If you gunsmith for others, you need to know what models are popular in your area and what parts are most often replaced in those models. You can learn a lot by asking questions and doing a lot of listening. Talk to firearms owners, gunshop pro-

Major parts such as bolts are not often needed. But this Sako bolt, eroded by the use of a cartridge that leaked gas around the primer, should be replaced.

prietors, gunsmiths and, if you run into them, factory representatives. Or call the manufacturers' customer service departments and ask them what you should inventory for the guns that interest you.

Owners of rifles that are seldom encountered, or discontinued models, should keep in mind that parts for such firearms may be hard to obtain. And the situation could degenerate to impossible in the future. In these instances, my advice is to stock up now on all likely needs, in quantities matched to the anticipated useful life of the firearms.

Guns that were or are manufactured in the millions of units result in great stores of parts. Owners of Winchester Model 70s or 94s, Marlin 336s or Remington 700s, 870s, 1100s, and so on, should have no difficulty in finding parts. But if you own a Winchester Model 61 or 62 or a Remington 141, a part may prove unobtainable or nearly so, or cost a king's ransom. Planning ahead is always worthwhile.

Guard screws are a common replacement item. They often get damaged, even by careful workman.

Parts are not always as sturdy (or fragile) as appearances make them seem. In 35 years, I've needed only one Winchester Model 70 bolt-stop retaining pin, despite its fragile-looking profile. But I've needed heaps of Springfield firing pins.

Guard screws may occasionally get chewed up, even by a careful workman. And a selection of front sights of varying heights, widths, and styles always make good sense, as does an extra set of scope rings and several recoil pads of assorted sizes and thicknesses. Experience is the best teacher as to what's needed in the parts drawer.

The factory of origin remains the best possible source of parts for current models, and sometimes they have limited parts for recently discontinued models. Some factories will provide parts literally by return mail. Others see nothing wrong with keeping the customer waiting—sometimes for months. So get your parts ordered before you need them.

Savage Arms is an exception to the parts-source advice. Savage (for Savage, Stevens, and several private-label brands) uses an outside

Spare sights and scope rings of all types are commonly needed items.

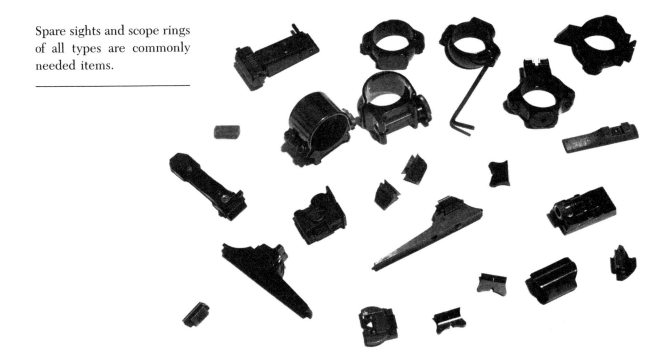

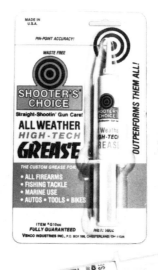

A good inventory of oils, greases, cleaning solvents, and degreasers are essential to the home gunsmith.

firm to service customers with parts or service.

Discontinued parts are often available from specialized dealers such as Gun Parts Corp., and some general manufacturers offer parts for specific firearms. For example, Williams Gun Sight offers firing pins (in kits) for a wide variety of single-shot and double-barreled shotguns, as well as some parts for Lee-Enfield rifles. The Appendix lists many parts dealers. Other dealers' names and addresses can be obtained from such periodicals as the *Gun Digest*, *Shotgun News*, and monthly gun magazines.

Some parts are totally restricted, for reasons of consumer safety or difficulty in fitting. Restricted parts are not available to the general public, but specific ones are sometimes made available to qualified gunsmiths.

Various maintenance and gunsmithing supplies, such as lubricating oils and greases, rust-preventing grease, emery cloth, sand papers of varying grades, a wide selection of stock finishes, gun-cleaning solvents, degreasing solvents, and similar items are best inventoried just as if they were needed parts. Get what's likely to be needed well ahead of time to avoid delays or disappointments.

When received, parts should be thoroughly degreased, cleaned, and amply protected with a totally effective rust-inhibiting grease such as RIG. Then they should be placed in accurately labeled envelopes or parts bins. This can save a lot of confusion later, and prevent the possibility that a good deal of money will turn into a pile of rusted or unidentifiable scrap.

The labeling of parts should include manufacturer, model number, part number, and part name. Any multiple application should be noted. In appropriate instances, also make notes as to whether the part is an old or new style.

Experience will teach when and which specific parts lend themselves to repair. Also, the data contained in Section III of this book include a number of suggestions on which parts can be reworked and which should be replaced. Keep in mind that surface hardness can play an important role in a part's functioning. If you cannot duplicate hardness, or if reworking would destroy the hardness of the original part, the only choice is to replace the piece.

When ordering parts, always state make, model, caliber, and, whenever possible, the serial number or serial-number range of the firearms in which the parts are to be used. Purchase of some parts may require the possession of a Federal Firearms License, so be sure to include a copy of yours with each order.

Finally, it's not a bad idea to mark the cost of a part on the package when you store it. If the part

Keep an adequate supply of stock finishes on hand to avoid touch-up problems.

Pressurized solvents and degreasers are some of the
greatest time-savers ever de-
vised for gunsmithing, eliminating the need for time-
consuming disassembly.

For cold bluing parts, as well as for touch–ups, the
Jenolite Gun Care Kit 1 is recommended. Cold bluing pen (foreground) may be all that is required for
heating scratches.

is installed in a paying customer's gun, or is
simply sold, it's often hard to remember that the
cute little gizmo cost $30 and the big ugly one
cost only 69¢. If you wish to keep your costs
confidential, code the packages. One simple
code is the word *BLACKSTONE*, in which each
letter stands for a number—starting with one,
proceeding to nine, and ending with zero.

If you purchase a part that cost you $13, the
code would be BA. To keep anyone from de-
ciphering your code, use the letters XYZ as
throw-in, meaningless values. For example,
write $13 as BZAX. Any easily remembered 10-
letter word, in which no letter is repeated, can
be used for a pricing code. And any three non-
value letters can be used so long as they do not
duplicate your 10 code letters.

7

Thinking Like a Gunsmith

Thinking like a gunsmith begins with understanding that firearms are mechanical devices that suffer from wear and quickly succumb to neglect. Also needed is the knowledge that firearms must be able to withstand pressures ranging from perhaps 10,000 pounds per square inch to 65,000 pounds per square inch, sometimes even a bit more. The gunsmith should realize that a 12-gauge shotshell producing 10,000 psi (pounds per square inch) is not actually producing only one-sixth the thrust against the bolt face of a 60,000 psi centerfire rifle cartridge. The actual total pressure applied to the bolt, or the chamber, of any firearm depends partly on the surface area of the cartridge. Remember that pressure levels are per square inch.

Thinking like a gunsmith includes a willingness to learn and to invest the time necessary to gain knowledge. Before any attempt is made to repair a firearm, a full understanding of that firearm's design, capability, and functioning cycle is essential.

Thinking like a gunsmith has begun when the owner realizes the consequences of an ill-fitted trigger and understands that few people are qualified to install this part. And when he accepts the fact that there is no way for the average owner to fit certain triggers, but that other triggers can easily be installed, and when he can accurately tell the difference between the two, then he is well along the road of routine gunsmith-like thinking.

The mere knowledge that we cannot possibly know everything will enable us to direct our efforts to those tasks best suited to our ability. This book does not cover the building of a gunstock from a log of wood, nor does it discuss the arts of checkering, carving, and engraving. Those who can excel in such areas will turn to literature dealing with these very highly specialized aspects of gunsmithing.

A lot can be learned by reviewing the material contained in Part III of this book. If you instinctively read material dealing with specific firearms that you do not own, you are, indeed,

thinking like a gunsmith. If you are inexperienced and the text is therefore less than 100
percent clear, and you automatically refer to the
firearms schematic drawing and parts lists to
better understand what is being said—well,
that's really thinking like a gunsmith. And if you
can visualize how another firearm's function
cycle is accomplished, based on what you have
learned about a similar type—indeed, you show
great promise.

The real secret of any worthwhile gunsmith is
the ability to look over a firearm carefully, repeatedly manipulate its action, and finally reach
an accurate conclusion about how it works. To
see all the built-in safeguards is to begin to understand the art of gunsmithing.

PART 2

BASIC MAINTENANCE AND REPAIR

8

Routine Maintenance

No single aspect of firearms ownership is more misunderstood than the need for cleaning. Cleaning a firearm's bore has been suggested by some to be a waste of time. Others have stated that a bore is never adequately clean except prior to the very first shot fired through it. Both extremes are pure hogwash.

Firearm bores must be truly clean if they are to shoot as well as possible. Even the old adage about a .22 rimfire bore never needing cleaning is garbage. Anyone who disagrees needs only to see the results that a truly clean bore will give with respect to accuracy.

I have seen countless barrels that shooters brought to me because they were "shot out." Looking into the bore from the breech showed that the rifling grooves were very nearly the same level as the lands. It doesn't take long to fill a groove that may be only 0.004-inch deep (or less) with copper fouling if the stuff is not removed frequently. A peek into the muzzle always revealed the telltale copper color that is the fouling left by bullets whose jackets contain a high percentage of copper. Barrels that use many lands and very shallow grooves sometimes foul up even more quickly.

The exclusive use of lead bullets does not eliminate fouling. Indeed, the smear of lead left on a bore's surface can be equally difficult to

Muzzle that shows traces of copper coloring in the bore is an indication that a good cleaning is required.

remove, can build up faster, and can have an even greater effect on accuracy.

Velocity is a major factor in metal fouling. The higher the velocity, the greater the fouling. With very hard lead bullets, the problem becomes severe when velocities approach or exceed 1,800 feet per second. With soft lead bullets, extensive leading may occur at 800 feet per second. With copper-jacketed bullets, the problem usually begins to get severe at about 3,000 feet per second.

Because velocity is a major factor in the build-up of heat caused by friction, rimfire barrel fouling often is worst at a point 16 to 23 inches from the breech (the distance at which the bullet reaches its highest velocity). Centerfire rifles usually have the worst build-up right at the muzzle.

The degree of roughness in a bore's surface is also contributory. The rougher the bore, the quicker metal fouling builds up. This is why barrels that have undue surface roughness, or pitting caused by rust, seldom shoot accurately for many consecutive rounds. It is also why a barrel may consistently foul severely at one particular point.

Barrels that have seen extensive use develop a very rough surface due to erosion caused by the hot gases of combustion. This roughness can escape detection except under a microscope. Thus, barrels having extensive use will foul more quickly than those with less use (all else being equal, of course).

Sometimes a new barrel has a somewhat rougher surface than one that has seen limited use. This is surface roughness left by machining and is quickly polished away by bullet passage. It takes only about 100 rounds of centerfire ammo to rid a bore of this roughness. About 500 to 1,000 rounds of rimfire ammo will accomplish the same task.

Because new bores foul quickly and because accumulated fouling becomes more difficult to remove with each succeeding shot, knowledgeable shooters clean new bores very frequently. When velocities of 2,800 fps or greater are standard, cleaning after every fifth shot is not unreasonable for the first 25 to 50 shots. Then cleaning after every 10 to 20 rounds is a good practice until a total of 100 rounds has been fired. Thereafter, clean the bore thoroughly every 15 to 20 shots to maintain peak accuracy. For velocities of 2,000 to 2,800 fps, cleaning frequency can be extended to perhaps cleaning after twice as many rounds have been fired.

When rimfire lead bullets are used, cleaning every 500 rounds (after the first 100) seems about ideal. Centerfire lead bullets demand varying frequencies of cleaning, depending the hardness of the lead. The rule is to clean as soon as the first smears of lead can be detected in the bore.

Solvents

Many shooters use bore cleaners that are not capable of removing deeply embedded barrel fouling, though many will remove the fouling that lies loosely on the surface of the bore. Moreover, some cleaners stop working after five or 10 minutes, and extensive soak periods have no benefit. Other bore cleaners are slightly abrasive, and while they will remove fouling, their abrasive action works on the barrel's steel, shortening the accuracy life of the barrel. I used one such cleaner in an experiment, side by side with a proven, satisfactory cleaner. Both were used in identical 270 Winchester Model 70 Featherweight hunting rifles, fired with identical ammunition an equal number of times under nearly identical conditions. The bore cleaned (carefully, mind you) with the ever-so-slightly abrasive product had a useful accuracy life of just over 2,500 rounds. The bore cleaned with the non-abrasive product maintained useful accuracy for more than 5,000 rounds and is still being used.

Bore cleaners that promise rapid cleaning without soak periods are suspect. However, in instances of serious bore fouling, an abrasive cleaner might be the only way to bring things back to normal. Such cleaners should never be used routinely, except perhaps in rough bores that foul badly with just a few shots. Accuracy life will then be short, but this is the lesser of two evils since a badly fouled bore has no accuracy. Obviously, abrasive cleaners have a specific niche.

The very first step in proper maintenance of a brand new barrel might be to have the bore hand-lapped, using a lead slug and extremely mild polishing compound or a slightly abrasive

Two effective cleaners for heavily fouled bores. Despite the wide choice available, good bore cleaners are not too commonplace.

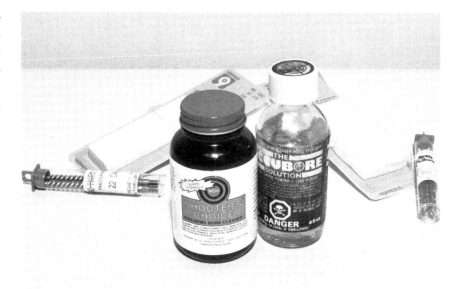

bore cleaner. However, because this is a procedure safely performed only by an expert, it's best left undone unless you know someone eminently qualified.

The second stage is to make sure you have a suitable cleaning rod, brush, jag, patches, and solvent. The use of an aluminum rod, an unforgivable error, has been discussed in the chapter on hand tools. Brass generally is a poor choice and ordinary steel is less than ideal, although it is a grand step forward. The best rod, for reasons given in Chapter 3, is a spring-steel one with a nylon or similar coating. And a good rod for rifled barrels always has a swiveling handle.

While a number of bore cleaners may prove satisfactory, depending on the barrel's smoothness and the velocity of the bullet, I recommend Shooter's Choice when fouling is very heavy. For normal cleaning chores, Shooter's Choice or the Canadian-made Accubore cleaner will prove effective. For lighter cleaning, Rig 44 and Hoppe's No. 9 solvents work well but may require more soaking.

Because of the strength of Shooter's Choice and Accubore cleaners, I do not suggest their use with a bronze-wire brush. They cause the rapid deterioration of any brush with a high

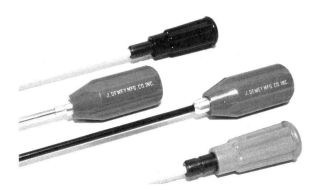

Swiveling handles, as on these Parker Hale and Dewey spring steel, plastic-coated rods, are important to proper barrel care.

copper content. Of course, either can be used with a stainless-steel brush, but such brushes should be used sparingly.

Steel brushes are extremely hard and can erode the bore unless used only when absolutely necessary—and then quite sparingly. Nonetheless, such brushes are useful in removing fouling from severely neglected or rough bores. When brushing, use a solvent such as Rig 44 or Hoppe's No. 9.

To test any bore cleaner for potential copper-

You can test a bore cleaner by immersing a jacketed bullet in a small amount of solvent and allowing it to soak for a few days.

Effective solvent will rapidly change color and, after several weeks, will cause the surface of the bullet's jacket and lead nose to deteriorate.

Difference between an ineffective solvent (*right bullet*) and an effective one (*middle and left bullets*).

the bullet. After several weeks, the best will produce a definite change in the bullet's appearance. It is possible to actually measure the difference in bullet diameter after a period of time if the solvent is very effective. Bullet color will change too, of course, and some solvents will even soften and begin to dissolve the bullet's lead tip.

fouling removal, drop a bullet into a plastic or glass vial that can be sealed. Place only enough solvent in the vial to nine-tenths cover the bullet. Every few days, agitate the container. When a number of solvents are tested simultaneously, the test results after about three weeks are most impressive.

Some solutions will simply show a separation of the "polishing" compound from its oil-like carrier. Others will exhibit no reaction at all with the bullet. Still others will display a discoloration of the solvent as it slowly dissolves the copper on

Jags and Rod Guides

Always use a rod tip that allows the patch to fall free after it has been pushed through the bore. Dragging the patch back into the bore only carries the grit on it back into the bore and increases the risk of scratching or the accumulation of grime in the locking-lug recess.

Always use a good cleaning-rod guide, such as the one made by J. Dewey Co., to protect the receiver from the sharp jag and also to protect the rifle's throat from damage. These are inexpensive and simple to use. They replace the

Dewey cleaning-rod guide, which replaces the bolt, being used in a Remington action to protect the chamber and throat from damage.

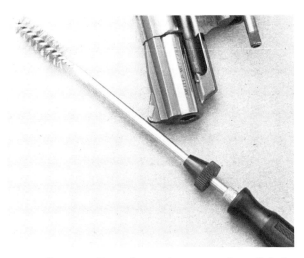

Brass "bumpers" used on cleaning rods will help prevent muzzle damage.

rifle's bolt, and allow the cleaning rod to align properly with the bore.

Wipe the rod's surface with a *lightly* oiled patch before beginning the cleaning operation in order to remove any grit or foreign material. Also carefully inspect the rod's surface for nicks that might cause barrel damage. And wipe the rod off before every successive insertion into the bore.

When possible, always put the rod into the bore from the chamber end to protect the muzzle from excess wear or damage. The last few inches of barrel are extremely important to accuracy, and wear or damage caused by a cleaning rod can ruin accuracy.

There are two suitable types of jags for your cleaning rod. The sharp, pointed style allows you to spear the patch and push it through the bore, and then allows it to fall off at the muzzle when the rod is withdrawn. The other suitable type is the cleated style, which allows the patch to be securely held by simply wrapping it around the jag's cleats. These also allow the patch to fall off at the muzzle—most of the time, anyway.

For firearms that cannot readily be cleaned from the chamber end (many semiautos, pumps, and lever-actions) great care must be used when inserting the rod into the muzzle. Always use a slip-on brass fitting to prevent the rod handle from bumping into the muzzle. Use care to guide the rod by hand as accurately as possible, in order to prevent undue contact that could damage rod or bore. In these instances, it is preferable to use a cleated jag that will hold the patch on the rod in order to prevent it from falling off into the action or chamber at the end of the stroke—unless it is easily retrieved.

Cleaning Procedures

It is always beneficial to push a patch only one way through the bore even if it means removing the patch by hand. Patches are for removing loosened fouling—they do not do the cleaning, as is so often assumed. Patches must fit very snugly if they are to wipe the bottoms of the grooves. Naturally, the fit of the patch depends greatly on the diameter of the jag being used.

Begin the cleaning procedure by pushing a thoroughly soaked patch through the bore. Repeat this operation, being sure you can observe an excess of fluid exiting the muzzle in front of the second patch. Then pass two dry patches through the bore. This will remove all loose fouling and grit.

Then pass another soaked patch through the bore. Remove the jag from the rod and install a bronze bore brush of the correct size. Soak the brush in solvent and push it through the bore, allowing it to exit the muzzle (or chamber), and the pull it back through the bore until it exits. Repeat this in-and-out brushing once for each shot fired since the last cleaning. Then run a dry, clean patch through the bore.

Now push a soaked patch through the bore. Follow with another soaked patch, being sure excess solvent exits the bore in front of the second patch, and then set the firearm aside in a horizontal position or with the muzzle down just a tad to keep solvent from running into the action. Allow the bore to soak at least 30 minutes. Three or four hours is better. Keep in mind that this advice applies to solvents that continue to work as long as the barrel remains damp.

At the end of the soak period, run a dry, clean patch through the bore. Repeat until the bore is dry. Proper bore cleaning always demands repeated applications of solvent over a period of time.

After the soak period, begin the same progress over again, omitting only the brushing step (which can be repeated if fouling is severe). If, at the end of the second soak, the cleaning patches come out heavily stained, consider the advisability of soaking a third time for a full 24 hours. It is counterproductive to allow a soak of more than 24 hours, but keep repeating the process until the dry patches come out without any green stain.

It may take three to five day-long soak periods (using a strong solvent) before all the fouling is removed from a smooth barrel that has been fired 15 to 20 times. A greater number of soaks will be necessary if the bore is rough or if a greater number of rounds has been fired. That's right—it can take a week or more to get a barrel really clean!

Don't be tempted to stop the cleaning process too soon. If you fired the rifle 20 times and remove the fouling from only 15 shots, think how much fouling will be left in the barrel when it has had hundreds of rounds fired through it. Then you may never get it truly clean.

If the barrel is truly clean, you will not see any traces of copper-colored fouling when looking at the rifling near the muzzle. A gray-colored appearance after cleaning is normal and is not related to fouling, but is rather the steel with the bluing worn away.

Does all this pay dividends? You bet, and big ones at that. I have done enough experimenting to know that rifles which routinely shoot 1½-inch groups with "cleaned" bores can actually shoot groups as small as ½-inch to ¾-inch when *truly* clean. And rifles that appear to be inaccurate, shooting five-shot three-inch groups at 100 yards, can often be restored to a level of 1½-inch groups after a thorough bore cleaning.

Immediately wipe any spills off the stock during cleaning. Any solvent that can effectively attack copper fouling, lead fouling, plastic residue (from shotgun wads), powder fouling, and primer residue will attack stock finish if it's given time to do its work. Those that are harmless to stock finishes are, at best, weak cleaners.

Remember to keep scope-lens caps in place during cleaning. More than a few scopes have had a lens pierced by a wayward cleaning jag. If you have not bumped a scope cap (or worse, a scope lens), you probably do a minimum of cleaning or are one of those few people who are truly careful all of the time. Whether or not you might run the cleaning rod through a scope lens, caps will keep powerful solvents from destroying the surface coatings on your scope's lenses.

After bore cleaning, it is imperative to get all solvent out of action recesses. Solvent left in a bolt-lug recess can eventually work down along the action screw, contaminating the stock or bedding material. If this happens, a stock's bedding might eventually be ruined. Special cleaning apparatuses, such as those made by Sinclair International, are available to ease the chore of cleaning lug recesses. But a few Q-Tips can do a satisfactory job of removing solvent, grit, and sludge from the lug area.

Generally speaking, wiping all remaining action surfaces with a solvent-soaked cloth and then drying them will clean the metal satisfactorily. Bolt faces may need to soak a bit before drying to remove all traces of brass accumulation. Use a solvent-soaked toothbrush to reach hard-to-get-at spots. When finished, a *few* drops of oil should be sufficient to coat the entire working surfaces of any action.

Caution: After cleaning, always visually inspect the bore to insure that no patch, piece thereof, or excess fluid remains in the barrel. Firing a gun with an obstruction in it can wreck the gun and maybe even the shooter.

Strip Cleaning

After every 800 rounds or so, consider dismantling the entire action to rid it of accumulated oil, dirt, combustion by-products, and any other foreign material. A complete strip cleaning is also in order whenever the firearm has been subjected to immersion or heavy rain, sleet, or snow. A few drops of moisture can rust internal parts and surfaces beyond repair.

Normally, most actions do not need to be stripped of every part for thorough cleaning. In fact, it is best to avoid unnecessary dismantling, especially of triggers, ejectors, and extractors. Also note that retaining pins, clips, springs, and plungers wear with each stripping, and these parts are easily lost and sometimes broken during disassembly and reassembly.

Once an action is free of the stock (with the bolt removed) most surfaces, even deep inside sub-assemblies, can usually be cleaned with a pressurized solvent. However, many bolts should always be separated into two pieces (the bolt body and the assembly consisting of firing pin, spring, and cocking piece). This two-piece takedown of most bolts will suffice for proper cleaning.

There are a number of pressurized gun-cleaning products. Select one that is non-gumming, that will displace moisture and remove all foreign material, and that dries without leaving any residue. A product with sufficient viscosity to flow smoothly is essential to insure that all of it drips free of the various mechanisms. A blast of dry air (such as the canned air available at photographic shops) can be employed to help remove all the cleaner. Do not use compressed air of the gas-station variety, as such air usually contains a great deal of moisture. Keep your eyes shielded with glasses whenever using compressed air or

When using pressurized cleaning solvents and degreasers, especially with compressed air, wear glasses to protect your eyes.

pressurized cleaners. The cleaner I like best is Birchwood Casey Gun Scrubber. Others also work well.

Parts cleaned with a pressurized cleaning solvent should be set aside to allow ample time for complete draining of the cleaner—usually overnight. Shaking parts before positioning for good drainage will help rid them of a lot of the cleaner. I do not like to use any cleaner containing oils or preservatives, as these tend to attract dirt.

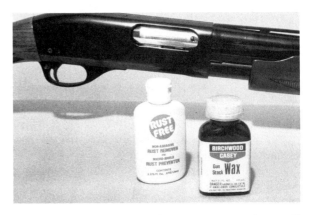

Dry rust preventatives and stock waxes work as well as oils on outside metal and wood surfaces and are not nearly as messy.

Oiling

Naturally, all parts should receive a light coat of friction-reducing and rust-preventing oil after cleaning. But I hasten to point out that oiling is often overdone. When correctly used, oil cannot be seen and almost cannot be felt on the parts. To use more than this invites the accumulation of dirt. Apply a drop to your fingertip and wipe all parts carefully. A one-third drop applied to hinge joints and moving parts is adequate. Spread it over these parts by working the action repeatedly. Because oil should be used sparingly, I usually avoid pressurized cans.

One of the best lubricants available is Rem Oil. Whatever oil you choose, be sure it is non-gumming at low or high temperatures. Any oil that freezes can render your rifle useless, causing misfires and jams.

If a rifle is to be used in extremely cold weather (10°F. or less), I prefer to use no oil at all. However, a rifle used extensively without lubricant will suffer unnecessary wear. Happily, this seldom applies to hunting rifles since relatively few shots are taken when afield.

It is important to keep exposed surfaces protected from the elements. A good coat of gun wax works as well as a light application of oil and will not be messy. One product I have been using that seems to protect smooth finishes from rust, if applied after each use, is Rust Free (manufac-

tured by MJL Industries). Others are available, and many auto waxes work well, too.

Stock Protection

Stocks should be protected from the ravages of weather, perspiration, and plain wear and tear. A good coat of auto or furniture polish works very well. Wax that gets unto checkering or hard-to-reach places can be removed with a soft toothbrush. Commercial gunstock waxes can also be used. Waxes behave differently under varying conditions, so if one does not prove satisfactory try others until you find one that suits your needs.

Degreaser

For severely gummed actions, a pressurized degreasing fluid is useful. And after cleaning a firearm to be used in extremely cold climates, a spray of pressurized degreaser such as Rig 3 will be good insurance that every trace of cleaning solvent has been removed. Another application of pressurized degreaser is for the removal of oil from screws and screw-hole threads when mounting sights. This will be covered in a later chapter. A degreaser is also necessary for other maintenance chores such as touching up bluing scratches.

Cold Bluing

Before cold bluing is applied, the surface must be prepared by removing any burrs or deformed metal. This usually can be done with the very careful application of a fine file and/or crocus cloth. Take pains not to remove bluing from surrounding areas. Keep your repair confined to the damaged metal. When the surface is properly smoothed (often simple scratches or bluing rubs require no pre-polishing), the area should be sprayed with short blasts of a pressurized degreaser to prepare it for application of the cold blue. Then wipe the area dry with a clean cotton patch before applying the cold blue.

The bluing used for touch-up is available in liquid and paste forms. With a cotton swab, the liquid blue is easily applied just to the area to be touched up. I find the paste far more difficult to use.

Some touch-up bluing solutions adversely affect the original blue of surrounding areas. For this reason, a bluing pen (ballpoint applicator), can be advantageous. In any case, test any cold bluing in an area that cannot be seen. Naturally, do this sparingly. If you want to touch up a barrel, test the solution on part of the barrel. Checking on another part, such as the receiver or bolt handle, may not tell you what you want to know because these may be made from a different type of steel and react differently to the touch-up bluing.

Touch-up cold bluing can often be satisfactory. Kits are available for doing a complete bluing job.

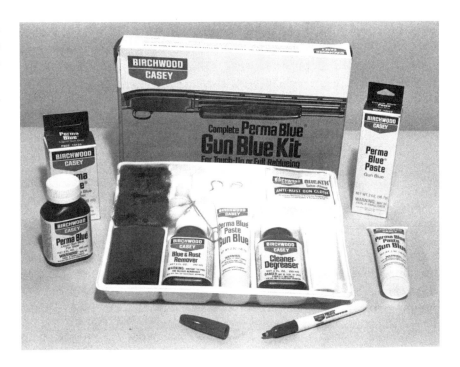

Routine Checks and Disassembly Tips

Proper gun maintenance means more than cleaning. All screws and fasteners must be periodically checked to insure that they are doing their jobs. Check each one with the appropriate screwdriver or other hand tool.

It is important to realize that fasteners, by their physical size, require specific degrees of tightness. Attempts to exert undue pressure can result in broken screw heads, stripped threads, or ruined hand tools. Failure to keep fasteners adequately tightened can cause inaccuracy or malfunctions. Specifics on the proper amount of effort to be applied have been covered in Chapter 3. When checking fasteners, do not attempt to increase the torque previously applied. Simply exert enough to insure that the fastener has not worked loose.

Cleaning should include a dismantling into basic component groups whenever a gun's been used in inclement weather that has resulted in water penetration into the action or between metal and wood. When a firearm has been exposed to saltwater spray, cleaning should start as soon as possible, certainly within a few hours after the hunt. A strip-down to basic subassemblies should also occur after every 100 rounds fired through most semiautomatic centerfire guns. Rimfire semiautomatics should be stripped to basic subassemblies about every 1,000 rounds. The use of pressurized cleaning solvents on subassemblies is suggested in lieu of disassembling complex part groups. This can result in a perfect job without the danger of lost, broken, or mutilated small parts, and the job will go much faster.

Bolt-actions should have the internal parts separated from the bolt body when cleaning, but do not remove extractors or ejectors, or reduce the firing-pin assemblies into component parts. Doing so will increase the possibility of needless wear. Clean all the internal surfaces that can be reached with swabs.

Do not further disassemble a bolt gun, because every time a rifle is removed from its stock and is reassembled, it will need a sight adjustment or at least verification of point of impact. Of course, if you suspect that moisture has seeped between the stock and metal parts or penetrated to the trigger group, etc., it will be necessary to disassemble the rifle.

If this is necessary, minimize the possibility of a point-of-impact change by tightening action screws in the reverse order of their removal, and try to duplicate the same amount of torque on each that was present before disassembly. A bolt gun is usually rugged enough to last its entire accuracy life without a complete strip cleaning if it does not get wet internally. And useful accuracy will be extended if you don't have to fire extra rounds to check sight adjustment after disassembly.

Semiautomatics need to be stripped for cleaning after approximately every 100 rounds if reliable functioning is to be assured. There are exceptions, however. If you are using a light, clean-burning target load in a semiauto shotgun, you may be able to go 500 rounds without a strip cleaning. Use common sense, based on how dirty the gun actually is when you first strip clean. Needless take-aparts will cause needless wear. However, if your semiauto seems excessively dirty because of the ammunition used or other factors, more frequent cleaning is appropriate. If you experience malfunctions caused by accumulated dirt, combustion by-products, or unburned propellant in the action, obviously your cleaning is not nearly frequent enough.

Pump and lever firearms tend to get a bit dirtier than bolt guns. Yet complete disassembly is seldom required. Indeed, due to the complexity of many such firearms, shooters often do not disassemble the actions until there is a real need to do so. This is acceptable if the shooter pays close attention to such warning signs as an action that gets a bit more difficult to operate or does not function as smoothly as it should.

Strip cleaning, in normal firearms maintenance, never means the disassembly of subgroups, complicated gas systems, mainspring housings, firing-pin assemblies (particularly in bolt-action firearms), and so on. I cannot overstress that the disassembly of such part groups should never be undertaken except to replace worn or broken parts. Even after total submersion in saltwater, such assemblies can *usually* be cleaned effectively with repeated applications of pressurized solvents, degreasers, and oils.

Parts Replacement

Other routine maintenance might include the replacement of extractors, ejectors, or springs and plungers. When a firearm begins to close hard on cartridges, the cause often is a rough extractor face that binds as it attempts to slip over the cartridge rim. A gun that begins to eject weakly may need a new extractor, a new ejector, or a new ejector plunger and spring (assuming these parts and related working surfaces have been checked for proper operation after a thorough cleaning). Such replacements are easily accomplished. But be careful, as small springs, plungers, ejectors, and extractors are easily lost when they escape under compression and bounce about. The replacement of these parts will be covered in the sections dealing with specific models.

Handgun Maintenance

Revolvers and semiautomatic handguns need special attention, especially when lead bullets are used. Lead build-up at the front of a cylinder and the back edge of a revolver barrel can quickly cause difficult cylinder rotation in guns having minimum barrel-to-cylinder gaps. If left to accumulate, such build-up can be extremely difficult to remove.

Lead in handgun bores can sometimes be quite severe. It is not wise to continue the use of lead bullets that cause excessive leading, nor is it wise to shoot lead bullets in a handgun whose bore is rough and therefore leads excessively. But leading needs to be dealt with, even in good bores using good ammunition.

Normally, a bronze bore brush soaked with solvent and vigorously applied will rid the bore, cylinder face, rear of barrel, frame area at rear of barrel, and outside of the cylinder of accumulated lead. This method is to be preferred over all others as it is not harmful to metal surfaces and will not cause any noticeable blue wear.

The use of lead-removing cloths is not suggested for blued or plated surfaces as these cloths soon wipe away finishes. Torn to patch size, such cloths can be useful in bores, but their performance is only about on a par with a solvent-soaked brass or bronze wire brush.

Power Cleaning

In cases of really stubborn or very heavy lead deposits, cleaning time can be shortened drastically by motorizing the brushing operation. Simply mount a cleaning-rod shaft (no handle) in an electric drill, preferably one with a variable speed. Then screw a solvent-soaked brush to the rod. Run the motor at medium speed and slowly push the barrel (or leaded surface) over the brush. This will quickly brush the leading free of the metal.

Take care in any brushing, whether by hand or power, to allow only the soft brass or bronze wires to contact the bore or metal surfaces. Any contact by the rod (or power-drill chuck) can cause accuracy-destroying or finish-marring damage.

Brushing, even with a power assist, is not particularly beneficial in the removal of copper fouling. Only a soaking with a copper-dissolving solvent is effective. Avoid any excessive brushing

Using a power drill to spin a bore brush at moderate speeds is an effective way to rid a handgun bore of extremely heavy lead deposits.

to help rid a bore of this type of fouling.

Power brushing can sometimes be useful in cleaning up severely leaded shotgun bores or in removing excessive plastic residue. However, great care must be taken to keep the long cleaning rod from contacting the bore. Some older shotgun barrels are quite soft and should not be subjected to power brushing.

The soft steels sometimes used in .22 rimfire barrels should never be subjected to any form of power brushing. Even the relatively soft copper or bronze wires used for brushes can be damaging to such barrels.

Generally speaking, avoid the use of steel-wire bore brushes, and never use such brushes for power brushing or on outside finished surfaces.

Naturally, it's wise to avoid firearms that require excessive amounts of maintenance. For most sport, a bolt-action rifle will prove completely satisfactory, will be as accurate as possible, and will require minimum maintenance. An autoloader can be quite satisfactory if you remember its special requirements for routine cleaning. Keep in mind that some autoloaders prefer light applications of a high-pressure grease, rather than a few drops of oil, to maintain reliable functioning. Lever- and pump-actions may be appealing but sometimes require more complicated maintenance. There are exceptions, of course. The Marlin lever-actions, for example, are as simple to maintain as any type of rifle.

Scope Maintenance

Don't forget your scope when doing your cleaning chores. After the gun is clean, remove the scope caps and examine the lenses for accumulations of dirt and smudges. As needed, apply a single drop of camera-lens cleaner to a lint-free lens-cleaning tissue (never directly to the lens). Start at the middle of the lens and clean in a circular pattern out to the edge of the lens. Repeat with a dry lens tissue and the job will be done.

Remember that not all lens-cleaning tissues are lint-free. Those that leave a dusty lint on the lens are about useless. Good tissues have a crisp feel rather than a soft, textured one.

Keep oil, grease, solvents, and any cleaning compounds away from scopes. The gaskets that keep lenses tight and scope bodies waterproof can be adversely affected by chemicals. Use only a clean silicon-impregnated wiping cloth on the scope tube, and avoid contact with lens surfaces when wiping the tube.

Miscellaneous Reminders

When performing routine maintenance, keep in mind each firearm's specific requirements. A trace of oil needs to be present on a revolver's ratchet, hand (pawl), front and rear lock-up points, and all surfaces around which the cylinder rotates. Tubular magazines, which accumulate interior moisture, will rust horribly if they are not cleaned as needed. The same applies to the inside surfaces of detachable clips. Revolver ejectors need special attention to insure that no action-stopping grime builds up underneath or around them. Some gas-operated semi-automatics build up unbelievable deposits in and around the gas port and piston.

Learning what is needed starts with reading the owner's manual. And knowing what is needed should also come from getting quite familiar with an individual firearm's characteristics. Routine maintenance, carefully and slowly performed, provides a great deal of insight into the special requirements of individual firearms. One thing is certain, the more complex a firearm's design, the more parts it will have and the more maintenance it will require.

9

Correcting Accuracy Problems

Every shooter cherishes an accurate rifle or handgun, although individual definitions of accuracy vary so widely that one person's inaccurate firearm may be another's treasured favorite.

Technically, accuracy has two distinct meanings. In one, accuracy is the measure of a firearm's ability to shoot a very small group. After placing three, five, or perhaps ten shots into a single group, the acceptable level of accuracy will vary with shooter and application. Shooters generally agree that a big-game rifle producing an average group size of 1½-inches (for five five-shot groups fired at 100 yards) is quite accurate. Some will use three three-shot groups as a criterion, though such limited shooting will not precisely reflect a rifle's true capability. Others, usually those who are truly fascinated by accuracy, will use the average group size of five ten-shot groups as a measure. Obviously, if a rifle's individual group size varies greatly, the average group size may not reflect the firearm's field capability.

Serious varmint hunters will demand that the average group size be one inch or less before a rifle is considered satisfactory. Dedicated

Accuracy can differ according to the shooter's firearm and ammunition. This squirrel hunter's definition of accuracy is one-inch groups from 10 shots at 75 yards.

66

For ultra-long-range varmint shooting most hunters will settle for no more than ¾-inch groups for 10 shots at 100 yards.

benchrest shooters will junk a barrel that shoots only ½-inch groups, while a rimfire squirrel hunter will be looking for one-inch capability at 75 yards.

Accuracy also means the ability of a rifle to place one group at the intended point of impact today, tomorrow, next week, and even next year. To a hunter, it is perhaps more important to have a consistent point of impact than to be able to shoot small groups. The hunter correctly reasons that a small group at the intended point of impact today, followed by a small group that is two inches to the left tomorrow, followed by a small group that is six inches low next week or next season, is not what he needs. The hunter wants to place his shots at the intended point of impact whenever he shoots, and would gladly accept two-inch groups that always print where intended, rather than one-inch groups that wander about the target randomly with the passage of time.

Accuracy and Actions

Accuracy is closely related to the type of firearm used. In general, bolt-action rifles and some single-shots are the most accurate. Surely any of these that cannot group under two inches at 100 yards, after tuning, is not a particularly good specimen. Semiautomatics tend to be less accurate, with 2½- to 3½-inch groups (again at 100 yards) considered good. Pump guns are often slightly less accurate than semiautos. Accuracy of lever-action rifles tends to be the poorest. Lever guns grouping four to six inches are often considered typical.

Of course, exceptions occur with any action type. Indeed, I have shot more than a few Marlin Model 336 lever-action rifles that were capable of consistent 2½-inch groups and, occasionally, even better. And I have fired a few other lever guns that would not average six inches regardless of what was done with them.

When evaluating a rifle's performance, it is necessary not only to consider the type of action being evaluated but also the known performance of similar models of the same make or style. For instance, a Remington Model 700 or Winchester Model 70 that cannot be made to shoot 1½-inch groups, or less, would be a rare exception deserving all the scornful terms often applied to a gun with poor accuracy.

Yet another bolt-action model, of which I have shot a great many, is just as apt to turn in 2½-inch groups as one-inch groups—even when tuned to perfection. I won't use a rifle that's not more

Bolt-action rifle is usually the most accurate type of firearm for hunting.

predictable than that. But many folks do, and then they want a magic formula that enables these guns to shoot consistent 1½-inch groups. As a rule, it's just not possible to obtain their goals.

Ammunition and Accuracy

Ammunition plays an important role in accuracy. As you buy it in the local gunshop, factory ammunition is seldom capable of better than two-inch groups—and then only when fired from a very accurate bolt-action rifle. Sure, there are exceptions; some mighty fine lots of ammunition have been produced. I have fired groups as small as ½-inch with factory loads. But such lots of ammo are exceptional. In fact, I regard two-inch accuracy from factory ammo as exceptional and

two- to three-inch groups as normal.

Thus, if a rifle's accuracy is to be truly evaluated, the shooter must have ammunition that performs somewhat better than average. A discussion of this requirement will be undertaken later. For the purpose of this chapter, it's assumed that the shooter has established that any ammunition used for accuracy testing is good enough to be useful for the purpose.

Bedding

The initial shooting with a rifle can tell you much about its potential. For example, if a rifle strings shots vertically on the target, perhaps covering four to seven inches between the highest shot and the lowest, while the left-to-right spread is minimum, you can reasonably suspect that the bedding of the rifle is at fault. It would be safe, on most such occasions, to assume that the upward pressure of the fore-end against the barrel varies considerably from shot to shot.

The cause may be as simple as a barrel expanding as it heats, creating additional contact with the fore-end. If this is the case, allowing the barrel to cool completely between shots should result in a notable shrinking of the group size. But the problem can also be due to a barreled action that shifts its position in the stock under the stress of recoil.

If groups string horizontally but are small over the vertical measurement, you can assume the barrel is being influenced by contact with the stock on one side or the other, for the reasons just stated, rather than contacting the bottom of the barrel channel.

Not surprisingly, most serious shooters long ago abandoned all the wood-contact bedding methods for hunting rifles, and accepted the free-floating barrel (one with no fore-end barrel contact, even when the barrel is hot) as the best solution to a consistent point of impact and small group sizes. When a barrel is free-floated, it eliminates changing points of impact due to the fore-end warping. And it has been my experience that 98 percent of all hunting rifles will group best when the barrel is free-floated.

There are rare rifles that will shoot good to so-so groups with a pressure-bedded barrel, but when free-floated do not group as well. There are even rarer hunting rifles that shoot very well with pressure-bedded barrels and then do poorly with a floated barrel. For the most part, these rifles simply are not right to start with, and there was a pressure point which, just by chance, helped correct a barrel stress or other problem.

Sometimes, too, such rifles are suffering from poor receiver inletting, and the barrel/fore-end contact is all that gives the gun half a chance of shooting. If this is the case, when the barrel is floated the barreled action is free to wander about in the ill-fitting receiver mortise as recoil is applied, making accuracy about as bad as it can get.

In most instances, these problem rifles can be corrected by insuring that the action is correctly bedded in the receiver area. The surest way to

accomplish this is to bed the offending rifle's action in some form of epoxy. This procedure will be discussed in detail later.

For the remaining few rifles that simply favor a stock-pressure point against the barrel (or several such points), I'll go on record as stating these are best used for trading. A rifle that depends on pressure points in the barrel bedding will need its point of impact checked frequently as the stock warps with seasonal changes. Indeed, if such a rifle is sighted-in with a dry, moisture-free stock, its point of impact may be so altered after exposure to several days of heavy rain as to cause a missed shot when hunting. If my condemnation of pressure-point bedding is strong, it is based on years of hunting experience. Unless a synthetic stock is used, pressure bedding has no place on a hunting rifle.

Rifles with synthetic stocks are free from any problems caused by moisture. Without the water-absorption that occurs with wood (even well-finished wood), these stocks will hold their point of impact quite well. But even with synthetic stocks, I find that pressure bedding usually results in less accuracy than can be obtained with a free-floating barrel.

Those who shoot only three-shot groups may never detect the difference; but if you are an accuracy enthusiast who shoots ten-shot groups, a free-floating barrel will correct a great many problems or simply make a good rifle better.

To determine the type of barrel bedding on a rifle, fold a dollar bill in half and, with the rifle supported in a cleaning vise, attempt to slip the folded bill between the barrel and forearm. With a correctly floated barrel, the bill will slide easily from the tip of the fore-end to the receiver, without drag. If you notice any drag or resistance, the barrel is contacting the fore-end, or will do so when hot, and (intentionally or unintentionally) it has pressure bedding. This test should be done first with a cold barrel and again immediately after firing a five- or ten-shot group. A heated barrel sometimes expands significantly and may contact the stock when hot, though it did not do so when cold.

Further checking of a rifle's bedding needs to be made if accuracy is a problem. A free-floated

Checking a barrel to determine if it's free-floating is easily done with a folded bill. If the bill binds when slipped from fore-end to receiver, the barrel is not properly floated.

barrel makes such inspection easier. The rifle should fit into the receiver quite exactly. The back of the recoil lug should bear firmly against the corresponding stock mortise. Also, the bottom and side of the recoil lug should locate with uniform contact in the recoil-lug mortise. If, with the action screws removed, you can detect any front to rear movement or lateral twist (when the recoil lug is fully seated into its mortise), the rifle's bedding needs work. Usually, it's possible to correct any such problems with an epoxy ("glass") bedding compound.

When the recoil-lug mortise has been properly bedded, contact at other parts of the action can be checked using lamp black or other inletting highlighter. This is discussed in detail in Chapter 12, dealing with glass bedding. It is important that the action be properly supported at each point where an action-retaining guard screw is employed. Any twist or bending of the action that occurs as guard screws are *tightened* will cause varying levels of inaccuracy. Additionally, the guard screws must be free of any contact with the stock material.

Keep in mind that improperly bedded actions, or guard screws that contact the stock, not only can destroy accuracy, but also can cause stock splits and repeated loosening of guard screws when shooting.

The stock inletting should also be checked to insure that any moving action parts are free of stock contact over their entire movement range. This also applies to the bolt handle on bolt-action rifles.

When the bolt handle is locked fully into place, its base should contact only the steel portion of the corresponding receiver cut. If the bolt contacts the stock, accuracy can suffer. If such contact is excessive, it may cause difficult operation of some safeties (depending on the type of safety).

Defective Crown

Poor rifle accuracy can be caused by a defective barrel crown. The barrel crown is the radius, or undercut, at the muzzle that insures the bullet's simultaneous release around its entire circumference as it exits the muzzle. The barrel crown also helps prevent any minor nicks and burrs around the muzzle from interfering with the uniform and non-damaging release of the bullet. However, the crown cannot always prevent damage that adversely affects accuracy.

The muzzle needs to be inspected for any dents, nicks, burrs, or other abnormalities that encroach on the all-important junction of the bore's actual termination and the crown of the muzzle. Damaged areas that do not encroach on the bullet's exit will, of course, have no effect on accuracy. If a crown has been so damaged as to cause poor accuracy, repair can be made easily with a lathe and a crowning cutter, discussed in Chapter 14.

Bore Fouling and Wear

Accuracy problems can, obviously, have other causes. Perhaps the most common problem is a fouled bore. Do not eliminate the possibility of a dirty or fouled bore until you are certain this is not the problem. As noted in Chapter 8, a bore cannot be cleaned properly with just a few passes of a bore brush and some patches wetted with a weak solvent. And remember that with some rifles—particularly those using high-velocity loads—the bore should be cleaned after surprisingly few shots. If you are in doubt, re-read the maintenance chapter.

Worn rifling, creates accuracy problems, so bear in mind that improper cleaning of the barrel is as often the cause of rifling wear as repeated firing.

Generally speaking, a bore reaches peak accuracy capability shortly after being placed into service (after 100 or so rounds). This peak accuracy may last 4,000 or 5,000 rounds on lower-intensity cartridges (.222 Remington, .30-30 Winchester, .35 Remington). With cartridges of medium intensity, such as the .30-06, .270 Winchester, .308 Winchester, etc., peak accuracy will last perhaps 3,000 to 4,000 rounds. With higher-intensity cartridges, such as the .264 Winchester Magnum, 7mm Remington Magnum, and .300 Winchester Magnum, peak accuracy may last only 2,000 rounds or so.

Heavy powder charges cause more rapid bore wear, and long bullet bearing surfaces also cause greater bore wear. The higher the chamber pressure, the greater the bore wear. Cartridge intensity describes bore-wearing conditions that add to the total amount of heat (calories) produced in the bore and the maximum temperatures reached, as well as all other erosive or friction-inducing conditions.

But even when a bore has passed its peak of accuracy, it may provide a satisfactory accuracy life for several thousand more rounds, depending on the needs of the shooter.

Trigger

Equally important to accuracy is a clean, crisp trigger pull of about three pounds for a sporting rifle. A trigger that has a creepy or jerky movement will greatly undermine the shooter's ability to obtain maximum accuracy. A heavy trigger pull is self-defeating when accuracy is tantamount. A pull of 2½ pounds is about right for a very experienced rifleman under target-shooting conditions. The same shooter may find a

A uniform crisp trigger pull is essential for getting the most out of a rifle. Accuracy will suffer with a heavy, creepy trigger. A pull of about 2½ to 3 pounds is right for most shooters.

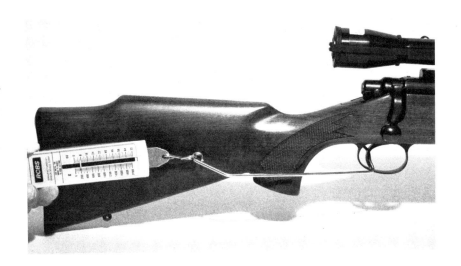

trigger pull of three pounds right for most big-game hunting. An inexperienced shooter would be best off with a 3½-pound pull.

Keep in mind that a too-light trigger pull can cause unintentional discharges. Such firings can occur when attempting to use the firearm with cold hands, gloved hands, or in haste. And no trigger should be adjusted so light as to fire if the gun is bumped or dropped.

A trigger that fires by breaking clean, like a glass wand, always makes it easier to shoot accurately than one that is spongy, creepy, jerky, or has considerable after-travel (movement after the sear has been released). Anything less than a good pull and the shooter will not be able to realize the firearm's full accuracy potential. For a detailed discussion of triggers, see Chapter 13.

No-Slip Buttplate or Pad

Since accuracy is related to the shooter's ability to hold the gun motionless or very nearly so, smooth metal or plastic buttplate, especially if it is curved, can be a liability. A rifle so equipped is difficult to hold steady. Even from a benchrest

When looking for accuracy the flat, nonslip surface of a rubber buttplate is preferable to all other styles.

position, such a buttplate tends to slide about on the shoulder, making it very difficult to get even a modicum of accuracy. On the other hand, with a flat, checkered, metal, or plastic buttplate, it is far easier to control the firearm. And a gun with a flat, no-slip rubber butt or recoil pad will lend itself to very steady holding. When a recoil pad is installed, stock length is sometimes altered to provide an ideal fit for an individual shooter—one more reason such installations are among a gunsmith's frequent projects.

Sighting Equipment

Accuracy problems can often be traced to loose or improperly mounted sights. A sight and its base must be solidly mounted and free of all play. Each screw used should be checked to insure that it can be fully turned up without bottoming in its hole. A screw that comes to rest against the bottom of its hole cannot do an adequate job of securing a sight or base. To check for this problem, install each screw in the appropriate hole with all other screws removed. When the screw is snugged up, check to see that it is holding the sight or base very tightly. Then remove that screw and try another and so on. If any screw bottoms and won't hold the part tightly, shorten it a bit with a small file. Work carefully to avoid damaging its threads.

When inspecting sights be sure that beads or other aiming surfaces are tightly positioned in the front sight. Also be certain that any folding leaves, adjustable leaves, or other moving parts of open rear sights are all held snugly in position. In evaluating performance after everything is snug, remember that most shooters have difficulty in maintaining three-inch groups with open sights.

Inspect any aperture (peep) sight and its mounting to locate any loose parts or screws. As a whole, two-inch groups with a peep sight at 100 yards can be considered about as good as most shooters can expect.

Using a scope of known quality and performance is an important aspect of accuracy testing.

Scope rings and bases need to be very snug. Inspect each screw for bottoming, as mentioned earlier. A drop of Loc-Tite, a screw-locking liquid, applied to base screws will help prevent them from loosening under recoil. This compound can also be applied to metallic sight-base screws to help prevent problems.

When checking for causes of poor accuracy, inspect the scope. A scope whose objective bell rests against the barrel can bring on problems. Also, be sure that manipulation of the firearm's action does not cause the bolt handle or ejected cases to hit the scope. In some instances, a bolt handle can be altered to permit low scope mounting, but if the objective bell rests on the barrel or if the tube is being battered by ejected shells, the situation calls for a different scope or a different mounting system.

Further, the scope's internal parts and optical system can cause inaccuracy. One of the most frequent problems with inexpensive scopes is that the optics or other internal parts may actually move about under recoil. The number of times I've found a poorly constructed scope to be a problem are uncountable, but such problems are not easily isolated. The best investigative

technique is to replace a suspect scope with one of known quality and proven performance.

There is, however, one aspect of scope performance that can be easily inspected—that is, to determine if the scope has excessive parallax. Parallax is an optical condition in which the target image does not fall on the same optical plane as the crosshairs. When this condition is present, the reticle will move about on the target as the eye is moved behind the scope.

To check for parallax, aim the scope at a bull's-eye 100 yards distant, using sand bags or a similar rest to hold the gun and scope in alignment. Make sure that when your eye is centered with the eyepiece, the reticle aligns precisely with the center of the bull's-eye. Then, without moving the gun and scope, shift your eye to the left, right, up, and down while looking through the scope. If the reticle moves about on the target, then the scope has a parallax condition.

If the reticle moves only half an inch or less with extreme eye movement, the parallax can be ignored as it is not great enough to affect grouping. However, if the crosshairs move an inch or more about the center of the bull's-eye, it will be difficult to shoot good groups unless the eye is held *precisely* in the same position, in relationship to the scope's eyepiece, for every shot. I have examined scopes with as much as three inches of parallax at 100 yards and, unfortunately, such scopes are not rare.

One scope brand is built to be free of parallax at 100 yards. Another is designed to be parallax-free at 150 yards. Either is fully acceptable for a big-game rifle. But some scopes, when inspected for parallax, are so inferior as to make it seem the manufacturer was unconcerned with the problem.

Higher-power scopes, meant for very precise shooting, are often equipped with an adjustable objective (front) lens. By turning the sleeve at the front of the scope, the user can select the range at which he wishes his scope to be free of parallax.

This adjustment range is sometimes from 25 yards to 400 yards, and even to infinity. This parallax adjustment is an excellent feature for target shooting and for long-range varmint hunting. But poorly made scopes, even with adjustable objectives—and occasionally including expensive models as well as cheap ones—sometimes prove less than satisfactory with respect to providing a parallax-free sight picture. Checking a scope carefully for parallax can be an important step in correcting an accuracy problem.

I have found scopes with loose objective lenses, too. This problem, surprisingly, is not at all uncommon. In some instances the movement of the front lens can be detected with the finger tip. Other times, the problem evades easy detection. If in doubt, use a scope of known worth to check the firearm's accuracy.

There are a few scope mounts that are totally unsuitable to the task. If, with the firearm firmly supported, the scope can be moved when it is grasped at both ends by hand, the mount should be replaced. Brackets or rings that can be so moved are not conducive to accuracy.

Summary

Sometimes the cause of accuracy problems can be difficult to determine, but for the most part, if you consider the following points you will be able to isolate the cause. The points to cover are:

1   Shooter capability (flinch, lack of experience, etc.). Some shooters' ability fluctuates daily. Several trips to the range may be required.
2   Reasonable accuracy expectations (based on action type).
3   Barrel condition (fouled, worn, eroded, damaged crown).
4   Looseness (sights, screws).
5   Poorly designed buttplate.
6   Poor mount not offering stable base for scope.
7   Trigger pull (should be crisp and clean).
8   Barrel bedding.
9   Receiver bedding (action should be cor-

rectly supported and firmly held in position).
10   Moving action parts contacting wood (bolt handle should not touch stock when locked, etc.).
11   Scope problem (parallax, loose internal parts, etc.)

Unfortunately, accuracy problems can be related to many other things, some of which are not so easily uncovered. In semiautomatics the gas system or recoil system must produce a uniform operation of the action. Unduly fast or slow cycle times can bring on grief. Firearms with two-piece stocks (lever-actions, pumps, semiautos, and some bolts) seldom shoot as well as rifles with one-piece stocks. Heavy, stiff barrels sometimes shoot better than light ones. Action screws that protrude into the receiver deeply enough to contact the bolt, or similar problems, all can destroy the potential for fine accuracy. If the problem does not lie in the listed trouble areas and remains a mystery, you will need to proceed very slowly to find the difficulty.

Sometimes nothing will work short of a barrel replacement. But this is an expensive undertaking, so first rule out all other possibilities. If good records on firearms use have been kept and they indicate that 5,000 or more rounds have been fired, barrel replacement may be a likely candidate to correct accuracy decline.

Never forget that excessive headspace also can cause some accuracy problems. Use a "no-go" gauge; if a stripped bolt will close fully on this gauge, the gun needs corrective repairs. Headspace is adjusted by removing a small portion of the chamber end of the barrel, setting the barrel deeper into the receiver, and then rechambering. Such an undertaking is only for the very experienced gunsmith. But anyone can use a headspace gauge to detect the problem. More about this later.

As you become experienced in tracking down problems, you will learn to detect all the abnormal conditions that can destroy accuracy. But even with limited experience, careful checking as discussed in this chapter will lead to the correction of most accuracy problems.

10

Scope Installation

When the manufacturer has drilled and tapped a rifle for the mounting of a scope base, installation of a scope is a snap, right? Well, not necessarily. Quite a few gremlins can creep into what should be an easy task. Knowing the factors that can cause the job to go wrong may keep your work rolling as intended.

To determine if screws are too long for blind holes, install them one at a time with the mount base in position, and be sure the base can be tightened securely with only the one screw. Then remove the screw and repeat the procedure with the next screw and blind hole. Shorten screws as required. Screws for through-holes should be checked for protrusion. Trim these screws as required, so that they will be approximately flush with the receiver. As screws are checked, set them aside carefully so that they

Removing Plug Screws

Starting with the removal of the plug screws presents no potential problems unless the factory cross-threaded one. Fortunately, this is not a common occurrence. But the screws for mounting the scope base can be a source of trouble. It is essential to insure that each is not unnecessarily long. A too-long screw may bottom in a blind hole (one that does not go completely through the receiver) and lose its fastening power. A too-long screw can also protrude from a through-hole. Screws protruding into the receiver can interfere with the bolt or other moving parts.

Be sure mounting screws are not overly long. Check each screw as described in the text.

may later be installed into the same hole in which they were checked.

Excessively short screws should be replaced. A screw should be long enough to supply at least four full turns in the hole's threads. Less can result in insufficient holding power or may cause screw threads to strip when the screw is securely tightened.

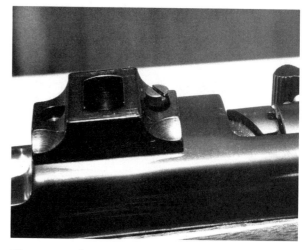

If mounting base is not level, place an appropriately shaped and drilled piece of shim stock under it.

Leveling the Mount

Next, if a two-piece mount is used, insure that the front and rear bases are level with each other. Check by first leveling the gun, then one of the temporarily installed bases. Then place the level across both temporarily installed bases. If they are not level, it may be difficult or even impossible to sight-in the rifle. Worse, you may damage the scope tube when everything is finally tightened up.

If a one-piece base is used, it must not be bent as it is tightened. First tighten the two front screws securely. Then look for space under the rear end of the base. Repeat the process with the front screws removed and the rear screws tightened, looking for space between the bottom of the base's front end and the receiver.

If the mount bases are not level, or if a one-piece base cannot be tightened without bending it, you will need to replace the base(s) or shim the offending base or base's end, or alter the base(s) as required. Do not proceed with the job until the bases fit perfectly.

Should it be necessary to shim a base or base's end, do so with a single thickness of shim stock rather than a build-up of multiple thinner shims. This will insure the best-looking job and help prevent looseness from later developing.

The best mounting job is attained by using a scope base that fits precisely. Due to variations in factory receiver dimensions, this is not always possible, but don't be too quick to blame the

firearm manufacturer. I have encountered more faulty bases than faulty receivers.

When base(s), and shims if necessary, have been checked with respect to proper fit, remove all screws and bases from the firearm. It is now necessary to clean and degrease each screw and hole. After this has been done, place a half-drop of a commercial screw-locking compound on each screw.

Installing Bases and Rings

Install each base using the pre-tested screws in the appropriate holes. Tighten all screws very snugly with a well-fitting screwdriver. Then place the screwdriver securely into each screw slot and lightly set the screws with a single light hammer blow to the screwdriver. The setting of the screws should allow you to get an additional 1/8- to 1/4-turn on the screw.

Next, install the scope rings carefully, according to the manufacturer's instructions. Do not

Setting base screws will give them that extra bit of tightness which will prevent them from becoming loose under recoil.

take any shortcuts. For example, if a Redfield Jr. mount (or similar mount) is used, a short length of appropriate-diameter pipe, tubing, or steel stock must be inserted through the front ring as a turning lever. The ring then needs to be turned in and out of its dovetail in the base several times. Never, never use the scope to accomplish this task. You might scar the scope tube or even severely damage the scope.

Make certain the front and rear rings are properly aligned. Use a short piece of pipe or steel stock to verify this alignment. Then remove the top half of the rings and lay the scope in place.

Keep in mind that the scope is just lying there and can easily be dropped or jarred loose. For this reason it is a good idea to have the rifle securely clamped in an appropriate work station. The Decker vise or a similar product is ideal for this.

With the scope lying in position, determine that the scope's objective bell does not contact any part of the receiver, barrel, or open rear sight. Then make sure the eyepiece of the scope does not contact the bolt handle when the handle is raised, or with any other part (safety, rear receiver bridge, etc.). If contact is made be-

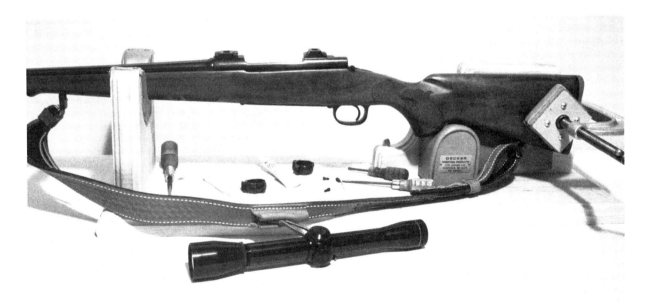

A Decker vise makes the ideal work station for scope-mount installation.

Mount the scope as low as possible, with adequate clearance between barrel and objective-lens housing.

tween the scope and any part of the rifle, it will be necessary to use higher scope rings.

It is always desirable to mount the scope as low as possible. This facilitates quick alignment of eye and scope, with stock support for the cheek. Higher rings always mean less cheek support, and this often leads to lost opportunities when a fast shot is needed—as well as a decrease in accuracy when shooting offhand.

Some dealers seem to have adopted a policy of not inventorying low rings. The exclusive use of medium and high rings reduces inventory requirements and the frequency of a customer's returning a too-low set for higher ones. But reduced also is the professional look of a low-as-possible scope mount and the gun's propensity for quick and accurate handling under field conditions.

An example of proper bolt-handle clearance.

Eye Relief

After scope clearance is assured, position the scope for correct eye relief. To do so, install the ring tops but do not tighten them. The most unprofessional mistake in scope installation is mounting the scope too far forward. Regrettably, due to many current scope designs, this seems to be a trend.

Keep in mind that when you're hunting in shirtsleeves, a scope mounted comfortably with respect to fore and aft positioning will be too far forward for hunting in heavy clothing. Long underwear, a heavy wool shirt, an insulated vest, and a parka can easily add ¾-inch in the effective eye-to-scope distance. If the gun is to be used with heavy clothes, mount the scope ⅝-inch farther to the rear than the ideal position in shirtsleeves. Naturally this mounting position must be checked when fully dressed for the field.

When you slide a scope fore and aft, the tube is easily scratched and marred if the rings are even modestly snug or do not properly align or have burrs. Be certain the rings are loose, properly aligned, and smooth. Make no attempt to slide or turn any scope in any ring if even the slightest resistance is felt.

More often than you might imagine, a scope, mount, and rifle combination will prevent sufficient rearward movement of the tube in the mount rings. If this occurs, use rings that extend scope positioning. Extension front and/or rear rings are available in many brands and styles. Unfortunately, some rings are available, at this writing, in only medium or high versions. But a slightly too-high scope is a lesser evil than one that is mounted too far forward.

Well-mounted scope that is as low as possible and has the proper eye-relief positioning will handle effortlessly in the field.

Aligning Crosshairs

When satisfied that proper eye relief has been obtained, check again that the scope is still clear of all contact with the firearm. Then turn up the ring screws, using only light, two-finger pressure on the screwdriver. At this point, the scope's horizontal crosshair must be made level

Make sure the scope does not contact an open sight.

with the true horizon when the gun is held level in a shooting position.

This is often a trial-and-error undertaking, but there are better ways to get the job done. Make sure the firearm is level in the holding fixture. Then place a small level on top of the scope turret. Tighten the ring screws carefully to maintain the level position of the scope. But crosshairs and scope turret tops are not always perfectly aligned so even this approach may not give the desired results without a little bit of further adjustment.

Another way, when applicable, is to remove the bolt and insert a B-Square scope-leveling jig into the receiver. Then carefully align the vertical crosshair with the jig's vertical scribe mark. Be sure to hold the jig firmly against the bottom receiver rails as this adjustment is made. The use of the B-Square jig requires level receiver rails, and also requires some practice in being able to see its vertical scribe mark and the vertical crosshair simultaneously—but it is a knack quickly learned. This method eliminates any chance of canting.

Tightening Screws

Scope-ring screws should never be coated with thread-locking compound; some day it may prove necessary to change eye relief, scope, or rings, and if the screws are locked in place, it may not be possible to do so without damaging the scope.

Rings that have clamping screws on each side generally will not cause the scope to turn as they are tightened, but it's best to tighten screws evenly and progressively. Take a slight amount up on one screw at a time. When you have snugged up all the ring screws, verify that the scope is still level. When properly installed, the ring halves will have an identical gap between them on each side of the scope.

Naturally, it is important that all screws and fasteners be made tight to prevent base, ring, or scope movement, which might otherwise occur under recoil or normal banging around. Yet, you must consider the future need to remove the

A scope square, such as this one made by B-Square, can make reticle leveling a simple task, but receiver rails must be perfectly level.

scope rings and mount from the gun. You may decide the scope was the wrong choice, that it needs repair, that the rings and/or base are unsatisfactory, or that the firearm needs rebluing. Whatever the reason, it is essential not to make the scope installation permanent.

Screw locking compounds are acceptable on base screws as there are ways of horsing these screws free. Several setting blows to the screws are often all you need to back them out of a receiver. And if the worst comes to pass, such screws can be drilled out if the rifle is held securely in a good drill-aligning fixture, such as the Forster Universal Drill Jig.

But ring screws cannot be subjected to such handling without a strong risk of scope damage, so use only hand pressure with the appropriate screwdriver or Allen wrench when turning them up.

In years gone by, slotted head screws were standard—and as I mentioned in an earlier chapter, I am not enthusiastic about hex screws for scope mounts. Hex-head base screws, installed with a locking compound, quite frequently will round out their wrench-mating surfaces on the first attempt to remove them—that is, if the wrench does not first round out its own edges. I have had occasion to service more than one receiver with a stubbornly stuck-on base. Often the owner loosens one or two hex screws, and the remaining ones defy extraction. I've seen receivers ruined by frustrated owners who attempted to drill out a screw without a satisfactory drill-aligning jig.

It's no better with ring hex screws. Often the hex size of these ring screws is small, the screw too soft, and the hex dimension somewhat sloppy. Many times wrenches are also sloppy with respect to dimensional tolerances, and sometimes too soft. All this can lead to a rounded-out hex hole or wrench and a screw that cannot be removed without drilling.

Hex screws can be satisfactory if they are sufficiently large to allow for an ample hex, and if they are hard enough to resist deformation and made to very close tolerances. Even then the wrench used must be an exact fit and of proper hardness. And you may still get a rounded hole if it is not deep enough to allow sufficient wrench purchase.

Properly made hex screws and wrenches are rarer than elephants cutting through my backyard. I go far out of my way to replace hex screws with slotted ones. The only good hex-head screws I have found (when used with an exact-fitting wrench) are those on the Redfield scope rings.

The use of Weaver-style rings or any that have ring-tightening screws on only one side will always result in the scope twisting (to the side of the rings on which the screws are located) as the screws are tightened. To compensate for this, you cant the horizontal reticle to be low on the side away from the screws. The proper degree to cant the scope is learned only by experience, and it usually takes several tries to get the crosshair level. Also be careful not to overtighten this type of ring as it has less than 100 percent circumferential purchase on the tube and some unsightly dents in the scope tube can result if screws are stressed too much.

There are still other pitfalls. For example, scope rings do not always fit the bases perfectly. Carefully check, before scope mounting, that each ring is adequately tightened to the base. This problem occurs most often when rings and base are of different manufacture.

Bore-Sighting

The final step in scope installation is bore-sighting. This aligns the crosshairs with the bore so that they optically intersect on a target. This procedure insures that the first shots fired will strike on, or near, the target at 100 yards or so. It also insures that there is no misalignment between bore and scope that would make it impossible to sight-in. Because such misalignment may necessitate dismantling rings and base from the firearm, it is essential to complete the bore-sighting before any screw-locking compound sets up on base-mounting screws.

Best way to bore sight a rifle (or handgun) after scope installation is to use a collimator.

Bore-sighting can be accomplished by visually aligning the bore on some distant target and then adjusting the scope's elevation and windage so that the crosshairs also align on the target. To accomplish this you must look through the bore from the rear, which means the gun must have a removable bolt and a visual access from rear of gun through the bore. A bore-scope mirror can be used to look down the bore on firearms from which bolt removal is not practical. When aligned on the target, the gun must be held motionless while the scope is adjusted to place the reticle on the center of the target, as seen through the bore. All of this is possible, even practical. But it is far easier and infinitely faster to use a collimator to align bore and scope. I described the procedure in my discussion of special tools in Chapter 5, but it's worth repeating here in brief form.

Lightly oil a collimator spud and insert it into the bore. Then attach the collimator to the spud. Next, while looking through the scope, square up the collimator's reticle with the scope reticle. Then adjust the scope reticle to coincide exactly with the collimator reticle. It's a fast, simple, very accurate way to bore-sight a rifle. In most instances a rifle that's bore-sighted with a collimator will put its first shots at 100 yards within four inches of the aiming point. That can save needless preliminary shooting at 25 or 50 yards, and save a good many rounds of ammunition that normally would be consumed.

11

Ten Easy Gun-smithing Projects

Because many popular firearms see extensive use by millions of shooters, certain repairs have become comparatively commonplace. In addition to these repairs, there are minor modifications—such as replacing basic sighting equipment or adding accessories—that fall into the category of easy tasks.

This chapter will deal with 10 common repairs and alterations that should be among those first attempted by firearm owners. Perhaps you own several of the firearms covered, but do not skip sections dealing with firearms you do not possess. The general knowledge contained here will be useful later and is essential to the overall understanding of basic firearm repair. Here's a list of the 10 projects:

1 Replacing Marlin .22 rimfire cartridge guide.
2 Replacing open sights.
3 Replacing Remington Model 870 trigger group with adjustable unit.
4 Repairing and improving Ruger Mark I .22 magazine.
5 Disassembling Winchester Model 70 bolt.
6 Plating small parts.
7 Removing broken cartridges from chamber or resizing die.
8 Measuring headspace.
9 Installing detachable clip in long-action Remington Model 700.
10 Installing aperture sight.

Job 1

Replacing Marlin .22 Rimfire Cartridge Guide

Marlin bolt-action 22 employs a cartridge guide that can become broken or damaged.

More than nine million Marlin .22 rimfire rifles have been sold, and many employ a uniquely shaped spring-steel cartridge guide which positions cartridges being stripped from the magazine so that they enter the chamber smoothly. When broken away or severely distorted, the guide cannot do its job, and attempts to feed cartridges into the chamber will invariably jam the cartridges against the end of the barrel. Happily, replacement of this Marlin cartridge guide is quite simple.

Remove the bolt, clip, and stock from the rifle and be certain, naturally, that the chamber is

Cartridge guide as it should appear on Marlin .22. When broken or distorted, it can be easily replaced.

Begin the Marlin cartridge-guide repair by removing clip, bolt, and stock.

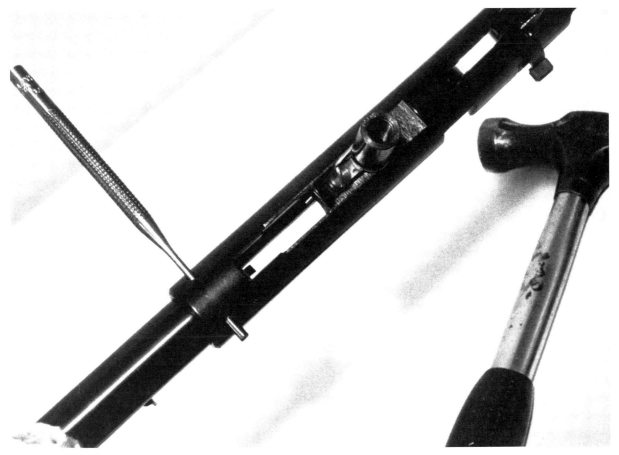

Drive out the barrel-retaining pin by using a medium-weight hammer and a pin punch. Then separate barrel from receiver so as to expose the groove at

the top of the barrel's chamber end which holds the cartridge guide. Replace the cartridge guide and reassemble the rifle.

---

unloaded. Next, drive out the pin that holds the barrel and receiver together. Do so by firmly supporting the barrel, right up to the receiver, in a well padded vise. Use a moderately heavy hammer and a large-diameter pin punch to drive out the retaining pin. Next, separate the barrel and receiver. (If barrel and receiver do not separate easily, consign the job to a person familiar with the correct procedures or return the gun to the factory.)

You will note that a portion of the original cartridge guide will still be in the retaining groove at the rear top of the barrel. Remove the

broken part and replace it with a new cartridge guide. Reassemble the barrel to the receiver and reinstall the retaining pin. Be certain the holes in barrel and receiver align perfectly before driving the pin into place. It may be beneficial to stake the end of the pin hole, on the receiver, to make sure the pin does not come loose.

Prior to reassembling the barreled action to the stock, it is wise to give all the metal surfaces a light coat of rust-preventing oil or a good application of firearm wax. And check the clip-retaining screw, as well as the safety-mounting screw, for tightness.

Job 2

Replacing Open Sights

Front and/or rear sight replacement can become necessary for a number of reasons. A sight may be broken, lost, or simply not allow enough adjustment to sight-in properly. Replacement of these sights goes easily.

Front and rear iron sights generally will be attached to the barrel with either one or two screws or a dovetail arrangement. Often, a front ramp may have one screw hidden beneath a dovetailed front bead or blade.

Never attempt to drive out a dovetail front or rear sight if it is dovetailed to a screwed-to-the-barrel base or ramp. This could cause the retaining screws to shear or strip their threads and leave you with a headache you hadn't planned on. To remove a sight dovetailed to a screwed-on base or ramp, use a tool such as the Williams Front Sight Pusher (it works well on rear sights too). This tool is also essential in adjusting such sights for windage when sighting-in. Always remove the sight by pushing it from the left side out to the right.

Front or rear sights dovetailed directly to the barrel have to be removed with a brass punch and hammer. Again, always remove from left to right.

When replacing a front sight, be sure to use the appropriate style to match the rear sight. Round beads should be matched to U-notch rear sights, while a blade or post is correct for a square rear notch. The bead or blade should always be small enough to be seen with adequate light on both sides when viewed through the rear sight.

If the front sight is being replaced to correct a deficiency that prevented proper sighting-in, remember a lower-than-original front sight will cause the gun to place its group higher on the target, while a higher front sight will lower the point of impact.

If a gun is to be equipped only with open sights, do not use a rear sight that can be folded down. Sooner or later it will be in that position when a quick shot needs to be taken. Very fine

Remove dovetailed open rear sights by driving them from left to right using a brass punch and hammer.

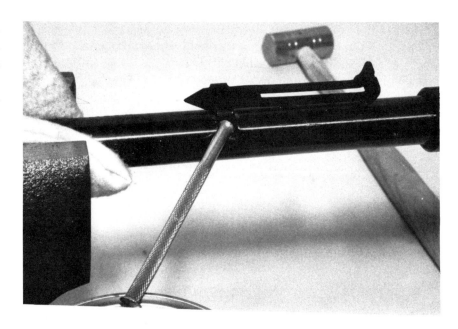

Remove base or ramp-mounted dovetail sights only with a Williams front-sight pusher. Hammering on these sights might shear off the screws that hold the base or ramp to the barrel.

Always drive replacement rear sights into position from the right side to the left. If a replacement sight is not tight in the dovetail, remove it and peen the edges of the dovetail slightly with a ball-peen hammer or a punch and hammer. Do so carefully, bending over just the edges of the dovetail no more than necessary to insure a tight-fitting sight.

If there still is excessive play between the sight and slot, the sight's male dovetail can be enlarged slightly by using an old cold chisel and setting a long crease in the base of the dovetail that will parallel the edge of the sight along the dovetailed edge. Naturally, the sight will need to be properly supported, and a very healthy blow is required to move the metal outward. The chisel should be held very close (approximately

Loose dovetails can be peened a bit with a punch (or ball-peen hammer) to tighten up the raceway.

A sight's dovetail can be enlarged somewhat by using a cold chisel to broaden its dovetail base.

and deep notches, as well as rear sights with large ears (buckhorn style), should also be avoided. These are slow to use, hide a lot of target, will give varying points of impact under different light conditions. Select sights that have shallow aiming notches of good proportion and flat tops.

1/16-inch to 1/8-inch) to the edge of the sight if this procedure is to be effective.

Rear dovetailed sights require movement left and right during sighting-in. Therefore, do not make the dovetail fit so tightly as to prevent movement when a brass punch and light hammer blows are used for adjustment.

Job 3

Replacing Remington Model 870 Trigger Group with Adjustable Unit

The Remington Model 870 pump shotgun has been sold in millions of units, and shooters are generally happy with its non-adjustable trigger. However, those who use slug barrels, smooth or rifled, as well as serious clay-bird shooters, may desire a cleaner, crisper pull. Happily for 12-gauge 870 owners, there is an easily installed trigger unit available.

Hastings and Timney have cooperated in developing an all-steel trigger assembly that offers a very clean, crisp pull. The weight of pull is adjustable within reasonable limits, as are take-up and backlash (overtravel). And all the parts are machined steel, an improvement that proud 870 owners might like to make, even without the advantage of a trigger that rivals those in many bolt-action rifles.

Remove the original trigger group by driving out the two retaining pins and lifting the entire

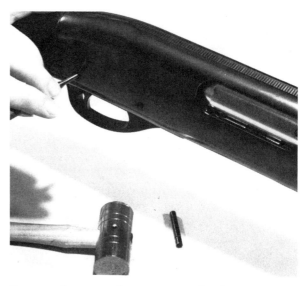

Remove the original trigger group by driving out the two retaining pins and lifting it free.

Remington 12-gauge 870 trigger group can be replaced with a fully adjustable Hastings-Timney trigger.

triggerplate assembly free of the shotgun. The Hastings/Timney trigger unit should be adjusted for an appropriate pull before installing it in the shotgun. The spring that clearly shows in front of the trigger (near its top) has a threaded screw and two lock nuts in front of it. By moving the lock nuts toward the trigger, the weight of pull will be increased, and moving the lock nuts away from the trigger will lighten the pull. Generally, it can be adjusted from 2¼ to 4½ pounds. A pull of approximately three pounds will be about right for most shooters.

The adjustment for take-up is located on top of the trigger. Loosen the lock nut and turn the screw (hex type) inward to decrease take-up, but do not reduce take-up excessively. Ample sear engagement must be maintained to insure that the gun will not fire if bumped or dropped. Be certain that both weight of pull and engagement adjustments are locked up tightly.

Backlash is adjusted at the rear top of the trigger guard. Insert the appropriate hex wrench

Replacement trigger should be adjusted to the desired pull before it is installed. This screw and its lock nuts control the weight of pull.

After the pins are removed simply pull the trigger group outward and away from the receiver.

This screw and its lock nut control the amount of trigger travel (take up) before the sear is released.

After-travel (backlash) is controlled by the screw located in the rear top of the trigger guard.

It may be necessary to remove some metal at this point if cartridges do not properly feed from the 870's magazine after the installation of the replacement trigger group.

into the adjusting screw and turn it in ¼-turn at a time, checking for proper trigger release. Keep turning until the trigger just will not release the hammer. Then back the screw out one full turn and the adjustment is complete.

Do not allow the hammer to move forward violently while testing trigger adjustments. Doing so can damage the unit. Prevent the hammer from flying forward by holding your thumb against it. Recocking is easily accomplished by pressing the hammer rearward with the thumb.

After the trigger has been adjusted for a clean, crisp three pounds, install the triggerplate assembly into the shotgun and make a final test of the adjustments. Often it may be decided to remove the triggerplate for a final adjustment.

After completing the adjustment and installation, the shotgun must be checked for proper feeding. Load *dummy* 12-gauge shells into the magazine and cycle them through the action. Never use live ammo. If the shells do not fully escape from the magazine and up onto the shell carrier, further fitting of the unit is required. Remove the triggerplate assembly and mount it in a well padded vise by grasping it in the area where the rear retaining pin passes through the assembly. Grasping the unit in a vise at any other point may irreparably damage it.

Lift the cartridge follower into its uppermost position. Now carefully remove a small amount

of material from the top front edge of the triggerplate assembly in the area contacted by the carrier when it is in its full down position. Be careful not to remove material from the rearmost portion of this area, as doing so will bring your file into contact with the piano-wire spring that lies across the trigger guard.

Remove only enough metal to allow the carrier to drop low enough so shells emerging from the magazine will clear its edge and lie fully rearward on top of the carrier. This is a trial-and-repeat process. Remove only small amounts of metal at a time. It should never be necessary to remove more than ¹⁄₁₆-inch of material in total. Reinsert the trigger group into the shotgun and check feeding each time you make three or four cuts with your file. Check that the cut is carried far enough back into the trigger guard to allow the follower to drop fully onto the cut.

Also be certain to wash away all metal filings carefully with a good solvent so they run off the forward edge of the triggerplate assembly, never into the unit.

Properly installing the steel replacement unit will enhance the durability and beauty of any 870. And it's bluing can be easily touched up if required—something not possible with the original aluminum unit. The clean, crisp pull may well mean better slug groups or perhaps more broken clay targets.

Job 4

Repairing and Improving Ruger Mark I .22 Magazine

Ruger Mark I pistols are available in a number of model variations, but each employs the same magazine. If any fault is common to the Mark I pistols it is that magazine. After extensive use, reliable feeding will be impaired and the pistol will begin to jam. Also, the Mark I magazine (unlike the Mark II, which is not interchangeable) will not cause the bolt to remain open on the last shot. This can lead to needless dry firing if the shooter does not carefully count his shots. But the feeding (and resulting jamming), as well as the bolt closing on the last shot, can be easily corrected.

The feeding problem arises when the two ears of the clip (one on each side near the mouth) lose their inward bend. This is a natural occurrence caused by the repeated loading and feeding of

Ruger Mark I semiautomatic pistol bolt will not stay open on the last shot if a standard magazine (*left*) is used. But a specially converted magazine (*right*) will cause the bolt to be held in the open position when the last shot is fired.

ammunition through the clip. To clarify the description, the ears are that section of the magazine (approximately ¼-inch wide) at the open end of the clip, lying between the permanently shaped front and rear sections. Each cycle flexes the two small ears outward and then relaxes them. Eventually they no longer return to their original position. This allows the cartridge to rise up too high as the rim of the case clears the turned-in portion of the clip and, in turn, the bullet hits the rear of the barrel, over the chamber, causing a jam.

To correct the problem you need a thin needle-nosed plier. Pull down on the thumb piece, causing the cartridge follower to be withdrawn into the magazine. Then insert a punch through the slots in the magazine, above the follower. Slowly release the tension on the thumb piece so that the follower bears against the punch. This will hold the follower down in a withdrawn position. Then, using the needle-nosed plier, carefully bend the two clip ears inward. Do not bend in the front edge of the clip (this actually has a slight outward flare). The ears should be bent inward about ¹⁄₁₆-inch inside the magazine walls. Excessive bending can cause irreparable damage. The use of a plier with a rounded inside nose will help prevent putting a sharp crease in the ears.

It is always wise to compare any clip causing jams with a clip that is working properly. It is an easy matter, then, to bend the ears of the faulty clip to match those of the working clip.

Converting a Ruger Mark I clip to hold the bolt open on the last shot requires that the magazine follower be replaced by one that will protrude sufficiently from the magazine to engage the bolt on the last shot. Such a follower can be built by duplicating the original follower dimen-

Replacement cartridge follower in the Ruger Mark I clip will protrude far enough into the receiver to interrupt the bolt's forward motion when the last shot is fired.

Ruger Mark I clip as supplied by the factory and the replacement follower which holds the bolt open.

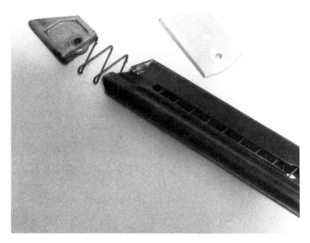

Removing the thumb pin on the Ruger clip (with follower completely depressed) will allow the follower to be withdrawn from the magazine.

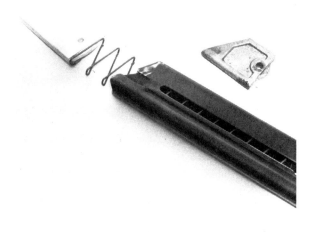

Replacement follower is simply seated on the magazine spring and the magazine reassembled.

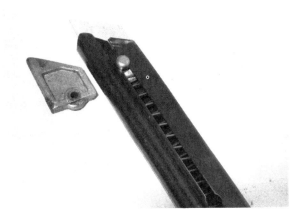

Bolt hold-open follower will protrude significantly from the magazine.

sions, but making the replacement exactly ⅜-inch longer at the front edge and ½-inch longer on the rear edge. Or you can purchase a new follower such as that made by Heritage Gunsmithing and sold through Brownells (in sets of two).

If you make your own, use only a fine grade of aircraft aluminum. This will prevent damage to the bolt face and give maximum follower life.

To remove the old follower, fully depress it into the magazine using a suitable-size screwdriver. Take care not to bend any part of the clip's open end. Fully depress the follower so that the thumb piece may be withdrawn from the left side of the clip. You may have to reduce pressure on the follower slightly to align the thumb piece exactly with the enlarged area of the cut in the side of the magazine. Then slowly release the pressure on the follower. Take care that it or the spring does not fly free.

Remove the follower and work the follower spring carefully back into the magazine. The spring will tend to get caught on the clip's ears, but by pushing each segment of the wire spring

fully to the rear you will be able to work it under the bent-in ears. Insert the follower, compress it fully to the bottom of the magazine, and insert the thumb piece into the left side of the clip. Be sure the thumb-piece retaining step slips up along the inside of the clip as you release tension on the follower.

In use, the new follower will pop up in front of the bolt face when the last shot is fired, preventing the bolt from closing.

Because the bolt now bears against the clip follower, under tension of the return spring, the clip sometimes cannot be dropped free until this pressure is removed. Do so by fully pulling the bolt rearward while simultaneously applying the safety. This locks the bolt open and allows easy magazine withdrawal. Some pistols will allow the magazine to be withdrawn without this step, but the bolt will close as the follower clears the bolt face. In this case, make certain no cartridge is left in the chamber.

This alteration will reduce the magazine capacity by one round—from nine to eight. It's a small price to pay for a major improvement.

Job 5

Disassembling Winchester Model 70 Bolt

Proper cleaning of a bolt-action means that occasionally the bolt body must be disassembled. The Winchester Model 70 bolt lends itself easily to such disassembly.

To begin, cock the firing pin by raising and lowering the bolt handle. Then move the three-position safety to its middle position—sticking out at a right angle to the bolt body. Remove the bolt from the rifle by depressing the bolt release button at the left rear of the action while simultaneously pulling the bolt handle rearward. The bolt will slip effortlessly from the receiver.

Now depress the spring-loaded plunger on the left side of the bolt (between the bolt body and the cocking piece) and, while holding it inward, unscrew the cocking-piece assembly by rotating it counterclockwise. The plunger needs to be held in only for the first full turn of the cocking piece. Completely unscrew the cocking piece and withdraw it from the bolt body. With it will come the firing pin and firing-pin spring as a complete assembly.

For most purposes, complete cleaning of the bolt mechanism can now be accomplished with a pressurized solvent.

For further disassembly, if needed, push the safety to its forwardmost position. Then carefully compress the firing-pin spring rearward. This is

Before removing the Winchester Model 70 bolt, move the safety to its mid-position.

Begin disassembly of the Winchester Model 70 bolt by depressing the spring-loaded plunger on the left side of the bolt while simultaneously unscrewing the entire cocking assembly.

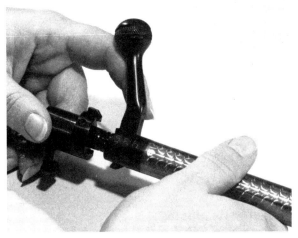

Entire cocking assembly can be withdrawn from the bolt body; then the inside of the bolt and the cocking assembly can be cleaned with pressurized solvents and degreasers.

best accomplished by inserting a tool designed for this purpose between the spring and the retaining washer and clip (located at the front end of the spring). With the rear of the firing pin resting against a table, compress the spring sufficiently to allow the retaining clip to be slid off to the side. Then lift off the retaining washer and allow the heavy spring to gradually relax.

Take care—the firing-pin spring is very strong and if care is not taken, the retaining clip and washer, as well as the spring itself, can escape to become lost or possibly cause personal injury.

With the spring and retainers removed, the screw through the cocking piece may be taken out, allowing it to be separated from the firing pin. The safety can then be removed by wiggling it upward and away from the cocking piece. However, it is seldom necessary to do so. Since the safety spring and its plunger are easily lost during disassembly, it's best not to remove it unless necessary.

There are a few variations on the Model 70 bolts. Some used a firing-pin retainer that required rotation of 180 degrees before it could be slipped forward from the firing pin. Others used

a pin to hold a bolt cap over the end of the firing pin. Other minor variations are sometimes encountered. Though each requires a somewhat modified disassembly, each change will be obvious.

To remove the extractor from the bolt, push a fine punch into the hole in the extractor and slide the extractor out of its groove. Take care not to lose the spring or plunger.

To remove the ejector, hold the bolt in a padded vise. Compress the ejector slightly and drive out the retaining pin. Then slowly release the pressure on the ejector. Withdraw it and its spring from the bolt.

Because extractor and ejector parts are easily lost during disassembly, it's best not to remove them unless replacement parts are on hand.

Reassembly is easily done in reverse order.

Earlier Model 70 Winchesters used a Mauser-type extractor and ejector. To remove the extractor from the bolt, rotate it out of its retaining groove (at the front end of the bolt) and push it forward off the bolt and its retaining collar. On these earlier models, the ejector is mounted to the rifle's receiver.

Job 6

Plating Small Parts

There is often a need to refinish small parts. A screw that has been burred, for instance, can often be saved by careful reshaping with a file, but it then needs to be refinished. Or a lost screw may be replaced but the blue finish (if there is any) on the replacement may not match. Small parts that have been made or repaired will require finishing, as well.

Often it is not practical to reblue a small part in a hot bluing salt bath. And the cold blues, while much better than nothing, seldom match the color desired and seldom last more than a brief period before the color fades or the part begins to rust.

The solution to all these and many other difficulties is to plate the screw or small part. Indeed, many firearm owners feel that plating all of the screws on a revolver adds a personal touch to an otherwise ordinary-looking gun. Others plate the slide of semiautomatic pistols or the floorp-

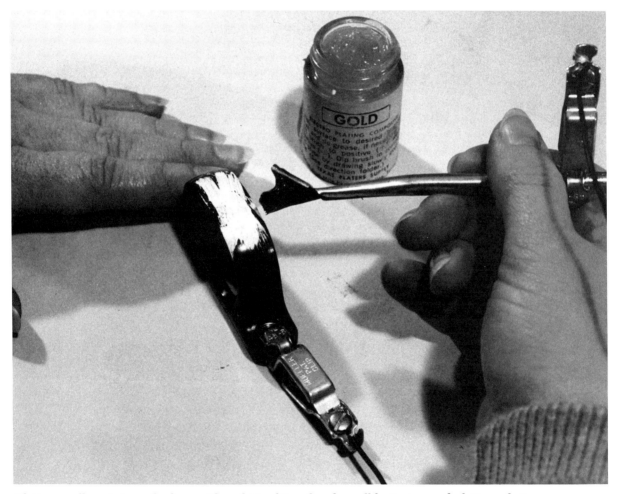

Plating small parts is easily done with a plating kit, a few dry-cell batteries, and plating solution.

late of a rifle or whatever to add a bit of distinction. It's extremely easy to plate small parts.

The secret to success is in the preparation of the steel parts to be plated. The final finish will reflect the degree of polish the part receives before plating. If you want a bright, lustrous finish, the metal must be polished to a mirror-reflective level. This may be done by hand or it can be done with professional polishing wheels. It is essential that all old bluing be removed, along with any rust or foreign material.

The part must then be completely degreased. This is easily accomplished with one of the pressurized solvents. All traces of oil and grease must be removed. If you attempt to plate over oil, grease, dirt, rust, old blue, or anything else, it will turn out tarnished. After degreasing, wipe the part carefully with a *clean, soft* cloth to remove all traces of the solvent. You are now ready to plate.

The best small-part plater I have used is the simple unit sold by Texas Platers Supply Co. Their plating solutions are tops and their small brushes and clamps are entirely adequate for the purpose.

You will need a source of electric current. Depending on the size of the part and its make-up, a three-volt direct current will be minimum and 4½-volt will be about perfect. This current can be obtained from two or three fresh dry-cell batteries (No. 6 size) of 1½ volts each. Connect the batteries in a series.

For two batteries, connect one battery's plus (positive) terminal to the other's minus (negative) terminal. Then connect the unused minus (negative) terminal to the work to be plated. The unused plus (positive) terminal is then connected to the plating brush.

In a three-battery hook up, connect the first battery's negative terminal to the second's positive terminal. Then connect the third battery's positive terminal to the second's negative terminal. The unused positive terminal of the first battery is then connected to the plating brush. The unused negative terminal of the third battery is then connected to the work to be plated.

However, it is more cost-effective to use a battery charger or battery eliminator of the proper D.C. voltage. Depending on the composition of the metal to be plated, it may sometimes be useful to use higher voltage, as much as six or eight volts. Keep in mind that three volts will be adequate only when plating a part with a *total* surface area of less than four square inches. For larger surface areas, 4½ volts seems about right. More voltage will speed up the work but also necessitate far more careful brushing. Always connect the positive lead to the brush and the negative lead to the work to be plated.

Begin by dipping the plating brush into the plating solution, making certain all the bristles and the underside of the anode (the metal hood of the brush which covers a portion of the bristles) are well covered with solution,. Then apply the plating to the work area using very short circular motions. The anode area of the brush must always be on top of the bristles and pressed lightly against them. The brush must be kept in constant motion while plating. Dip the brush frequently into the plating solution to renew the supply of metal. Each square inch of work must be plated for 30 seconds minimally for a light plating. Longer periods will be required for a heavier plating.

Copper, nickel, and brass platings can be applied directly to the steel part. If you wish to plate gold or silver, you will first have to apply an undercoat of copper.

All white metals (except thin coats of nickel), as well as gold will have a foggy appearance when the plating is finished. Immediately after plating, wash the part with running water and wipe dry to improve appearance. To further enhance appearance, lightly polish to a *bright* finish with metal polish. Great care must be taken to avoid excessive wear on new plating when you polish it.

A complete plating outfit can be purchased for less than $50 and includes ample supplies of gold, silver, nickel, copper, and brass, along with brushes and some wiring. Such an outfit will enable you to do a variety of jobs, perhaps even an entire handgun. But gain some experience first by working on practice parts before you plate a valuable part or handgun.

Job 7

Removing Broken Cartridges from Chamber or Resizing Die

It's rare for a factory case to separate into two pieces during firing, unless the gun's headspace is dangerously excessive. But when an over-zealous reloader uses a case once too often, the rear of the cartridge case may extract and eject, leaving the front half stuck in the chamber.

While at first it may seem like a monumental gunsmithing task to remove the broken half of the shell, it is a simple operation. You will require an old Marble's broken-shell extractor or one of the newer but similar Alex cartridge extractors. You will also need a strong cleaning rod.

Begin by removing the bolt. If the bolt cannot be easily removed, simply lock the action open. Make certain the sliding extractor portion of the broken-shell extractor has ¼-inch of free travel. This is adjusted by screwing in (or out) the base portion of the unit on the central shaft. Then

insert the broken-shell extractor fully into the chamber.

It is important to seat the broken extractor fully into the chamber to insure that the claw section enters deeply enough to pass the end of the case. Now point the barrel upward and push the cleaning rod into the barrel. Gently tap the rod until you feel the claws engage the front end of the cartridge case. A moderately sharp blow on the cleaning rod will now drive the shell extractor and broken case free of the chamber.

Do not attempt to use the bolt to push the shell extractor into position or to withdraw it and the broken case from the chamber. Doing so can damage the bolt face, especially its extractor and ejector.

To remove a broken shell (from which the rim has been torn) from a reloading die is almost as

Proper broken-shell extractor can make fast work of removing the front half of a broken cartridge from any chamber. A cleaning rod is also needed.

Shells firmly jammed in a resizing die can be quickly removed with the aid of a tool like the E-Z Way Stuck Case Remover.

easy. In the past, reloaders drilled and tapped the broken case and used a large screw to withdraw it from the die. This was slow and not always effective if the case was very tightly stuck. There is a better way.

The one special tool for quick, simple removal of a case jammed in a resizing die is the E-Z Way Stuck Case Remover (Superior Products Development Co.). This tool works with all RCBS, Bonanza, Forster, and similar reloading dies and will not damage the die in any way.

The sizing die should be screwed tightly into the press. Begin by removing the lock nut and adapter nut (through which the decapping rod screws) from the top of the die. The screw-in top portion of the E-Z Way unit should be turned all the way in. Place the E-Z Way Case Remover over the die's threaded decapping rod.

Now place the supplied washer over the decapping rod so it sits on top of the E-Z Way unit. Install the original die adapter nut, in an upside-down position, on the threaded decapping rod. Screw it on until it rests solidly against the washer. Then install the die's original decap-

ping-rod lock nut and bring it firmly against the upside-down adapter. This must be a tight fit, as the decapping-rod stem must not turn during the next step.

Holding the bottom of the E-Z Way unit with an appropriate wrench, unscrew (counterclockwise) the top half of the E-Z Way, using another appropriate wrench. This will move the entire decapping rod away from the die, drawing the expanding button free of the case. When it has been freed, remove the entire unit from the die.

Drop the supplied knock-out rod (use the largest one that will fit into the die) into the top of the die so that its end rests on the bottom of the stuck case. Now apply a few smart blows to the rod with a hammer and the jammed case will pop free of the die.

The whole process can be accomplished in four minutes or less, without drilling or tapping.

If a case separated in the die with the head end coming away with the shell holder, first remove the decapping rod as described. Then use the method and tool described for removing a similarly broken shell from a firearm chamber.

First step in removing shell jammed in die is to remove the decapping rod and expander button.

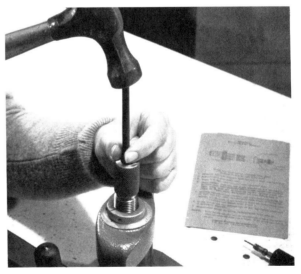

After the decapping rod and expander button have been removed, it is a simple task to knock out the jammed cases with one of the supplied steel rods and a hammer.

Job 8

Measuring Headspace

The headspace dimension in any firearm is critical. If there is too little headspace, a cartridge may not allow the action to close over it. If there is too much, a cartridge may fit loosely in the chamber and could rupture upon firing, perhaps damaging or wrecking the firearm and possibly the shooter. Correct headspace insures that there will be neither too little nor too much space between a fully seated cartridge and the bolt face. Basically, there are four common ways of obtaining this crucial dimension.

With rimmed cartridge cases (.22 rimfire, .38 Special, .30-30 Winchester, .45-70 Government, and shotshells), headspace governs the chamber area that houses the case's rim. Thus, the distance from the face of the bolt to the bottom edge of the rim recess is the headspace dimension.

Belted magnum cases do not have a rim in the conventional sense. For these cases (.224 Weatherby Magnum, 7mm Remington Magnum, .300 Winchester Magnum, and .375 Holland & Holland Magnum), headspace is measured from the bolt face to the bottom edge of the chamber area containing the cartridge's belt.

Headspace is measured differently for cases that have neither a rim nor a belt. For rimless cases with a shoulder, headspace is measured from the bolt face to a datum point (of given diameter for each cartridge) on the chamber's shoulder area. This method is used for cartridges such as the .222 Remington, .270 Winchester, .30-06 Springfield, and the .358 Winchester. The fourth method of headspace measurement is the distance from the bolt face to the end of a chamber for a straight case (no shoulder). This is the system used for such cartridges as the .25 ACP, .380 ACP, 9mm Luger, and .45 ACP.

The only practical method for measuring a chamber's headspace is to use headspace gauges of the correct caliber and size. The use of shim stock applied to the back end of a case can lead to

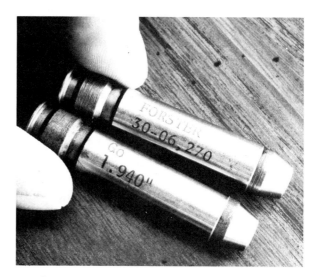

Headspace gauges are vital tools for firearms maintenance, reloading, and verifying ammo quality.

a great many errors, as cases vary and the case will be of unknown dimension.

For a specific caliber, headspace gauges are generally available in three different sizes commonly called "go" gauge (minimum), "no-go" gauge (maximum), and "field" gauge (very dangerous). The chamber's acceptance of the "go" gauge indicates that the chamber is sufficiently deep to accept a cartridge that has a maximum headspace dimension. The chamber's acceptance of the "no-go" gauge indicates that the chamber's headspace is excessive and the firearm should be removed from service because of potential hazard to firearm and user.

The "field" gauge was designed for military use on the theory that every possible firearm might be needed for combat. Firearms that accepted a "no-go" gauge could be retained in use on an as-needed basis, and only a firearm that accepted the "field" gauge was promptly removed from service—as it posed a real and immediate hazard to its user and bystanders. For our purposes, only the "go" (minimum) and "no-go" (maximum) headspace gauges have a practical value.

Generally, there is a difference of 0.006-inch in length between a minimum and maximum gauge, depending on the caliber. The military "field" gauge was 0.004-inch longer. Thus, it can be seen that there is very little difference between an acceptable chamber and one large enough to be considered dangerous.

A firearm's headspace dimension is not an absolute. Handloads that are loaded to a pressure only slightly higher than normal can, after an indefinite amount of use, slowly increase a firearm's headspace measurement. This is caused when the locking lugs are repeatedly driven against the mating receiver surface under great pressure. Eventually, enough metal is displaced to increase headspace. If the original headspace dimension was midway between minimum and maximum, it will take a change of only 0.003-inch to change it from safe to dangerous. Compare this to the average thickness of a human hair—which is 0.002-inch thick.

Checking headspace is not merely a matter of dropping a headspace gauge into a firearm and closing the bolt or action. For a number of reasons, the bolt must first be stripped. These gauges are made of very hard steel, and the rim area is not designed or dimensioned to necessarily allow for extractor clearance. Moreover, because checking headspace demands a very accurate feel of the firearm's bolt interaction with gauge and chamber, the presence of a spring-loaded, bolt-mounted ejector would interfere with an accurate appraisal of headspace. Nor can headspace be accurately gauged (felt) if a firing pin under spring tension is left in the bolt.

It is possible to permanently damage a bolt face, extractor, or ejector when using a headspace gauge. This is especially true of the small, light extractors used on many firearms. Before measuring headspace, strip all working parts from the firearm's bolt. This includes extractors (with springs and plungers), extractors collars, bolt-face-contained ejectors (with springs and

plungers), cocking pieces, firing pins, firing-pin springs, etc.

Then carefully clean all oil or grease, residue, and foreign material from the chamber and the headspace gauge. Ditto for the bolt lugs and their matching recesses in the receiver. Finally, clean the face of the bolt.

Next, drop the "go" headspace gauge into the chamber, gently closing the action. The bolt should fully close without any felt interference from the headspace gauge.

Now drop in the "no-go" gauge. Gently begin to close the action. It should never close fully on the "no-go" gauge if the gun is to be considered safe. (The degree of closing will vary with the specific dimensions in the individual chamber.)

Make careful note of the amount of closing that takes place. When headspace is again measured, you will then be able to determine if the headspace dimension is growing larger. This can occur with extensive use or with ammunition that produces above-normal pressures.

Handloaders will do well to measure headspace every 1,000 rounds or so. Users of factory ammunition might be content with measuring every 5,000 rounds. But if a problem is suspected, check immediately. *Some* of the warning

A backed out primer is a good reason to check chamber headspace. Be sure to strip all working parts from the bolt before inserting a gauge in the chamber.

signs that indicate the need to check headspace are: primers that partially back out of the case upon firing; cases with bright circumferential rings after firing; cases that give evidence of incipient splitting—and so on.

Just as chambers must be within a very narrow range of headspace dimension, so must ammunition. If a cartridge has too much headspace length, it may not properly fit into the chamber, preventing the action from being closed, or making it difficult to close. If a cartridge has too little headspace, it will be too short to be supported by the chamber and may rupture when fired. With factory ammo, headspace is verified before it is packaged. However, reloads should be carefully checked, except in the instance of rimmed or belted cartridges. Rims and belts are not normally dimensionally altered by the firing and

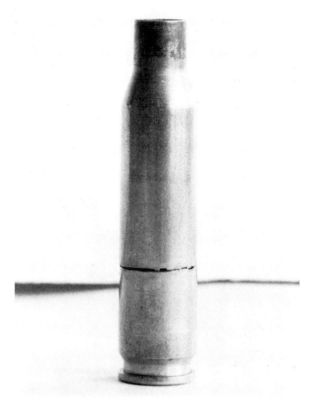

This case separation could have been avoided if the firearm's chamber and the ammo's headspace had been checked beforehand.

reloading process, so there is no need to be concerned with case headspace.

However, rimless cartridges, both bottleneck and straight styles, need to be checked because cases stretch as they are repeatedly fired and reloaded. Straight rimless cases .32 ACP, 9mm Luger, .45 ACP), will stretch continuously until headspace (measured from base of case to mouth) has become so long as to prevent proper chambering. To avoid this problem, a reloader trims his cases back when they reach or exceed the suggested maximum length. Unless he makes the cases too short, proper headspace will be maintained. The only tool needed to check headspace dimensions on straight cases is a vernier or dial-indicating caliper.

For rimless bottleneck cases (.223 Remington, .243 Winchester, .270 Winchester, .30-06 Springfield, etc.) the headspace dimension is from the base of the case to a specific datum line on the case shoulder. Headspace on these cartridges can be dangerously reduced by a resizing die of improper dimensions or a too-thin shell holder or a combination of both. All it takes is several thousandths of an inch to create a problem, so it is best to carefully measure the headspace of all rimless bottleneck reloads. This is easily done with a cartridge-headspace gauge such as the one supplied by Forster.

Cartridge-headspace gaugers are chambers into which the loaded rounds are dropped. The rear of the chamber has two steps. The lower of the two is a minimum-headspace step. The loaded round should never drop below this level. The upper step indicates maximum headspace, and a loaded round should never extend beyond flush with this step. The mouth end of the same die is used for gauging minimum and maximum cartridge length.

Every rifleman should have firearm-headspace gauges for each caliber he owns. Some gauges will do double duty—that is, a .30-06 gauge also works in a .270 Winchester, while a .243 Winchester gauge is suitable for the .308 and .358 Winchester chambers. Further, every reloader should have a cartridge-headspace gauge for every rimless bottleneck caliber for which he loads.

Job 9

Installing Detachable Clip in Long-Action Remington Model 700

The Remington 700 series of bolt-actions are the most popular rifles of this type. However, many owners long for the easy, quick loading and unloading of a clip-model rifle. Such shooters are often those who frequently change locales during a day's hunting and therefore welcome the ease of popping a clip in and out of the rifle.

It's not difficult to convert almost any *long-action* Remington 700 rifle to clip use—that is, any 700 chambered for the .25-06 Remington, .264 Winchester Magnum, .270 Winchester, 7 × 57 Mauser, .280 Remington (7mm Express Remington), 7mm Remington Magnum, .30-06 Springfield, or .300 Winchester Magnum. The only long-action 700s not convertible are the .300 H&H Magnum, 8mm Remington Magnum, .375 H&H Magnum, .416 Remington Magnum, and .458 Winchester Magnum.

You will need a Kwik Klip magazine conversion for the 700LA, made by Trexler Industries, Inc., and sold by Brownells. This unit consists of a one-piece trigger guard and clip holder, and is factory fitted with a push-lever clip release. Also included is a magazine suitable for any of the cartridges just mentioned.

After making sure the rifle is unloaded, remove the two action-retaining screws on BDL or Classic models. (The 700 ADL can be fitted with the Kwik Klip but requires special inletting which will be discussed a bit later.) Remove the complete hinged floorplate, trigger guard, and magazine—setting them aside. Retain the two action screws. Set the barreled action carefully aside where it will not become damaged. If the original magazine box remained in the stock, slip it out and set it aside.

After removing the original Remington 700 hinged floorplate, position the Kwik Klip trigger guard and clip housing into the stock.

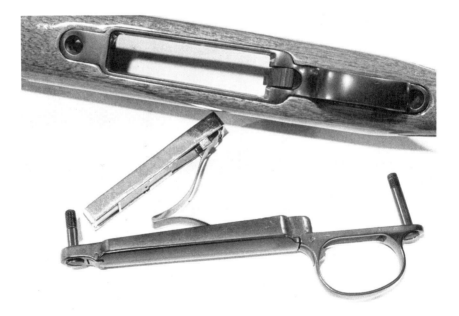

With the clip removed from the replacement trigger-guard group, attempt to slip the trigger guard into place in the stock. Most likely, it will not slip into position, and you will need to remove wood from the inside stock area which surrounds the clip housing of the trigger guard unit. Most often, only the sides of the front half of the magazine mortise require wood removal. This can be done with the careful use of a wood rasp. Be sure not to hit the stock edges, top or bottom, when working with the rasp. If you've gained experience and skill working on stocks, you may prefer to use chisels to remove the excess wood. Be sure to remove only enough to allow easy entry of the replacement trigger guard.

When the trigger-guard unit is properly fitted, place it in the stock, holding it in position with one hand. Then insert the clip and insure that it goes in easily and snaps into position. If it does not, the housing is being distorted by pressure from the stock, and a bit more wood needs to be removed.

After the trigger-guard unit is fitted properly, remove it and give any raw wood a coat or two of stock finish. When the finish has completely dried, you can continue the job.

Place the barreled action in the stock and put the Kwik Klip trigger-guard unit into place. Check the action's bolt release to be sure it is properly working. (Some rifles may require a bit of filing to get the bolt release to clear the replacement trigger guard. It's best to file the release because it is made of steel and can be easily touch-up blued, whereas the Kwik Klip trigger guard is aluminum and cannot be easily touched up if it is filed.)

Now replace the guard screws snugly. Insert the clip. If it does not easily latch into the locked position, you will need to add one or more washers between the rear of the trigger guard and the stock. These washers are pre-drilled for ample action-screw clearance. Do not add any more washers than necessary to have the clip lock smoothly into position.

Now manipulate the bolt carefully. If it binds or rubs against the clip, you will need to add one or more washers between the front end of the trigger-guard group and the stock. As in the rear, these washers are positioned so that the action screw passes through them. It is unlikely that any installation should require more than a total of three washers. Most require only one.

The complete alteration should be checked for clearance behind the rear of the trigger guard. If the trigger guard binds tightly to the stock, repeated firing may cause the wood to split. There should be a few thousandths of an inch of clearance between the wood and the rear of the trigger guard. If wood needs to be removed at this point, do so carefully with a suitable wood chisel. Don't forget to add stock finish over any exposed raw wood.

Customizing a 700LA with a detachable clip will enhance the gun's usefulness and add value. The new clip will hold four rounds, except with magnum calibers which hold three rounds. The clip should always be loaded from the front end, and the cartridges pushed to the rear *under* the clip ears. Do not attempt to snap cartridges down past the ears.

It may be necessary to use one or two special washers between the Kwik Klip trigger guard and clip housing. If the original trigger guard had a washer(s) under it, replace it (them) with the washer(s) supplied with the Kwik Klip.

Be sure the clip will slip in and out of its housing easily before attempting to reassemble the rifle. If it does not, some wood removal, as described in the text, may be necessary.

Because the Kwik Klip feeds each cartridge from a central position under the bolt (rather than feeding first from the right and then the left side), smooth feeding is assured. Indeed, a Kwik Klip could solve some feeding problems encountered with handloads of varying lengths.

The Kwik Klip will shorten the maximum length of a loaded round that can be used in the 700. All factory ammo will fit, but handloads will need to be kept to a maximum overall length of approximately 3.240 inches.

Because the 700ADL has no cut for a floorplate in the bottom of its stock (using instead a blind magazine) it will be necessary to carefully alter the stock. First, using a punch, drive out the washer that serves as a stop for the front action screw. Insert the punch through the top of the stock and, using repeated light blows with a mallet, carefully work the punch around the edge of the washer to drive it straight out. Take care—if the washer is driven out at an angle or if unnecessary force is used, the stock could be split.

Next, position the replacement trigger guard over the stock and trace its outline lightly on the wood with a soft pencil. It will require great care, using the appropriate chisels, to inlet the stock to accept the new trigger guard. This is a job most easily done by someone with stockmaking experience, but it's also a good way to begin getting that experience. Go slowly and remove only a tiny bit of wood at a time. Be careful not to cause any splits or to let the chisel curl away too much wood. Stay well within your penciled outline until you have cut completely through the stock into the magazine mortise. By going slowly you will prevent unsightly gaps between the wood and the replacement trigger guard.

By carefully drilling a number of holes through the stock into the magazine mortise, the job can be made easier. But this operation requires great care not to remove wood where it will be needed.

The installation of a detachable magazine in a 700ADL stock makes a fine beginner's stockmaking project, though it's not without risk since less than careful work could result in a ruined stock.

Completely installed, the detachable clip adds a nice custom touch to any Remington 700 long-action rifle.

Job 10

Installing Aperture Sights

Most shooters prefer a scope on a hunting rifle, but that is not invariably the best choice in sighting equipment. If a rifle (or a shotgun to be used with slugs) will be getting a lot of hard knocks and general banging around, and if it's going to be used only at modest ranges, an aperture (peep) sight may well be ideal. A good peep sight, such as the Williams FP (Fool Proof) and similar models, will be a better, more rugged sight than a cheaply made telescope. And it will be less expensive.

A peep sight can be an excellent choice not only on a deer rifle or slug shotgun but also on a rimfire rifle to be used on running rabbits and such. Thus, the installation of peep sights is a fairly common gunsmithing task.

There are a number of installation styles for peep sights, depending to some extent upon the firearm to which they will be mounted. Some are as simple as slip-on dovetails while others require the drilling and tapping of two holes in the receiver.

Generally speaking, most older firearms (rifles built prior to the early 1970s) are pre-drilled for peep sights. Because most of today's shooters use scopes, the factory drilling and tapping of peep-sight holes has become less common. But some, such as the Marlin Model 336 carbines, are always drilled and tapped, and so are current Marlin Model 39A and Winchester Model 94 rifles, among others.

The front sight may have to be changed to a higher one for use with a peep. This can be checked before installation begins by simply tapping the peep sight to the receiver and attempting to adjust it to align with the open front and rear sights. If the peep will not adjust far enough downward, you know a higher front sight will be required. This can be accomplished with a higher bead or blade, a higher ramp, the addition of a riser between ramp and sight, or the addition of a ramp to a gun not so equipped.

For .22 rimfire rifles equipped with a dovetail designed to accept a scope mount, several dovetail aperture sights are available. Among these are the Williams Guide Sight and the Williams FP. The Guide Sight incorporates a simple dovetail base with another dovetail on top. Elevation adjustment is obtained by sliding the aperture housing up or down along this dovetail. A simple set screw locks the adjustment. Another set screw, when loosened, allows

A peep sight, this one a Williams FP, can make a practical addition to any shotgun used for deer hunting with slugs in heavy cover.

The accuracy of a muzzleloading rifle can be enhanced by the addition of a good peep sight.

for windage adjustment. The FP model has ¼-inch (at 100 yards) click adjustments which can be positively locked once sighted-in. Either of these sights is secured to the rifle by sliding it onto the dovetail of the rifle's receiver and locking a set screw. As with all aperture sights, the most rearward position (on the receiver dovetail) is correct.

Invariably, a peep mounted to a .22's receiver dovetail requires a higher-than-normal front sight. Front sight replacement was discussed earlier in this chapter.

When installing a peep sight using factory-drilled holes, such as on a Marlin 336 or a Winchester 94, remove the two filler screws from the peep-sight mounting holes. Then carefully degrease the holes and the mounting screws, using a commercial pressurized solvent such as Rig #3. Next, install the peep sight and one of its mounting screws snugly. Insure that the screw does not protrude into the receiver or that, in the case of a blind hole, it is not too long to prevent complete tightening of the aperture sight's base. Remove the screw and repeat the procedure with the second screw. Shorten any screw that protrudes into the receiver or bottoms in a blind hole until it is flush with the receiver. This can be done with a small file. Be careful not to damage the screw's threads.

Place one drop of a screw-locking compound on each screw and securely mount the base to the side of the receiver. After the screws have been hand-tightened, set each one by giving the screwdriver a light, sharp rap with a small hammer. This should enable you to gain another ⅛-turn or so on each screw. Then assemble the sight staff to its base.

If the gun was previously sighted-in with open sights, adjust the peep so it aligns with the open rear and front sights. This will bring the peep's adjustment very close, even closer than bore-sighting. If the peep cannot be properly aligned, a higher front bead will be required. After installation of the higher bead, bore-sight the gun using a collimator.

Always remove any fixed-position open rear sight and replace it with a slot blank or install filler screws as appropriate. Rear open sights which will fold down do not require removal, but by removing them you will avoid any accidental raising of the rear sight in the field and give the gun a cleaner look.

On some rifles, and with some peep sights, mounting is accomplished by removing a factory aperture sight and using part or all of the original mounting system to install a replacement peep. H&K, the Ruger Mini 14, and others call for this type of installation.

If you choose to mount a peep sight on a rifle requiring drilling and tapping, a jig such as the Forster Universal Sight Mounting Fixture will be required to obtain precise location of the screw holes. Use of this jig, or similar ones, is covered later in this book.

For a rifle that will see plenty of rough use, or be limited to short range hunting, a good peep can prove to be the best possible sight selection.

Peep sights come in many configurations. This one slips into the receiver dovetail designed to accept a scope mount often found on .22 rimfire rifles.

12

Bedding Barrel or Action

Bedding or rebedding an action and/or barrel with epoxy compound (glass bedding) is worthwhile whenever faulty bedding prevents a rifle from shooting as accurately as it could. Epoxy will enable the average gunsmith to obtain a perfectly fitting stock with several hours of work, as opposed to the 40 or 50 hours it would take a highly skilled stockmaker to carve and fit a new stock. Perfect stock fit will add a great deal of accuracy.

Almost universally, the action is bedded in epoxy in a manner that completely supports the recoil lug and bottom area at the front end of the receiver in a skin-tight sheath. This maintains a rigid, uniform position of the action in the stock during recoil and at all times.

Many firearm owners choose to bed the *entire* action in epoxy. This may add some strength to the stock and surely also waterproofs the inside of the entire receiver mortise. In addition, it will prevent any possible action twisting or bending as the action screws are evenly tightened.

The bedding of the barrel can be done simultaneously with the action or separately, depending on the type of barrel support desired. Simul-

A free-floating barrel will provide a consistent point of impact over the months and years despite great variations in humidity and temperature.

taneous bedding is appropriate if you want a full-bedded barrel, total end-to-end contact with the fore-end. However, this is perhaps the least desirable method with respect to accuracy. As I emphasized in Chapter 9, a free-floated barrel is the top choice for accuracy.

There are three common types of bedding. Most commercial manufacturers leave a small pad of wood, an inch or two from the fore-end tip, in the stock's barrel channel to supply upward pressure against the barrel. This is a good enough system for some guns and some shooting but is subject to varying pressure by the fore-end against the barrel as the stock warps against or away from the metal. Such warping is inevitable as the stock gains or loses moisture.

Either of the two other common methods is generally preferred for custom bedding. One is to bed the receiver and the first inch or two of the chamber end of the barrel, leaving the remaining barrel free of any fore-end contact. This provides the desired stability for point of impact and generally affords better accuracy than the pressure-point bedding used for most mass-produced rifles.

The third method is a variation in which only the receiver is bedded, leaving the entire barrel free-floating. Some shooters contend that this provides the best accuracy; others say there is no difference from the second method. A full coat of epoxy is often used in the barrel channel, but not touching the barrel, to insure fore-end stability, though some feel this step is unnecessary.

Either of these last two methods should be selected when bedding in epoxy.

Generally speaking, epoxy bedding compounds require very exact mixing. You usually cannot slow down or speed up the hardening process by using less or more of the catalyst (hardening compound). Indeed, if the materials are not mixed exactly, hardening may not occur at all. So be very, very precise and follow exactly the instructions that come with the bedding material you buy.

There are two basic consistencies for properly mixed bedding materials, depending on the product you choose. One type has an oozing consistency that allows it to flow freely into recesses, with the excess bleeding out of stock/barrelled action junctions. This is an effective mixture, but a messy one. Excess material must be cleaned up before the compound hardens or it will take a great deal of time-consuming effort to be cleaned up—and the material can ooze into crevices it was not intended to occupy. One such compound is the excellent Acraglas currently sold by Brownells.

Recent years have seen the development of

Epoxy bedding compounds are offered in rather simple kits, but care must be taken when using them to insure the desired results and to avoid a ruined stock.

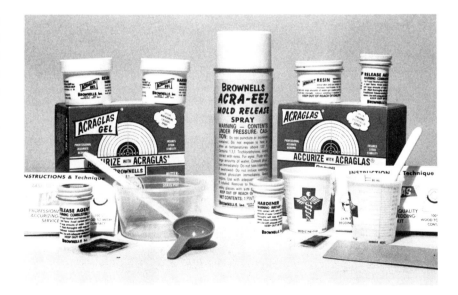

non-running gel-like materials, whose consistency I prefer. They are easier to work with, result in far less mess, and are unlikely to flow where not wanted. My instructions will assume the use of this type of compound—specifically, Acraglas-Gel, currently sold by Brownells.

Inletting

Whether you are building a custom stock or refitting a factory stock, the inletting is important. You need not be precise with the fit of wood to metal, but an irregular or grossly oversized barrel channel will still be visible in the finished effort, regardless of how closely you match the epoxy to the wood color. It pays to take great care. Besides, if the barreled action and trigger guard do not screw together with a reasonably proper fit, there will be the devil to pay in getting the action to seat to the right depth.

Inlet the stock so you have approximately ¹⁄₁₆-inch space at all the wood-to-metal surfaces. A space of ¹⁄₃₂-inch is ideal where there are visible wood-to-metal seams—around action, barrel,

and trigger-guard edges. There is no reason to be concerned with smooth internal wood surfaces, as the bedding will fill in all uneven areas.

Bedding the Barrel

It will be necessary to bed the barrel first, as a separate operation, if free-floating is desired. Adequately cover the barrel and nearby action parts with several coats of release agent. Be sure to get plenty of release agent into the front action-screw hole and on the screw itself. Allow ample drying time between coats. An extra coating of Simonize automobile wax on screw threads and in screw holes is a good safeguard. Just wipe on the wax, do not buff it.

Next, cover all outside stock areas with masking tape. Later, when the bedding material oozes out of the barrel channel, this tape will prevent it from ruining the stock and finish.

Then apply a liberal amount of properly mixed bedding compound in the barrel channel. Screw the barreled action, stock, and floorplate to-

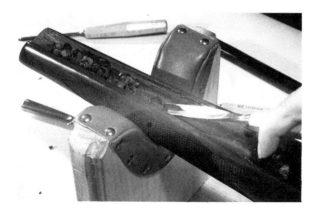

Stock inletting should be carefully done with chisels and gouges. Do not be concerned with some inexactness as the bedding will fill in uneven areas.

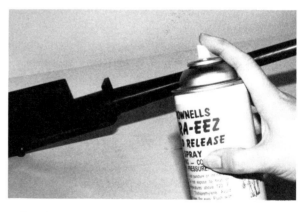

Liberal use of a release agent is extremely important to prevent stock and barreled action from being permanently glued together.

gether and set aside to harden—approximately 18 hours.

Do not use too much bedding material or it can squeeze excessively into the action mortise of the stock. Keep in mind that if an inadequate amount of the release agent is used on metal parts, the epoxy will glue the stock and barrel together in a manner that will prevent separating them unless you are willing to destroy the stock with an ax.

Before the bedding material sets, in approximately five hours, remove the excess that has oozed out along the barrel channel. It can be peeled away with a sharp knife. A wetted blade will help. Be extremely careful not to mar the barrel finish during this operation. Do not at-

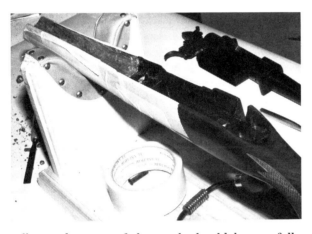

All outside areas of the stock should be carefully masked to keep any oozing epoxy from the finished wood surface.

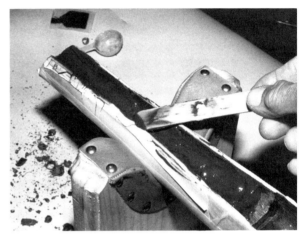

Apply a liberal but not excessive amount of epoxy to the surface areas to be bedded.

Allow ample drying time.

After 5 to 6 hours, remove excess bedding material using a sharp, wet knife blade.

tempt to get a smooth, even fit at the top of the barrel channel at this time. Simply remove the major excess. You will sand the stock channel edges to a perfect fit later, when you remove the barreled action.

After 18 hours, remove the barreled action from the stock and sand the edges of the barrel channel. Do this carefully and no refinishing of the wood will be necessary. Then remove the masking tape from the outside stock areas on the fore-end.

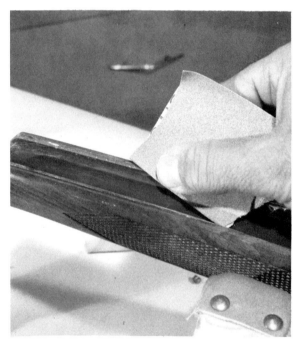

After 18 hours, remove the barreled action and carefully sand the edge of the epoxy to match all stock lines. Then remove masking tape from fore-end.

You should now have a perfectly bedded barrel channel. If there are minor voids in the epoxy, they can be ignored or filled. Major voids should, of course, be filled. This can be done by simply mixing a small bit of bedding material and placing only enough epoxy into the voids to precisely fit them and cause no run-over. Do not forget to get at least two coats of release agent on

all metal, and re-tape the stock if such touch-up is necessary. However, it's far better to get the job done perfectly the first time without any need for touch-ups.

Bedding the Action

After the barrel has been bedded, you need to bed the action while raising the barrel perhaps $\frac{1}{32}$-inch to $\frac{1}{16}$-inch off the fore-end bedding to obtain the free-floating feature. This is the time to be certain you have removed $\frac{1}{32}$-inch to $\frac{1}{16}$-inch of wood all around the recoil-lug area of the stock mortise. It is important for accuracy that you give the stock mortise full bedding coverage in the area of the recoil lug.

You are now ready to begin bedding the action. It is strongly advised that you remove trigger, bolt stop, and other action parts that might accidentally be glued into the stock mortise. All hollows, holes, recesses, and any other action area that might provide a river of flow for the

To bed the action, remove sufficient wood from the recoil-lug mortise to insure full coverage of bedding compound. This is important for accuracy.

bedding compound must be filled with putty or other inert material—this is imperative. It's not enough to put release compound in such areas because any pegs, claws, or protrusions formed by the bedding compound in any action recess or orifice will permanently affix the action in place in the stock. Be sure any plugs are covered with suitable tape and that the tape is, in turn, adequately covered with release compound. Sometimes tape and release compound can be used in place of undesirable disassembly.

Carefully give all metal surfaces a double coat of release compound. Some auto wax, applied liberally on top of the release agent, is a good idea for all screw holes and screws.

Before applying the epoxy, you must make sure that when the barreled action is in position, the barrel will be held at least ⅟₃₂-inch off the bedding in the barrel channel. One convenient way to do this is to carefully apply several layers of heavy tape to the barrel, which will give a ⅟₃₂-inch or more thickness. The tape will have to be trimmed exactly at the receiver, and then several coats of release compound should be applied to the tape. Or, alternatively, shims can be placed in the bottom of the receiver mortise.

Be sure all outside surfaces of the stock are

When bedding the action, tape the barrel to a thickness of ⅟₃₂ inch to give the desired free-floating barrel channel. Then apply release compound to tape.

protected with masking tape. Replace the tape previously removed at the rear of the barrel channel. Then carefully apply the bedding compound to the action mortise. Use enough to fill all voids but not so much as to cause displacement into the magazine, trigger, and safety or bolt-release areas of the mortise. Any bedding that flows into those areas will have to be removed later. Be especially careful at the receiver/barrel joint area. Because of the ⅟₃₂-inch or more space created by the tape on the barrel, some bedding material may find its way into this area. When the job is complete you will need to clean up any such "flash."

Be certain—and this cannot be overemphasized—that you have adequately filled all action recesses with putty (or otherwise prevented the entry of bedding material) and adequately covered all metal parts and any tape with two coats of release compound. Allow adequate time for the release compound to dry between coats and after the final covering.

Now assemble the barreled action, turning up the front action screw quite snugly but not enough to cause any bending of action or barrel. A firm, one-handed hold on the screwdriver will provide adequate tension. The rear action screw should not be as tight.

Once again, after about five hours, remove any excess bedding material from outside areas in the magazine well or on action parts. Then let the bedding harden for 18 hours.

After removing the barreled action, clean away all surplus material, trim and sand the edges and, finally, remove all tape from the stock and the barrel.

Now assemble any removed parts such as trigger, safety, magazine, bolt release, and so on. Check for proper working of all moving parts. It may be necessary to remove bedding material around moving parts if any interference is detectable. This can be done with wood chisels or rasps and sandpaper. A properly bedded stock will have a skin-tight fit to the action, with the barrel free-floating.

If, for some reason, the free-floated barrel will not group as well as when it was pressure-bedded, you can add a small pad of glass bedding to

A free-floating barrel will provide enhanced accuracy and a nonshifting point of impact.

the barrel channel, (perhaps an inch-long pad one to two inches behind the tip of the fore-end or fore-end-cap/stock junction). A height of about ⅛-inch will be right. Allow this pad to harden completely without the barreled action in place. Then, by trial and error, you can sand down the glass pad a bit and try for accuracy until you are satisfied.

Don't try to rush any of this. While the bedding material will appear quite hard after 18 hours or so, the rifle should not be used for 60 hours to insure that full hardness has been obtained.

For added strength, incidentally, some folks add powdered aluminum or steel to the action-bedding compound. This should be done only in exact accordance with the bedding manufacturer's instruction.

Good bedding material will provide an acid-proof, waterproof, solvent-proof surface that is not only durable. but also very, very stable. It's not damaged easily and will provide the maximum accuracy potential that can be achieved by proper bedding.

Fitting and Bedding Synthetic Stocks

After-market synthetic stocks are popular, but sometimes they are not the easy bolt-on additions we are led to believe. Still, the addition of any of these stocks is easily accomplished by anyone capable of bedding a barreled action with epoxy compounds.

The synthetic stocks, such as the "Six," can often be installed very rapidly. Simply sand or chisel away any tight spots to obtain a drop-in fit, and then, if the receiver's recoil-lug area does not fit snugly, glass-bed that portion of the new stock following the procedures outlined in this chapter. I have installed "Six" stocks on Remington 700s without any difficulty other than relieving a bit of stock material around the magazine housing.

The installation of a Clifton Arms synthetic stock was accomplished on an extremely accurate Model 70 Winchester. To insure that the maximum accuracy potential was realized, the action area was fully glass-bedded. The job resulted in a reduction of the rifle's weight and a slight gain in accuracy. The Clifton Arms stock also adds a good deal of usefulness to the rifle as it has a fold-away (and disappearing) bipod built into the fore-end. This restocking proved very worthwhile.

13

Triggers and Safeties

The safety of a well-designed firearm is not easily compromised, yet each year thousands of firearms are rendered unsafe by owners who decide to lighten or improve a trigger pull or smooth up a safety switch. No other area of home gunsmithing exposes the firearm owner to more potential hazards than the alteration or repair of trigger or safety assemblies. All firearms manufacturers caution against any alteration or repair of these parts. In view of the potential hazards involved, the untrained person should return to the factory any firearm that needs trigger or safety repair.

All the same, a careful, meticulous gunsmithing enthusiast may perform certain trigger and safety improvements in order to increase accuracy and insure proper functioning. For example, trigger assemblies and even certain safeties can sometimes be replaced with after-market units. A trigger pull that is extremely heavy or is creepy with excessive travel will prevent the shooter from obtaining full accuracy. And a safety that is difficult to switch on or off may well become a safety that goes unused. To avoid the inconvenience and expense of returning a firearm to the factory, many owners make minor adjustments of the kind I will describe, or install suitable replacements.

But when contemplating any adjustment it is essential to understand that safety and trigger assemblies usually require very precise physical dimensions. You cannot expect to remove material or change angles or parts engagements and have the firearm be as safe as intended.

Testing Trigger Adjustment for Safety

With respect to the weight and travel of a trigger, what is correct in one firearm may well be unsafe in another. A trigger that is properly adjusted will not allow the firearm to fire if it is dropped, when cocked. I test rifle triggers by rapping receivers with a rubber mallet and by hitting the assembled rifle's buttplate against a padded section of my bench. Care must be taken to avoid cracking the butt, yet to jar the gun sufficiently to cause the trigger to release the sear if it is improperly adjusted.

Any trigger adjustment must also be checked with regard to the function of the mechanism. Forcefully and repeatedly slamming a bolt closed, on bolt- and pump-action rifles, should not result in discharge. Test semiautos by allowing the bolt to slam shut repeatedly under spring pressure. Naturally, all such tests should be done with an empty firearm.

Finally, after a trigger adjustment has passed the impact and rubber mallet tests, the firearm should be cocked and the safety switched on. The trigger should then be pulled as hard as possible. The gun should not fire.

Practically speaking, a minimum trigger pull of 2¾ to 3¼ pounds can be obtained on most firearms having close-fitting parts and a good trigger design. Lighter pulls often will not stand up to the required tests.

Remember that light pulls often contribute to accidental discharges in the field. Cold fingers, gloved fingers, or merely an attempt to shoot quickly can, when combined with a too-light trigger pull, cause an unintentional discharge.

Trigger adjustments are commonly made when original triggers are replaced with aftermarket triggers. Such triggers are often similar enough that a basic understanding of one will result in the understanding of several. At least two such replacement triggers adjust identically to the factory trigger used in the Remington Model 700 and Model Seven, as well as earlier Remington rifles. For the purpose of this text I have selected a Timney trigger to explain the adjustments.

Trigger Installation— Remington 700

The Timney trigger, which I installed in my Remington Model 700, comes with slave (keeper) pins to keep all parts in alignment during installation. If the trigger you select does not have slave pins, making and installing them will help the job go smoothly. Not every trigger replacement for other types of rifles requires such pins.

To begin, after removing the barreled action from the stock, clamp the receiver in a vise so that the trigger mechanism is fully exposed and horizontal. Carefully disassemble the original bolt stop and safety lever from the original trigger. Take special care not to bend or distort these parts. There is a small spring and detent ball under the safety lever—do not lose it. Next, transfer these parts to the replacement trigger. Now remove the original trigger by driving out the two retaining pins. (Military barreled actions frequently have only one retaining pin.)

Install the new trigger in the action using the original two mounting pins. Be sure the replacement trigger is correctly aligned in the receiver. As the mounting pins are tapped into engagement with the new trigger housing, they will drive the slave pins from the unit. As the retaining pins are fully seated, the slave pins will exit the retaining-pin holes. (If the pin holes cannot be properly aligned, contact the replacement-trigger manufacturer.) Be sure the replacement trigger is held snugly in position. There should be no discernible movement of the housing in the rifle's receiver.

Backlash Adjustment

The first step in adjusting any trigger of this type is to remove excessive backlash (trigger travel after the sear is released). This is accomplished using the backlash-adjusting screw, which is the top screw located on the front of the trigger housing. Loosen its lock nut and turn in the screw a half-turn at a time. Continue doing so until the rifle will not fire. Then carefully back out the screw an eighth-turn at a time until the rifle will fire. Now back out the screw an additional half-turn and lock it in place.

REPLACING REMINGTON 700 TRIGGER

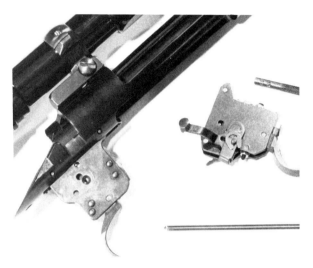

When replacing a Remington 700's trigger with an after-market trigger, first remove all the safety-switch and bolt-stop parts from the original trigger and install them on the replacement trigger.

Remove the original trigger. Some of the parts will separate as the retaining pins are driven out. The replacement trigger is then ready to install.

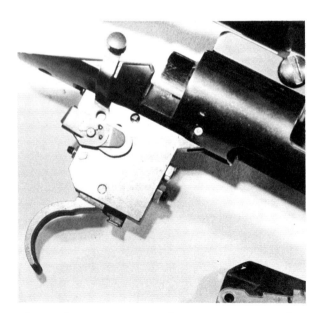

The replacement trigger slips into position and is secured by replacing the mounting pins.

When replacing a trigger, it is often necessary to chisel away a bit of wood from the front end of the stock's trigger mortise to allow clearance for adjusting screws and locks.

Trigger-Pull Weight

The weight of the trigger pull is controlled by the bottom screw on the front edge of the trigger housing. Check the weight of pull with a trigger-pull scale or weights. Most replacement triggers can be safely adjusted from approximately 2½ pounds upward. To decrease the weight of pull, loosen the lock nut and back out the screw a half-turn at a time. Check the weight of pull three or four times with each adjustment.

On some trigger assemblies, the pull-adjusting screw is located on the bottom edge of the trigger housing, directly in front of the trigger guard. This location allows for trigger-pull adjustment (within reason) without removal of the stock. Light trigger pulls may require adjustment of the sear-engagement screw.

Sear Engagement

The sear-engagement adjusting screw is located at the back edge of the trigger housing. This adjustment can normally be left as received if a trigger pull of about three pounds or more is used. If a lighter trigger pull is desired, it's necessary to reduce the amount of sear engagement.

There is a delicate balance between the engagement adjustment and the adjustment of a light trigger pull. It is especially important to check carefully that the gun will not fire if bumped, dropped, or manipulated aggressively, as described earlier. If uncertain about your ability to balance sear engagement with a light pull, adjust the trigger to no less than three pounds and do not move the sear-engagement adjusting screw.

Improper trigger weight or sear engagement can cause accidental discharge which can lead to personal injury or death. Be safe, not sorry. Al-ways use a trigger-pull gauge or weights to check adjustment.

After the trigger has been properly adjusted, it may be necessary to carefully remove some wood from the stock to provide ample clearance for the new trigger housing, especially for the adjusting screws which protrude from it. After wood removal, apply a good stock finish to any raw wood.

Frequently, the wide trigger used on a replacement trigger group will bear against the stock and/or opening in the trigger guard. Carefully check for this condition. If necessary, trim away stock wood and open up the trigger guard with a small file. This is important, and not just for smoothness of pull, but for safety. If the trigger binds on the stock or trigger guard, the gun might fire as the action is closed. Make sure the trigger can be moved from left to right for its entire travel without touching either the stock or trigger guard.

When the firearm is assembled be certain that clearance is maintained between trigger and stock, as well as the trigger guard. On some rifles, it is possible to shift the stock position slightly, causing interference. After the firearm has been assembled, check that impact will not cause the gun to discharge and that the safety will prevent the trigger from being pulled. Also be sure the safety fully snaps into position when the safety switch is placed "safe."

Trigger Adjustment— Winchester Model 70

The adjustment of the Winchester Model 70 trigger and some replacement after-market triggers for this model, is a straightforward operation.

Trigger travel is controlled by how far in or out the trigger-adjusting screw is positioned. Begin by loosening the single lock nut on the outside of the trigger-adjusting screw. Then turn in screw to decrease the amount of backlash. When the trigger will just fire the rifle, back out the adjusting screw a full turn and lock it in position with the lock nut.

The weight of pull is governed by the amount of compression applied to the trigger spring. To increase trigger-pull weight, compress the spring farther. To decrease weight of pull, release compression on the spring. This adjustment is made using the two nuts next to the spring. The lower nut is loosened to allow the upper nut to be turned in or out for the desired weight of pull. It has been my experience that the factory trigger unit should not be adjusted lighter than 3½ pounds or it will not withstand the safety checks mentioned at the beginning of this chapter.

Use two small wrenches to adjust the trigger-pull weight and lock nuts. Be sure the two nuts are locked up tightly against each other after making the adjustment.

After reassembly, check to insure that the trig-ger will not fire when the butt is impacted or the receiver is struck repeatedly with a rubber mallet.

Untrained hobbyists are cautioned not to attempt any stoning of the trigger and sear-engaging surfaces. The experienced person can use a stone only to carefully remove any burrs from the sear or trigger-engagement surfaces. All the original angles and the degree of engagement must remain as initially provided by the factory. Stoning should serve merely to clean up any burrs and give engagement surfaces a light polish. The stoning of any sear or trigger-engagement surface can cause a hazardous condition. Stone with great care and only if you are qualified to do so.

Some replacement triggers of the Winchester Model 70 style, such as the Canjar, have a single set feature. When pushed forward, these triggers allow a thin set-trigger release to protrude from the face of the trigger and lock it in the set position. In this mode, a pressure ranging from a fraction on an ounce to perhaps several ounces

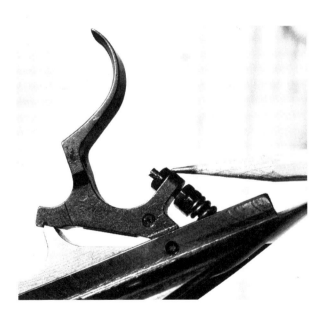

To adjust trigger of Model 70 Winchester, begin by loosening the outside lock nut (indicated by the pencil pointer), then turn in the screw a half-turn at a time to decrease the amount of backlash.

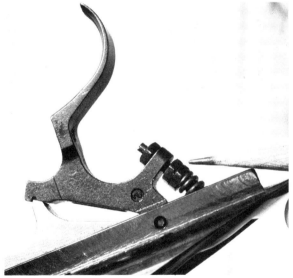

Weight of pull on a Model 70 Winchester is adjusted by changing the amount of compression on the trigger spring. This is done by moving the compression nut and lock nut up or down on the trigger screw.

Use two small wrenches to lock together securely the trigger-weight adjusting nuts.

will fire the gun. The amount of pressure required in the set mode is controlled by a small hex screw in the side of the trigger.

Additional Cautions

The weight of trigger pull on many handguns and some rifles is controlled, at least in part, by the tension of the hammer's mainspring and the trigger-return spring. Some shooters attempt quick but improper trigger-pull adjustment by decreasing the tension of these springs. Shortening of the coil springs or the grinding of flat springs amounts to gunsmithing butchery. Problems of misfires and tied-up mechanisms during rapid firing can be the result. If a spring treatment is desired, purchase replacement springs designed for the purpose. Even then, an occasional misfire or tied-up action can result.

Attempts to change sear, firing-pin, and trigger-engagement surface angles or dimensions are sure to lead to grief. It's best to get along with a less than perfect trigger when the alternative may be trying to explain why an accidental discharge caused personal injury—or worse.

How Safeties Work

A safety is not an all-inclusive preventer of unintentional firearm discharges. Some safeties are designed to prevent only the firing of the gun if the trigger is pulled or accidentally impacted while the safety switch is in the safe position. With this type of safety it is possible that a severe jolt, such as when the firearm is dropped against a hard surface under high-impact circumstances, can cause the gun to fire even with the safety switch in the safe position.

Other safeties are designed to withdraw the firing pin rearward and prevent it from moving forward regardless of the circumstances. So long as the safety is fully on, the firing pin is withdrawn from the sear and fully blocked from forward motion, and the gun cannot be fired. The Winchester Model 70 uses such a safety. A variation of this style leaves the firing pin in contact with the sear but prevents any forward movement of the firing pin by blocking its passage. The Ruger 77/22 uses such a safety. Regardless of safety design, parts can wear, bend, distort, and break. Thus, no safety should ever be assumed totally foolproof.

Testing Safeties

Safeties can be tested by cocking the firearm, applying the safety switch, and then, using two fingers, squeezing the trigger as hard as possible. The firearm should not fire. Next, release the safety switch. If the safety is defective, the gun may well fire as the switch is moved to the fire position. Improper trigger and sear engagements can also cause this problem.

Naturally, a safety should hold its selected position under moderate impact. A safety that can be moved inadvertently can cause an accident.

There are many safety designs, and a discussion of their functioning and maintenance would require a large volume. However, generally speaking, safety repair should *always* mean the replacing of worn, broken, or malfunctioning parts, and should *never* mean the stoning or altering of any safety switch or related part. Bent parts should never be straightened, as bending them back and forth may severely weaken them.

Some safety replacements for military-style rifles are designed for easy installation. But some of these require the stoning of angle alterations to firing-pin parts such as on Mauser 98 and 1906 Springfield models. Follow the manufacturer's instructions exactly when installing such safeties and keep metal removal to an absolute minimum.

For most firearm owners, trigger and safety work will be limited to inspections to make sure these units function as intended. If you decide you are competent to undertake replacements or adjustments, remember that you must insure the safety of your work. Be meticulous and all should go well.

14

Crowning a Barrel

The crown of a barrel must be just right if it is to accomplish its twofold purpose. Its first function is to help prevent bumps from causing an irregular surface at the junction of the rifling and the mouth of the barrel. The other purpose is to help insure a very exact and uniform release of the bullet as it emerges from the barrel.

Barrel crowns come in many styles, including heavy radius, shallow radius, recessed flat, and other styles. Perhaps the most common are the radius, found on most hunting rifles, and the recessed flat, found on many target rifles. Regardless of configuration, the crown is intended to protect the junction of rifling and muzzle by recessing that junction below the highest point of the crown. If the end of the barrel is inadvertently run against a stone wall or the face of a

Good crowns vary in configurations but all insure a uniform release of the bullet from the barrel. The general configuration of a crown also helps protect the junction of rifling and muzzle from nicks, dings, and bumps.

cliff, for example, any damage usually won't involve the vital-to-accuracy area of the bullet's release from the muzzle.

The crown must be absolutely perpendicular to the bore to insure that the entire circumference of the bullet is released from the bore simultaneously. If the crown is so shaped that a portion of the bore bears on a portion of the bullet after it has been mostly released by the bore, accuracy will be abysmal. For this reason, except for temporary repair, a crown should always be formed or repaired with a good lathe and the appropriate cutting tools. Temporary repair is appropriate only in emergencies—when a lathe isn't available and you want to resume shooting without a substantial loss in accuracy. Even then, you'll need a vise, brace, and ball grinder bit, so this type of repair is uncommon. It will be covered at the end of this chapter.

Whenever a barrel is shortened, whenever a burr or dent occurs at the crown/bore edge, or when a new barrel is made, the barrel will need to be crowned.

movable tail stock when setting up the barrel. This insures that the bore, at the muzzle, is running true to center as it turns. Once everything is as it should be, the live center and tail stock are moved away from the barrel.

If the barrel is to be shortened before crowning, a parting tool can be mounted in the lathe's tool post and the barrel cut off at the length desired. However, many gunsmiths simply use a hacksaw on the spinning barrel, cutting it about ⅛-inch to ¼-inch longer than the desired finished length. While the hacksaw treatment works, care must be taken to prevent a chattering saw or broken blade from damaging the outside of the barrel surface. The use of a parting tool is the best way to shorten a barrel.

The forming of the crown is most easily accomplished with a cutting tool pre-shaped to the radius desired for the crown. When the cutter is mounted securely in the tool post and moved slowly inward over the muzzle end of the barrel, the crown will be formed without a hitch—if the cutter is properly aligned with the barrel. I prefer a cutter that is shaped to place the front end of its edge inside the bore and the back end of its edge beyond the outside edge of the barrel. A properly shaped cutter will allow a wide range of

Normal Crowning Procedure (Radius Style)

It is easiest to crown a barrel before it has been installed on a receiver. However, it makes no sense to remove a barrel from a receiver solely to crown it. A barreled receiver can be carefully chucked in a lathe, in a manner that will prevent any imbalance of the receiver from causing wobble as the lathe chuck spins. It is important that the chuck jaws be tightened securely against the barrel. Therefore, unless the barrel is properly padded it can be damaged. It will be difficult for the lathe chuck to maintain a secure and continuous purchase on the barrel if the padding is not appropriate. Leather strips of adequate thickness make ideal pads for chuck-to-barrel contact.

I prefer to use a live center on the lathe's

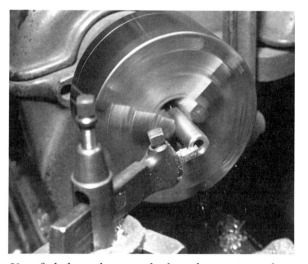

Use of a lathe and a properly shaped crowning tool are essential to a first-class job of recrowning.

Use a small piece of crocus cloth stretched over a finger tip to polish the crown as it spins in the lathe.

Finished crown should have a very high polish.

barrel diameters to be crowned with a single tool. But don't make the mistake of trying to use a too-small or too-large cutter. Grind a new cutter when faced with extra-small or extra-large barrel diameters.

As the crown cut is completed, decrease the speed of feed of the cutter to almost nil. Then allow the cutter to dwell a moment before backing it away from the barrel. This gives a very smooth cut. After cutting, the crown should be polished to a very high gloss in order to prevent rust from forming and to give the appearance associated with first-class work.

If the barrel is not to be reblued, polishing must be done with great care to avoid removing any bluing from the barrel itself. Only the crowned area should be polished. This is not as difficult as it sounds. A small piece of crocus cloth, stretched over a fingertip and carefully placed against the bore, will get the crown surface nicely polished as the barrel spins slowly in

the lathe. But take care—be certain there are no sharp edges on the barrel that could cut through the crocus cloth and cause personal injury.

Depending on how well the cutter was aligned with the barrel, only a very fine polishing grade of crocus cloth will be necessary. If multiple grades of paper are needed to produce a very high polish, you can bet the cutter wasn't properly shaped, sharpened, or aligned.

The proper polishing procedure is to press the finger, with a piece of crocus stretched over it, into the bore, as if you intended to plunge your finger through the barrel. Hold a bit of pressure and slowly manipulate your finger in a manner that causes the polishing action to move outward around the crown's radius. Stop in time to prevent any polishing beyond the crown's edge.

It is always best to remove any front sight and any detachable front-sight ramp before crowning a barrel. Spinning front sights and/or ramps can cause serious injury and property damage.

Producing a Recessed Flat Crown

To effect the stepped, flat crown common on target rifles, a straight cutter blade is used, but it is not positioned to attack the barrel flat-end-to-flat-end. Rather, only the tip is used (as when turning a piece of metal to a smaller diameter). Begin by cutting a single flat across the surface of the muzzle. Then cut a deeper flat, beginning at the bore's center and progressing outward. The second flat should be deep enough to give ample protection to the crown/bore edge, perhaps $\frac{1}{10}$ inch. The second cut looks best, to most folks, when it is made to equal half the barrel's diameter. Finally, to add a professional touch, "break" the sharp corner of the edge of the barrel with a small—very small—cut.

A flat crown is very difficult to cut smoothly. And it must be very smooth since this type of crown does not lend itself well to polishing. Some skill in the use of a lathe is essential to insure that a properly shaped cutter is used and that it is placed at the proper angle of attack to the metal. A person who is experienced in turning smooth outside diameters will have no difficulty and will realize the need for a very slow feed rate and a properly shaped cutter. Others would be well advised to choose the easy-to-cut radius crown.

Great care must be taken in all crowning efforts and polishing to insure that the rifling-to-crown junction maintains a very sharp edge. Any reduction of the lands at the end of the crown will impair accuracy.

Temporary Crown Repair

Sometimes crowns can be damaged when rifle and shooter are a long way from anything that looks like a lathe, yet some sort of repair may be called for if there is heavy damage. In such instances a vise, brace, and ball-shaped grinder bit

Hand drill and a ball-shaped grinder bit may be used for emergency crowns. Later, crown should be properly formed on a lathe.

may save the day. With the barrel *firmly* mounted in the vise and a grinder ball mounted in the brace, careful positioning of the ball grinder in the muzzle and a uniform rotation of it may produce a satisfactorily contoured temporary crown. It won't look like much but, if carefully done, it will be a much better performer than a badly damaged crown.

When attempting a crown repair by hand, realize that it is an emergency procedure only. The shape of the grinder ball is not critical because you are trying only to get a uniform and perpendicular parting line between bore and crown. Naturally, any emergency crown repair should be properly redone on a lathe as soon as possible.

A final caution: Always carefully wipe the bore free of chips and grit immediately after crowning. Firing a gun with any metal chips, polishing compound, or bits of a grinding ball in the bore can ruin the accuracy of the barrel or cause a catastrophic failure in the form of a burst muzzle.

PART 3

DISASSEMBLY, REPAIR, AND REASSEMBLY OF POPULAR FIREARMS

Firearms don't become popular unless they are well designed and manufactured. Some of the best remain in production for generations. A good many date back 30, 40, 50, or even almost 100 years. The Winchester 94 and the Marlin 336, for example, trace their heritage back to the 1890s. The Browning A-5 semiautomatic has roots in the first half of this century.

In addition, there are more recent firearms whose excellence of design and manufacture have caused them to sell in the millions of units. Examples are the Remington 870 pump shotgun, the Remington 1100 semiautomatic shotgun, and the Remington bolt-action high-powered rifles.

Because there are so many millions of these and other fine guns in use, some breakdowns will occur. After extensive use, even the finest firearms will require disassembly, if for no other reason than the need for a thorough cleaning.

The firearms selected for inclusion here are durable firearms which have become extremely popular. If you follow the advice and procedures given for each model, you will encounter no undue difficulty in disassembly, listed repairs, or reassembly.

Keep in mind that safety demands assuring yourself that any firearm you work on is unloaded. Safety also demands observance of every caution contained in the following pages. Whenever a doubt exists about safe procedure, it is best to consign the repair to a trained gunsmith.

In a single volume on home gunsmithing, obviously it's impossible to cover disassembly, common repairs, and reassembly of all the popular American sporting arms, let alone foreign arms, military rifles, etc. I've chosen representative examples of popular American firearms on the basis of several criteria. In addition to popularity, practicality was a major element; some models would require far too many pages for adequate coverage and might involve procedures beyond the scope of the average home gunsmith. Still another criterion was similarity of mechanism. Additionally, so much has been written about some firearms that it would be superfluous to repeat it here. An example is the Winchester Model 70, which has been dissected, worked over, and microscopically examined in so many books and journals. I therefore chose the enormously popular but somewhat younger Remington 700 and Savage 110, rifles about which less has been written over the years.

The eight firearms covered in this section are:

1   Browning A-5 semiautomatic shotgun
2   Remington 700 bolt-action rifle
3   Remington 1100 semiautomatic shotgun
4   Remington 870 pump-action shotgun
5   Winchester 94 lever-action rifle
6   Savage 110 bolt-action rifle
7   Marlin 336 lever-action rifle
8   Marlin 70 semiautomatic rimfire rifle

Many of the procedures discussed in this section will be applicable to similar firearms. For instance, many of the details for the browning A-5 are applicable to the early "hump-backed-receiver" Remington and Savage semiautomatic shotguns which were built under license from Browning. The same applies to material concerning the Remington 700, as many earlier-model bolt-action Remington rifles are very similar—even identical in some respects. You will recognize many other similar characteristics between firearms as you gain experience.

Keep in mind that successful disassembly, repair, and reassembly requires that you proceed in a thoughtful manner, never infringing upon the safety aspects of a gun's design. And it is always advisable to read through the complete section about a specific firearm before beginning disassembly.

Every effort has been made to cover model variations, but manufacturers occasionally change specification, designs, or parts. In some instances, changes may be very short-lived, and the passage of time will destroy any records of such temporary changes. So, if you encounter a slight variation, think the job through extra carefully. If doubt persists, consult an experienced gunsmith or the factory service department.

Parts nomenclature can be confusing. An "Action-spring tube nut" may simply be a nut for the action-spring tube or some esoteric tubular-shaped nut. Whenever such doubt occurs, refer to the parts list and schematic drawing for clarification. Usually, however, any confusion will be eliminated by following the step-by-step procedures, with the gun in front of you, along with the accompanying drawings and photos.

15

Browning A-5 Semiautomatic Shotgun

T he information provided herein is equally applicable to 12-, 16-, and 20-gauge A-5 shotguns. There are minor differences in the recoil springs for magnum-length versus standard-length receivers, but these will not interfere with the instructions given.

It is essential to remember that the A-5 shotgun is recoil-operated. The magazine tube, on which the recoil mechanism is mounted and on which the barrel slides rearward to function the shotgun, must be kept clean. Also, under normal circumstances, the magazine tube must be kept lightly oiled to insure proper functioning.

Cycle of Operation

The functional operation of the A-5 is quite simple. Indeed, it is the simplicity of function that makes the A-5 so reliable. When the chambered shell is fired, the expanding gases create equal pressure in all directions. Because the barrel is free to move rearward, it does so as the shot moves forward. Because of the heavy mass of the barrel, together with the inertia of the recoil spring and friction pieces, the majority of the barrel's movement does not occur until the shot column has left the barrel. As the barrel moves rearward, it carries with it the breechbolt assembly, which is locked into the barrel extension by the locking block. This entire unit travels rearward until its movement is arrested by the total compression of the recoil spring.

The manner of assembly of the recoil spring, friction ring, and friction piece is critical to proper functioning. The way these parts are positioned about the recoil spring allows the gun to handle light or heavy loads. Be certain the arrangement of these parts, in accordance with the ammunition type used, corresponds to the nearby illustrations.

For heavy loads, the proper assembly is to place the recoil spring over the magazine tube, then place the solid steel friction ring on top of the spring so its flat side rests against the spring, and then place the friction piece (bronze), with the steel-collar friction spring in place around it, on the magazine tube with its heavy bevel toward the muzzle.

For light loads, place the friction ring on the magazine tube first, with its inside bevel against the receiver. Then slip the recoil spring and the friction piece (with the steel spring collar in place around it) onto the magazine tube, with the bevel toward the muzzle.

Three-inch magnum models employ two bronze friction-piece assemblies and three friction rings when used with three-inch loads. Assembly begins for the heavy loads in a gun with a 2¾-inch chamber. Slip the spring onto the magazine tube and then a friction ring with its flat side against the spring and its inner bevel toward the muzzle. Then slip the collared bronze friction piece, bevel to the muzzle, onto the magazine tube. Next, another friction ring is added, with its inner bevel facing the bronze friction piece and its flat side facing the muzzle. Now add another steel friction ring so that its flat side bears against the flat side of the previous ring. Add the second collared bronze friction piece, with its heavy bevel facing the muzzle. That completes the recoil system for three-inch loads using lead shot.

For high-velocity 2¾-inch loads or steel-shot loads, set the three-inch recoil system the same way as the standard 2¾ inch gun using heavy loads. Do not use the extra two steel friction rings or the extra bronze friction piece and its spring collar.

When fired, as the A-5's breechbolt and barrel begin their rearward movement, the rear end of the link disengages the upper arm of the safety sear. The safety sear, under pressure from its spring and plunger, rotates the lower arm of the safety sear forward until it rests against the back edge of the trigger—until the trigger is released. When the trigger is released, the lower arm of the safety sear is rotated over the trigger, blocking it from being pulled again until the entire functioning cycle has been completed and the bolt is once again locked in firing position. At that time, the link is forward and in position against the upper arm of the safety sear, unlocking the trigger to allow it to be pulled for another shot. Should the breechblock fail to close fully into the battery position, the safety sear will prevent the trigger from being pulled.

The trigger must be manually released sometime during the firing cycle or immediately thereafter to allow the gun to be readied for another firing. This is necessary, as when the trigger is held rearward during firing, the hammer—upon reaching the cocked position—is caught by the rear safety notch of the trigger. Only when the trigger is released can the hammer be released from the safety notch and be engaged by the forward firing notch of the trigger.

As the bolt moves rearward during the firing cycle, the A-5's carrier dog is rotated rearward, compressing its spring. When the bolt reaches its maximum rearward travel, the carrier dog snaps upward, under its spring tension, into the area between the operating handle and the breechbolt, and locks the breechbolt in its rearmost position. The compression of the recoil spring then returns the barrel to its forward position.

As the barrel is moved forward, the locking bolt rotates out of the aperture in the barrel extension, and the two extractors hold the fired shell against the face of the locked-in-position

LIGHT 12- AND 20-GAUGE GUNS

2¾″ High-Velocity and Steel-Shot Loads (12 and 20 Ga.)

3″ Magnum Loads (12 and 20 Ga.)

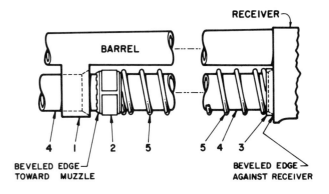

1. Barrel Guide Ring
2. Bronze Friction Piece
3. Friction Ring
4. Magazine Tube
5. Recoil Spring

3″ MAGNUM 12- AND 20-GAUGE GUNS

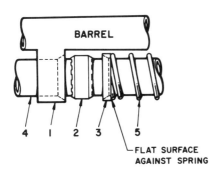
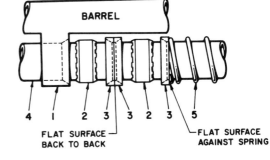

1. Barrel Guide Ring
2. Bronze Friction Piece
3. Friction Ring
4. Magazine Tube
5. Recoil Spring

15–2. Correct assembly of A-5's recoil system is shown in these diagrams. The A-5's recoil system must be assembled specifically for the type of ammunition to be used.

EXPLODED VIEW OF BROWNING A-5 SHOTGUN

Standard, Light, and Magnum Models
12, 16, and 20 Gauge

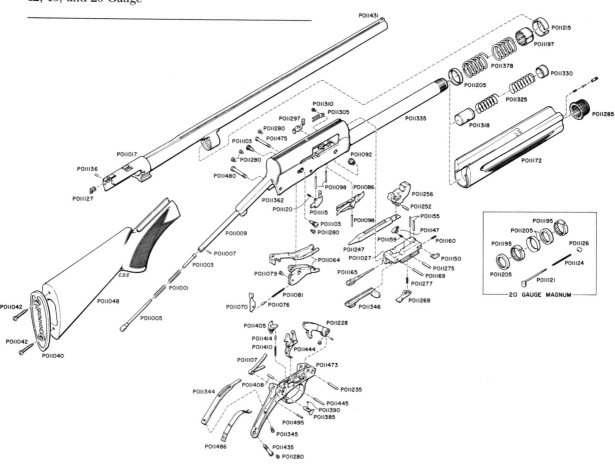

PART NO.	PART NAME	PART NO.	PART NAME	PART NO.	PART NAME
PO11001	action spring 12M-12-16-20-20M	†PO11022	barrel extension assembly 16	†PO11048	buttstock field 1⅝″ × 2½″ × 14¼″ 12
PO11003	action spring follower 12M-12-16-20-20M	†PO11024	barrel extension assembly 20	†PO11051	buttstock trap 1⅜″ × 1¾″ × 14⅜″ 12
PO11005	action spring plug 12M-12-16-20-20M	†PO11025	barrel extension assembly magnum 20-gauge	†PO11056	buttstock field 1⅝″ × 2½″ × 14¼″ 16-20-20M
PO11007	action spring plug pin 12M-12-16-20-20M	PO11027	breech block 12M-12	PO11057	buttstock swivel eyelet 12M-12-16-20-20M
PO11009	action spring tube 12M-12-16-20-20M	PO11032	breech block 16	†PO11062	carrier assembly (magnum) 12-gauge
†PO11015	barrel extension assembly magnum 12-gauge	PO11035	breech block magnum 20-gauge	†PO11064	carrier assembly 2 piece 12
†PO11017	barrel extension assembly 12	PO11036	breech block 20	†PO11066	carrier assembly 2 piece 16
		†PO11040	buttplate 12-16-20-20M	†PO11068	carrier assembly 2 piece 20-20M
		PO11042	buttplate screws 12-16-20-20M	†PO11070	carrier dog 12M-12
		†PO11046	buttstock magnum with recoil pad 1⅝″ × 2½″ × 14″ 12M	†PO11071	carrier dog 16-20-20M
				PO11076	carrier dog follower 12M-12
				PO11077	carrier dog follower 16-20-20M
				PO11079	carrier dog pin 12M-12

†Part must be fitted by Browning Service Department or qualified gunsmith.
††Part may be purchased only by holders of current Federal Firearms Licenses.

Note: Unless otherwise indicated, part is interchangeable between gauges/calibers.

PART NO.	PART NAME
PO11080	carrier dog pin 16-20-20M
PO11081	carrier dog spring 12M-12
PO11083	carrier dog spring 16-20-20M
PO11085	carrier latch assembly (magnum) 12-gauge
PO11086	carrier latch assembly 12
PO11089	carrier latch assembly 16
PO11090	carrier latch assembly 20-20M
PO11092	carrier latch button 12
PO11093	carrier latch button 12M-16
PO11094	carrier latch button 20-20M
PO11098	cartridge stop pin 12M-12-16-20-20M
PO11103	carrier screw 12M-16-20-20M
PO11107	carrier spring trigger plate type 12M-12
PO11111	carrier spring trigger plate type 16-20-20M
PO11115	cartridge stop 12M-12
PO11117	cartridge stop 16-20-20M
PO11120	cartridge stop spring 12M-12-16-20-20M
PO11121	ejector & ejector rod magnum 20-gauge
PO11123	ejector spring magnum 12-gauge
PO11124	ejector spring magnum 20-gauge
†PO11125	ejector magnum 12-gauge
PO11126	ejector spring retainer magnum 20-gauge
†PO11127	ejector 12 & prewar 16
†PO11134	ejector 16 & 20
†PO11136	ejector rivet 12
†PO11142	ejector rivet 12M-16-20
PO11147	extractor left 12M-12-16-20
PO11148	extractor spring follower magnum 20-gauge
PO11149	extractor magnum 20-gauge
PO11150	extractor right 12M-12-16-20
PO11155	extractor pin left & right 12M-12-16-20-20M
PO11159	extractor spring left 12M-12-16-20
PO11160	extractor spring right hand 12M-12
PO11162	extractor spring right hand 16-20
PO11163	extractor spring magnum 20-gauge
PO11164	extractor spring follower right hand 16-20
PO11165	firing pin 12M-12
PO11167	firing pin 16-20-20M
PO11168	firing pin stop pin 12M-12
PO11169	firing pin stop pin 16-20-20M
†PO11170	forearm 5-shot magnum 12-gauge
†PO11172	forearm 5-shot 12
†PO11183	forearm 5-shot 16
†PO11191	forearm 5-shot 20
†PO11192	forearm magnum 20-gauge
PO11195	friction piece bronze magnum 12-gauge
PO11197	friction piece bronze 12
PO11198	friction piece bronze magnum 20-gauge
PO11199	friction piece bronze 16-20
PO11205	friction ring 12M-12
PO11207	friction ring 16-20-20M
PO11215	friction spring 12
PO11216	friction spring 16-20
†PO11225	hammer assembly-magnum 12-gauge
†PO11228	hammer assembly-lightweight 12
†PO11232	hammer assembly-lightweight 16-20-20M
†PO11235	hammer pin 12M-16-20-20M
†PO11243	link (magnum) 20-gauge
†PO11245	link (magnum) 12-gauge
†PO11247	link 12
†PO11251	link 16-20
†PO11252	link pin 12M-12
†PO11254	link pin 16-20-20M
PO11256	locking block 12M-12
PO11261	locking block 16-20-20M
PO11264	locking block latch magnum 20-gauge
PO11265	locking block latch magnum 12-gauge
†PO11269	locking block latch 2-piece carrier 12
†PO11272	locking block latch 2-piece carrier 16-20
PO11275	locking block latch pin 12M-12-16-20-20M
PO11277	locking block latch spring 12M-12
PO11279	locking block latch spring 16-20-20M
PO11280	lock screw 12M-12-16-20-20M
PO11285	mag. cap-w/o swivel eyelet 12M-12
PO11287	mag. cap-w/o swivel eyelet 16-20-20M
PO11292	mag. cap-with swivel eyelet 12M-12
PO11294	mag. cap-with swivel eyelet 16-20-20M
PO11295	magazine cutoff-magnum 12-gauge
PO11297	magazine cutoff 12
PO11298	magazine cutoff 16
PO11299	magazine cutoff 20-20M
PO11098	magazine cutoff pin 12M-12-16-20-20M
PO11305	magazine cutoff spring 12M-12-16-20-20M
PO11310	magazine cutoff spring screw 12M-12-16-20-20M
PO11315	magazine follower-magnum 12-gauge
PO11318	magazine follower 12
PO11319	magazine follower 16
PO11321	magazine follower 20-20M
PO11325	magazine spring 12M-12
PO11329	magazine spring 16-20-20M
PO11330	magazine spring retainer 12M-12
PO11333	magazine spring retainer 16-20-20M
PO11335	magazine tube 5-shot 12M-12
PO11339	magazine tube 5-shot 16
PO11342	magazine tube 5-shot 20M
PO11343	magazine tube 5-shot 20
†PO11344	mainspring 12M-12-16-20-20M
PO11345	mainspring screw 12M-12-16-20-20M
PO11346	operating handle 12M-12
PO11347	operating handle 16-20-20M
††PO11355	receiver-magnum 12-gauge
††PO11357	receiver-magnum 20-gauge
††PO11359	receiver-standard 12
††PO11362	receiver-lightweight 12
††PO11366	receiver-standard 16
††PO11368	receiver-sweet 16
††PO11372	receiver-lightweight 20
PO11375	recoil spring-magnum 12M
PO11378	recoil spring 12
PO11381	recoil spring 16-20
PO11382	recoil spring magnum 20-gauge
†PO11385	safety crossbolt, right 12M-12-16-20-20M
†PO11386	safety crossbolt, left 12M-12-16-20-20M
PO11390	safety ball 12M-12-16-20-20M
PO11395	sight base-rear-buck special 12M-12
PO11397	sight base-rear-buck special 16
PO11398	sight base-rear-buck special 20-20M
PO11399	sight body-rear-buck special 12M-12-16-20-20M
PO11400	sight aperture-rear-buck special 12M-12-16-20-20M
PO11401	sight adjusting screw-windage-buck special 12M-12-16-20-20M
PO11403	sight adjusting screw-elevation-buck special 12M-12-16-20-20M
PO11404	sight roll pin-buck special 12M-12-16-20-20M
†PO11405	safety sear 12M-12
†PO11406	safety sear 16-20-20M
PO11408	safety sear pin 12M-12-16-20-20M
PO11410	safety sear spring 12M-12-16-20-20M
PO11414	safety sear spring follower 12M-12-16-20-20M
PO11421	sight ramp-front-buck special 12M-12-16
PO11422	sight ramp-front-buck special 20-20M
PO11423	sight-gold bead-front-buck special 12M-12-16-20-20M
PO11425	sight bead plain & vent-magnum 12M
PO11431	sight bead plain & vent-12-16-20-20M
PO11435	tang screw for pistol grip stock 12M-12-16-20-20M
†PO11444	trigger for crossbolt safety-gold plated-lightweight 12-16-20-20M
PO11445	trigger pin 12M-12-16-20-20M
†PO11466	trigger plate for crossbolt safety-12
†PO11473	trigger plate for crossbolt safety-lightweight 16-20-20M
PO11475	trigger plate screw-front 12M-12
PO11477	trigger plate screw-front 16-20-20M
PO11480	trigger plate screw-rear 12M-12
PO11481	trigger plate screw-rear 16-20-20M
†PO11486	trigger spring-pin retainer 12M-12-16-20-20M
PO11495	trigger spring retaining pin 12M-12-16-20-20M
PO11499	adapter, magazine, 3-shot 12M

bolt. As the barrel moves forward it is, in effect, stripped away from the fired case. As its motion continues it causes the ejector, mounted on the barrel extension, to be drawn forcefully against the shell's head, thus ejecting it from the shotgun.

As the barrel nears the completion of its forward movement, the cartridge stop, riding in the groove of the barrel extension, is moved outward. This allows a live round to pop out of the magazine.

As the live round moves from the magazine, it strikes the rear portion of the carrier latch and releases it from the carrier. The front of the carrier latch then locks the remaining rounds in the magazine table.

The released carrier is rotated, under pressure of the carrier-dog spring, lifting the round upward. As this occurs, the carrier dog releases the breech bolt assembly, which moves forward rapidly under the compression of the action spring (located in the buttstock). The forward moving bolt forces the elevated round into the chamber. The forward end of the link rotates and unlocks the locking-block latch, allowing the locking block to rotate into position in the barrel extension. The carrier spring then returns to its normal position completing the firing cycle.

The parts just mentioned and all other A-5 parts are shown on the exploded view. Each part is labeled with a part number that corresponds to the parts list.

move the barrel and recoil spring (about one inch rearward). This will relieve the pressure of the recoil assembly and allow the removal of the fore-end cap. With the fore-end cap removed, slowly allow the barrel to move forward until all compression of the recoil spring is released. Slide off the fore-end by pulling it forward. Then remove the barrel and recoil-assembly parts.

If a magazine cap is frozen in place, use the padded jaw of a vise to hold the cap and rotate the firearm about the cap sufficiently to loosen it. Then remove the cap by hand. Be sure to use a properly padded vise; leather-faced hardwood works well.

Further disassembly requires screwdrivers. Browning screw slots are unique in dimension, and it is necessary to have screwdrivers to fit or to grind existing screwdrivers to match the slots.

Removal of Buttstock

Place the shotgun in an inverted position and remove the lock screw and tang screw from the rearmost position on the lower tang. *Note*: Do not inadvertently remove the mainspring screw, which is positioned just ahead of the tang and tang-clock screws (Fig. 15–4).

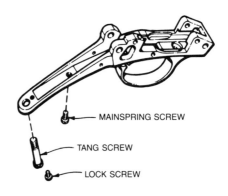

15–4. Remove tang screw and lock screw to allow for buttstock disassembly. *Do not remove mainspring screw.*

Basic Disassembly

Basic disassembly of the A-5 Browning shotgun is accomplished without the need for tools. Start by insuring that both the chamber and magazine are empty. Then pull the bolt handle fully rearward and position the buttstock on the workbench, in such a way as to prevent it from slipping. Grasp the barrel well ahead of the magazine cap and pull downward to slightly

15–5. After tang screw and lock screw (but not main-spring screw) have been removed, buttstock can be removed by striking back of receiver hump on padded bench and pulling down on buttstock.

Remove the buttstock as shown in (Fig. 15–5). Place a soft cloth pad on the bench; then, while holding the gun as shown, strike the back of the receiver hump on the bench, using a downward motion, while simultaneously pulling it down on the buttstock. If the buttstock has been previously removed, it may be possible to simply slip it off by pulling it away from the receiver. A long bolt-return spring housing extends from the rear upper tang well down into the buttstock. When removing the buttstock, take care to avoid damaging this housing.

Triggerplate-Assembly Removal

Press the carrier-latch button on the right side of the receiver while holding the bolt-operating

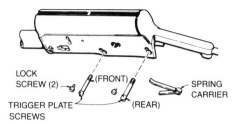

15–6. Triggerplate screw-assembly removal.

handle. Ease the bolt forward as far as it will go. Never allow the bolt to run forward under its return spring's compression when the barrel has been removed from the shotgun. Doing so will drive the operating handle forcefully against the front edge of the receiver opening, causing possible damage to receiver and operating handle.

Remove the triggerplate lock screws and retaining screws (Fig. 15–6). These are the two sets of screws in the lower rear portion of the receiver on the left side. Then remove the triggerplate assembly.

On new models, the carrier spring will come away from the receiver as part of the triggerplate group (Fig. 15–7). On older models, the spring will remain in the receiver. Remove it by gently prying it from under its retaining post, using a thin-bladed screwdriver.

15–7. Triggerplate removal. On this recent model, the carrier spring will come away, attached to the triggerplate group.

Carrier Assembly

Remove the carrier lock and carrier-retaining screws. There are two sets of these, each located approximately in the middle of the receiver, from top to bottom, and approximately one-third of the way from the rear. These are shown in Fig 15–8.

These screws must be returned to the same side of the receiver from which they were taken if the lock screw recesses are to align properly. You may wish to mark one of them with chalk.

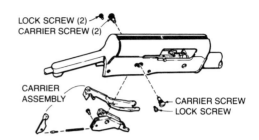

15–9. Action-spring removal.

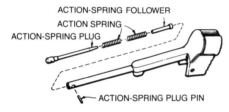

15–8. Carrier assembly removal.

On older-model guns, the right screw has a mark on its end for easy identification.

Note: Disassembly of the carrier group into its component parts is not normally necessary and I strongly advise against such effort when not required.

Action-Spring Assembly

Using a ³⁄₃₂-inch punch, remove the action-spring plug pin while slightly pressing inward on the plug. This plug is located at the tail end of the housing, projecting from the upper rear tang (Fig 15–9). There is considerable spring tension

on this plug so use care not to allow any parts to escape as the punch is removed. If they escape, they can cause harm and become lost or damaged.

Breechblock Assembly

Hold the action with the open side of the receiver on top. Using the long link rod, extending from the bottom of the receiver, position the bolt so the latch pin (Fig. 15–10) aligns with the half-hole at the bottom edge of the ejection port.

While holding the bolt in this position, rotate the receiver 180 degrees and drive out the locking-bolt latch pin. Use a ³⁄₃₂-inch punch and a small brass hammer for this operation. Place the punch in the appropriate receiver hole on the left side, driving the pin out with its alignment on the half-hole of the right side.

As the punch is withdrawn from the bolt and receiver, the locking latch and its spring will be free to escape. Take care not to lose these parts.

The operating handle can now be separated from the bolt. This is accomplished by pulling rearward on the operating handle while simultaneously pushing it forward on the long link. This will allow withdrawal of both parts of the forward end of the receiver. Set the bolt assembly aside and continue.

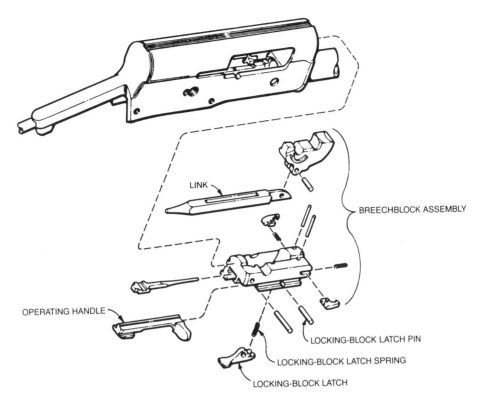

15–10. Breechblock assembly removal.

Magazine-Spring, Follower, and Retainer

Using a hooked tool held in a vise (Fig 15–11), remove the magazine-spring retainer. Take care not to allow the loss of this retainer as it is under considerable spring tension. After the retainer and spring are removed, the follower can be slid free of the magazine.

In some instances, the front end of the magazine tube may be beveled inward sufficiently to prevent the removal of the follower. If this is the case, consider carefully whether the follower needs to be removed. A magazine tube can be easily ruined if attempts to remove this bevel are crude.

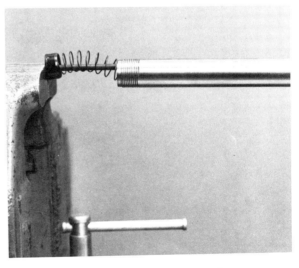

15–11. Magazine spring, follower, and retainer are removed with a hooked tool in a vise.

Cartridge Stop

With the receiver held upside-down in a padded vise, use a 3/32-inch punch to carefully drive out the cartridge-stop roll pin. This pin is driven inward from the receiver bottom to escape at the ejection port. Use extreme caution to insure that the punch aligns with the hole past the cartridge stop so that the receiver rails are not damaged. The cartridge stop can then be removed when the punch is withdrawn. It is under spring pressure so use care not to lose the stop or spring (Fig. 15–12).

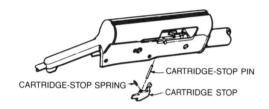

15–12. Cartridge-stop removal.

Note: On older models, the cartridge stop is retained by a screw that can be removed from the receiver bottom. A very small screwdriver is required. Be careful not to break off the screw head, as it is tiny and fragile. The location of the cartridge stop and its retaining pin is shown in Fig. 15–9.

Carrier-Latch Assembly

The carrier latch is removed in the same fashion as the cartridge stop. It is also located on the

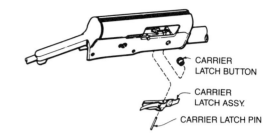

15–13. Carrier-latch assembly removal.

right side of the receiver. On older models, the carrier latch is held in place by a screw instead of a roll pin. Note Fig. 15–13 for location of the carrier latch.

Magazine-Cutoff Assembly

Fig. 15–14 clearly shows the location of the cutoff assembly and the relationship of its parts. First remove the cutoff-spring screw and spring from the left outside of the receiver. Next remove the cutoff in the same fashion as the carrier latch and cartridge stop.

15–14. Magazine-cutoff assembly removal.

Magazine Tube

The magazine tube is screwed into the receiver. It can be removed without damage only if it is properly supported with a special clamping device. Therefore, it is strongly suggested that no attempt be made to remove the magazine. *Note:* The magazine-cutoff spring screw must always be removed in order to unscrew the magazine tube.

Disassembly of Trigger-plate Group

Fig. 15–15 shows the relationship of all the parts in the triggerplate group. Refer to it before attempting disassembly of this unit. Normally, there is little reason to take this subassembly apart unless it has a broken or worn part.

Should the triggerplate group require dis-

assembly, begin by cocking the hammer and then putting the safety in the safe position. Using a small, thin-bladed screwdriver and extreme caution, depress the safety-sear spring follower and slide the safety sear off its pin, as shown in Fig. 15–16. Do not use the screwdriver for any manipulation other than depressing the safety-sear spring and its follower. Use caution to prevent the safety sear spring and its follower from flying free as they could cause injury or become lost.

After removing the safety-sear spring and follower, put the safety in the off-safe position. Holding the hammer in place, pull the trigger and carefully allow the hammer to move fully through it (Fig. 15–17). Remove the hammer pin, using a ⅛-inch punch, and then the hammer. Next, remove the mainspring screw from the tang and then the mainspring.

On older models, the trigger spring is held in place by grooves on the inside of the tang. To remove this type of trigger spring, insert a punch in the hole at its rear and pull the spring rearward out of the tang. On newer models, the trigger spring is retained by a small cross pin which must be driven out with a small punch. *Note:* The removal of both types of trigger springs will uncover the safety ball, which is easily lost. Being careful, invert the trigger

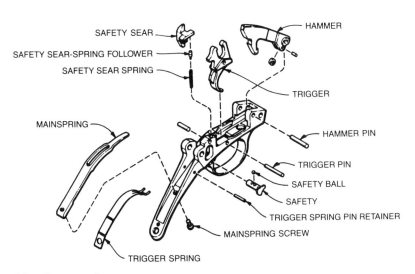

15–15. Disassembly of triggerplate group.

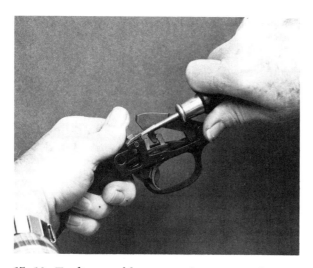

15–16. To disassemble triggerplate group, depress safety sear spring using thin-bladed screwdriver and slide it off its pin.

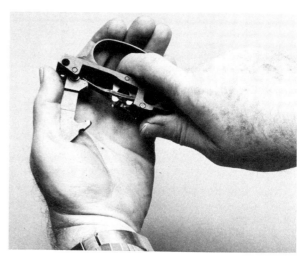

15–17. Next, uncock the hammer by supporting it and allowing it to move fully through its arc. Do not allow the hammer to snap forward.

group and allow the safety ball to drop into your hand.

Using a ³⁄₃₂-inch punch, drive out the trigger pin and remove the trigger and safety. Leave the safety-sear pin in place.

Inspection, Adjustment, and Reassembly of Triggerplate Group

With the disassembly complete, inspect the trigger guard for burrs and/or deformities. Burrs can develop in the portion of the trigger guard that houses the safety. Carefully remove them with a very fine round file.

If the gun has been dropped or mishandled so as to deform the trigger guard, this part should be carefully reshaped. This can be done with a small leather or plastic mallet and a suitable anvil. Work slowly and carefully.

Next inspect the safety-sear pin for looseness. If it's loose, restake it. To do so, locate the original stake mark on the triggerplate, just above the safety-sear pin. Use a suitable center punch, placed on top of the original stake mark, and restake the sear pin sufficiently to make it tight. A modest blow with a small hammer will be sufficient.

Place the safety in the triggerplate and insure that it slides from side to side freely. If it binds, remove any high spots or burrs. Do not remove any more metal than absolutely necessary. Clean away any metal filings and then reinstall the safety.

Next, install the trigger and its retaining pin, after visually inspecting the trigger surfaces. Replace the trigger if it shows signs of abnormal wear or damage. Be sure the trigger rotates freely on its pin. Also be sure that the trigger does not bind against the forward end of the cutout in the trigger guard when the trigger is pulled rearward.

Using a thin pair of needle-nosed pliers, install the safety ball while the triggerplate is held in a properly padded vise. Reinstall the trigger spring as appropriate to its style. The newer type

15–18. To reinstall trigger spring, position it, then depress it with a punch or appropriate tool and slip the retaining pin into position.

will need to be positioned and then depressed as the retaining pin is pushed into place (Fig. 15–18). Older-style springs need to be slid into place from the rear until the screw holes align with the hole in the tang. Be sure there is sufficient friction on the safety after the trigger spring has been installed. If the safety moves too freely, remove the trigger spring and bend the center prong to increase pressure on the safety ball. Inversely, if the safety is too tight, bend the center prong of the trigger spring to decrease the tension on the safety ball. It should take an operating force of about four to five pounds to make the safety work.

Any bending of the center prong must be done very carefully and in small increments. If it requires more than just a minor amount of manipulation, replace the trigger spring.

Next, install the mainspring and its retaining screw. Be certain the mainspring is correctly oriented as shown in Fig. 15–19.

Before installing the hammer, be sure it moves smoothly on its retaining pin over the entire surface of its elongated hole. After installing the hammer, it must be checked for correct functioning. To do this, place the safety in the off posi-

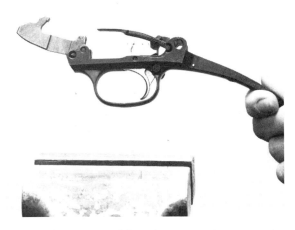

15–19. When reassembling the triggerplate group, be sure the mainspring is correctly oriented as shown.

tion. Cock the hammer, rotating it fully to the rear, and hold it in this position with the thumb. While maintaining pressure on the hammer, pull the trigger and hold it fully to the rear. Now release the thumb pressure from the hammer.

The trigger-sear notch should be engaged in the rear hammer notch, and the hammer is held in a past-, or over-, cocked position for as long as the trigger is held fully rearward.

When the trigger is released, the front trigger-sear notch should engage in the front hammer notch, holding the hammer in a cocked position. While preventing the hammer from flying forward and striking the front of the triggerplate, check the trigger pull with an appropriate gauge or weight. It should be between four and five pounds.

Then carefully observe that the sear has full regain. That is to say, when the trigger is partially pulled and then released, the sear should, in turn, go to partial disengagement and then return to full engagement.

If, when checking the trigger functions, the sear notches do not release or have a tendency to hang, the mating surfaces may be improperly shaped or have burrs, or the trigger spring may be weak. The problem or problems must be isolated and corrected. When it is determined that the trouble is with sear surfaces on the trigger or hammer, these parts must be replaced. Do not make any alteration whatever to these parts.

If, when releasing the trigger, the front notch of the hammer does not strike squarely in the front notch of the trigger, the U-shaped portion of the trigger is too wide and the trigger should be replaced.

Continue with the assembly of the triggerplate group by cocking the hammer and installing the safety sear, spring, and plunger. Make certain the lower shank of the safety sear can rotate into position to block movement of the trigger when it is pulled. If it cannot rotate into position to block the trigger, the lower shank of the safety sear is too long and a very small amount of metal should be removed (Fig. 15–20). *Note:* Use extreme care to maintain exactly the same angle as the original at the bottom of the sear. If too much metal is removed, the safety sear will be ineffective. This can be extremely dangerous.

If, after the gun is assembled and is ready to fire, the trigger cannot be pulled, it is possible

15–20. If the safety sear does not rotate into position to block the trigger, its lower shank is too long. If so, remove a very small amount of metal from it. (Lower shank is indicated by punch.)

that the top portion of the safety sear, which should strike the inside of the link, is too short, or the link itself is bent. If this is the case, the suggested procedure is to replace the safety sear and/or link.

With the hammer cocked and the sear safety disengaged, place the safety in the safe position. Pull the trigger with the full pressure of the index finger of both hands. The hammer must not fall. If it does, the safety and/or the rear tab of the trigger that contacts the safety are worn. Replace one or both parts as required.

Inspection of Carrier Assembly

As stated earlier, the carrier group does not normally require disassembly. On occasion, however, the carrier can lose its original shape. The two legs that extend to the rear may become

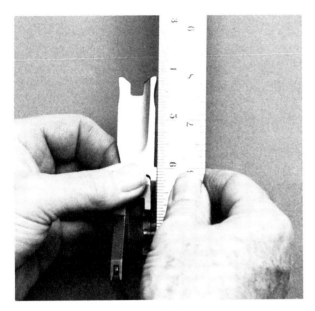

15–21. Check alignment of the carrier legs (which extend to the rear) by placing a steel scale along the outer edge of the carrier. The legs must be parallel with the lifting portion of the carrier.

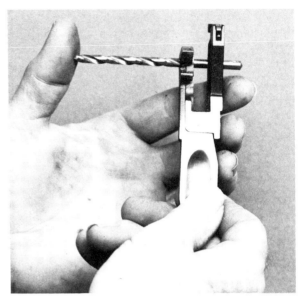

15–22. Check the alignment of the carrier screw holes by insuring that the shank of a #13 drill bit will slip freely through both sides.

misaligned. To check for this condition, place a steel scale on the outside of the carrier legs (Fig. 15–21) to insure that the legs are parallel with the lifting portion of the carrier. If they do not align, place the front of the carrier in a vise and use a small leather or plastic mallet to tap the legs back into shape.

The carrier screw holes must be in perfect alignment. To check their alignment use the shank portion of a #13 drill bit. The bit should slip from one side to the other as shown in Fig. 15–22. Do not use any force—the bit must slide freely from one hole to the other. If alignment is improper, the carrier leg can be bent or twisted as required. A mallet or parallel-jawed plier can be used to accomplish this (with the front end of the carrier secured in a padded vise).

The holding surface of the carrier dog must be maintained in the identical condition, as received from the factory. This surface is indicated by the pointer in Fig. 15–23. Do not alter this surface in any way. If altered, the carrier dog can

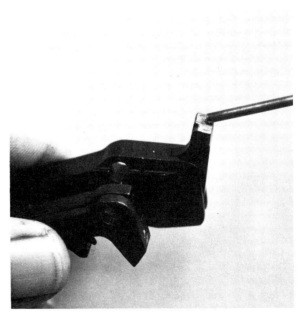

15–23. It is important that the holding surface of the carrier dog be maintained in the identical condition it was in when received from the factory.

fail to release from the operating handle. In use, if this happens, the carrier dog or the surface of the carrier upon which it rests will be worn excessively, allowing the carrier to rotate too far forward. Replace these parts as required, attempting no alteration to them.

indicated, drive the link pin from right to left, separating the link from the locking block. Newer models have a flattened pin while older ones have the pin staked on the left side. These variations both accomplish the goal of preventing the pin from protruding from the right side during cycling, which could cause a jammed action or possible damage. See Fig. 15–25 for

Disassembly of the Breechblock (Bolt) Group

Refer to Fig. 15–24 for the relationship of the various parts included in the bolt assembly. Using a ⅛-inch punch, remove the firing-pin stop pin (moving it from left to right) from the bolt and withdraw the firing pin. Rotate the locking block and link and lift them up and out of the bolt.

Disassembly of the locking block and link is not normally required. Should disassembly be

15–25. Correct relationship between locking block and link. Incorrect assembly can cause serious firearm damage.

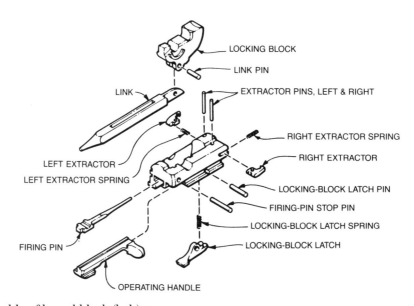

15–24. Disassembly of breechblock (bolt) group.

appropriate locking block and link relationship.

Both extractors and their springs may be removed by driving out their retaining pins. Drive the pins from the bottom of the bolt to the top, using a ³⁄₃₂-inch punch.

Inspection, Adjustment, and Reassembly of Breechblock (Bolt) Group

Carefully inspect all bolt parts for cracks, burrs, or unusual wear, and replace parts as required. Make certain the front portion of the link, that lifts the locking-block latch, is not worn or burred. Be sure the link is perfectly straight.

Reinstall the extractor springs, extractors, and their retaining pins. Inspect the fit and function of the extractors, using a dummy cartridge. Place the base of it between the right and left extractor just as a loaded round would be seated on the bolt face. Force the right extractor outward by sliding the dummy cartridge across the bolt face until the extractor has reached its maximum travel. Tilt the cartridge outward so it will show a space in clearing the left extractor, as in Fig. 15–26. The distance between the rim of the shell and the extractor should be from ¹⁄₆₄-inch to ¹⁄₃₂-inch. If it is larger than ¹⁄₃₂-inch, shells will occasionally drop off the extractors during functioning, resulting in sluggish ejection. To correct this, tap the hook end of the left extractor inward to give the required clearance.

After this adjustment has been made, position the dummy cartridge centrally between the two extractors. Tilt the shell outward, away from the left extractor, without sliding the shell across the bolt face. The rim of the shell should be retained by the left extractor until moderate tilting pressure causes it to release the shell. If it does not release the shell, the hook is too sharp or has too

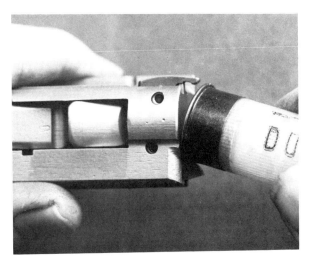

15–26. Clearance between shell rim and left extractor must be maintained between ¹⁄₆₄ and ¹⁄₃₂ inch (see text for details). If more, ejection will be sluggish.

great an angle. To correct this, use a fine small file and trim the sharp corner of the hook's end.

If the left extractor does not move outward when pressure is applied on its hooked end, there is a possibility it's misshapen or the last coil of its spring is lodged between the extractor and the bolt. Replace the extractor if required. Also be sure to turn in the last coil of the extractor spring (Fig. 15–30). Naturally, an accumulation of debris behind the extractor can also cause it to malfunction.

Continue to reassemble the bolt by installing the link and locking block. Be sure these parts are correctly positioned (see Fig. 15–22) if they have been separated from each other.

The tolerance between the breechbolt and the locking block is very important to prevent damage to the track on the locking block. Position the locking block to protrude approximately ¼-inch above the bolt. Then compress the two components by pushing the locking block forward, toward the bolt's face, as in Fig 15–27. Check to insure that contact is made between the forward surface of the locking block and the bolt when the parts are pushed together. If con-

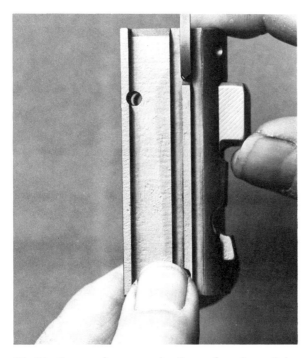

15–27. Contact between the forward surface of the locking block and the bolt is essential when the parts are positioned and compressed as shown (see text).

tact is not made, replace parts as necessary to correct this.

If the locking block and bolt rub excessively hard together the action will jam. Replace parts as required to correct this situation, too.

Note: On A-5 shotguns manufactured prior to 1958, it is necessary to replace both the breechblock and the locking bolt as a pair. This is due to a dimensional change in the breechbolt track. Additional parts that will be required are the left extractor and its spring, as these also differ.

Next, install the firing pin and its stop pin. Drive the stop pin in front, right to left. Be sure the rounded and polished end of the stop pin is located on the right side of the bolt.

With the locking block in its lowered position, apply pressure to the rear of the firing pin. As the block rotates upward, the firing pin will release approximately as the block reaches its maximum height. Pushing the locking block downward should cause the firing pin to move rearward. This prevents inertia from driving the firing pin into the primer as the bolt slams shut. It is

15–28. Installation of the operating handle.

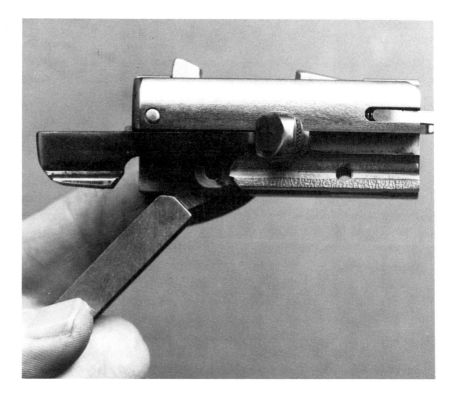

possible that cartridges might display a very slight primer indent after loading and unloading. This can be considered normal, as insufficient firing-pin inertia exists to cause ignition.

Next, install the operating handle on the bolt as shown in Fig. 15–28. The clearance between the operating handle and the locking block and its links is important. This clearance should be about 0.010-inch. To check, hold the assembly horizontally with the bottom of the bolt falling upward (Fig. 15–29). Depress the locking lug into the bolt and work the operating handle back and forth to be sure there is clearance between these parts. Then lift the link to insure that it is free to rotate. If there is binding of these parts, the gun will operate sluggishly and fail to lock or fire.

If there is insufficient clearance of these parts, use a mill file to remove a small amount of metal from the front end of the link, where it contacts the operating handle.

If there is too much play between these parts, you will find two lines at the top inside of the receiver. It will appear as if something has been scraped down the middle of the receiver. Additionally, when the gun is fired and the barrel has completed its rearward travel, the locking block will remain partially engaged in the aperture of the barrel extension. This will cause sluggish operation. To correct this excessive play, replace the link.

Note: When inspecting the locking-block latch spring make certain the last coil of the spring is turned inward as shown in Fig. 15–30. This will prevent the lock-block latch from being jammed in an open position, thereby damaging the carrier assembly.

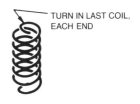

TURN IN LAST COIL, EACH END

15–30. Locking-block latch spring.

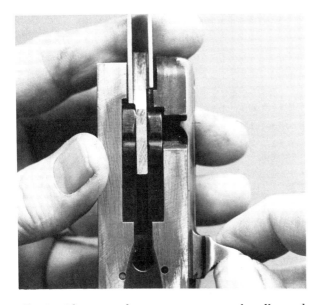

15–29. Clearance between operating handle and locking block is critical and should be maintained at about 0.010 inch.

Also inspect the locking-block latch-spring hole for burrs. If they develop in this hole, the spring may remain compressed, allowing the locking-block latch to remain open. This can damage the carrier assembly.

The operating handle and the locking-block latch spring are not installed until the bolt has been placed in the receiver.

Inspection of Disassembled Receiver

The important things to look for are cracks and burrs. Begin by inspecting the ejection port where the operating handle rests when the barrel is not assembled to the shotgun. Check both the inside and outside for burrs. If large burrs or any indentations are found, they may be caused by the bolt slamming forward when a barrel is not assembled to the firearm. Or they may be due to forearm wood that has been compressed where the barrel-guide ring comes to rest at the front of the forearm. This, in effect, causes the forearm to be incorrect dimensionally.

To check forearm length, assemble the barrel and forearm to the receiver. If the fore-end is satisfactory, the barrel extension will be flush with, or slightly inside, the receiver. If the barrel extension protrudes beyond the receiver, replace the forearm.

Next look at the rear inside surface of the receiver. If there is an imprint of the bolt on the back end, several causes can be suspected, including a weak or broken action spring, a broken action-spring tube, a missing action-spring plug-retaining pin, a weak recoil spring, or the improper setting of the recoil-spring mechanism (for instance, it may have been set for light loads when heavy loads were used). Replace the action spring and the recoil spring as a pair. If the action-spring tube is replaced, always ream it with a 0.413-inch-diameter reamer. Check the inside surfaces of the receiver for rub lines. If they are present replace the link.

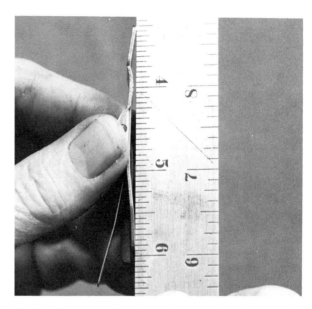

15–31. Use a steel rule to observe the bow in the carrier latch. The space between the rule and the *hump* of the latch should be approximately ¹⁄₁₆ inch.

square. Should the edges be rounded slightly from wear, a slight amount of metal may be stoned at that point to square it up. But it is essential to remove only minimal material to keep clearance between the latch and carrier at a minimum. If in doubt, replace the carrier latch, as excessive clearance will cause feeding malfunctions.

Inspection and Adjustment of Carrier Latch

Place a steel six-inch rule along the carrier latch (Fig. 15–31). The gap between the rule and the hump of the latch should measure approximately ¹⁄₁₆-inch.

The rear surface of the carrier latch, which locks the carrier, must be maintained in its original factory configuration. The angle on it must not be changed, and the edges must be kept

Inspection of Buttstock

If the stock was found to be loose on the action, check the tang-screw hole for elongation. If it has become elongated, drill the hole out with a ⅜-inch bit and plug it. Use a maple dowel with some glue on it to plug the drilled hole. Then refit the tang screw to the sock by drilling out the plug with an appropriate-sized bit.

Inspection of Fore-end

A fore-end with minor cracks at the receiver end may still be serviceable. However, if cracks appear in the fore-end where the barrel-guide ring strikes, the fore-end must be replaced or repaired.

Often, cracks can be repaired with an epoxy compound. However, for this to be effective the wood cannot be oil-soaked.

Reassembly of Magazine-Cutoff Group

If a magazine tube has been replaced, it will be necessary to drill through the magazine-cutoff spring-screw hole with a #38 drill bit before proceeding. Take extreme care not to damage the threads in the hole.

With the action firmly held in a well-padded vise, install the magazine cutoff and its retaining pin (or screw on older models). Be sure not to drive the pin in so far that it will interfere with the barrel extension or the breechblock rails. Then assemble the magazine-cutoff spring and its screw to the receiver.

Adjustment and Installation of Cartridge-Stop Assembly

Position the cartridge stop and spring in the receiver and install the roll-pin retainer (or

screw on older models). Check to be sure it moves freely. Once again, take care not to drive the retaining pin in so deeply as to interfere with the barrel extension or the breechblock rails.

Remove the receiver from the vise and position the barrel past the battery position, approximately two inches into the receiver. The forward end of the cartridge stop, which retains the shell in the magazine, should begin to rotate inward toward the receiver. Just before the barrel reaches the battery position, the forward end of the cartridge stop should be flush with the receiver's inside surface. If it is above the receiver, remove the cartridge stop and bend in the shank portion that contacts the barrel extension. If the cartridge stop is below flush, remove it and bend the shank outward.

After adjustment, remove the barrel from the receiver and check for protrusion of the forward end of the cartridge stop. It should protrude approximately 0.050-inch.

Installation of Carrier-Latch Assembly

Place the receiver in the padded vise with the bottom side up. Install the carrier-latch assembly, carrier-latch button and retaining pin (or screw).

Note: Use care when installing the retaining pin to insure that both holes in the carrier latch align with those of the receiver. And again be sure not to drive in the pin so deeply as to interfere with the breechblock rails.

After installation, inspect the assembly for free movement. Depress the carrier-latch button fully. If it does not fully return, the carrier-latch spring is weak and should be replaced. Of course, missed burrs or improper assembly can also be at fault.

Installation of Magazine Assembly

Remove any burrs from the magazine follower while inspecting it for excessive wear. Drop it into the magazine tube, followed by the magazine spring and, if it is to be used, the three-shot magazine plug.

Check to insure that depressing the carrier latch button does not cause the forward end of the carrier latch to interfere with the magazine follower. If it does, the follower and/or the magazine tube has excessive wear. Replace the offending part(s) as required.

Installation of Breechblock (Bolt) Assembly

Place the receiver in the upright position. Insert the operating handle in the receiver and position it to the rear of its operating slot. Insert the breechblock assembly and link from the front of the receiver, positioning the breechblock in the operating rails of the receiver. Pull the breechblock to the rear of the receiver by the link and engage the operating handle into position in the breechblock. Push the breechblock together (with the operating handle forward by the link) and position the locking-block latch-pin hole in the breechblock at the half-hole in the bottom edge of the ejection port.

Rotate the receiver assembly to bottom-up position, insert the locking-block latch spring in its hole in the breechblock, and position the locking-block latch, wide section aft, on the spring. Depress the locking-block latch slightly with the thumb to align all holes, insert the locking-block latch pin (insert the end opposite

the flattened end) in its hole, and seat it gently with a ⅛-inch punch.

Push the breechblock assembly forward in the receiver and install the action-spring follower, spring, plug, and its retaining pin. *Note:* Be certain the rear end of the link is properly seated in the action-spring follower.

Work the breechblock assembly back and forth to be sure it has unrestricted movement. Remove any burrs that may be inhibiting free movement.

Note: Do not let the breechblock assembly slam forward in the receiver, as damage will result.

Inspection of Locking-Block Latch

With the barrel assembly installed in the receiver, grasp the receiver with one hand, the barrel with the other, and push the barrel back against the breechblock approximately two inches past battery position. Maintain this position of the barrel by holding the barrel and magazine tube together with one hand, as shown in Fig. 15–32. With the other hand, slowly pull the operating handle to the rear and notice whether the locking-block latch engages the locking block and locks it in the down position (Fig. 15–33). If the locking-block latch is too long, it will not function in this manner and must be adjusted by removing material from the engaging surface. Be sure to maintain the same degree of bevel on the end to be adjusted.

Holding the barrel and breechblock assembly with locking-block latch engaged in the retraced (rear) position, slowly let the assembly move forward by the action spring and observe whether the locking-block latch becomes disengaged from the locking-block when the forward end of the breechblock is approximately ¾-inch from the forward end of the ejection port. If

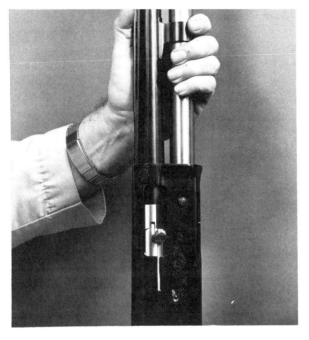

15–32. Proper positioning of parts to inspect locking latch (see text).

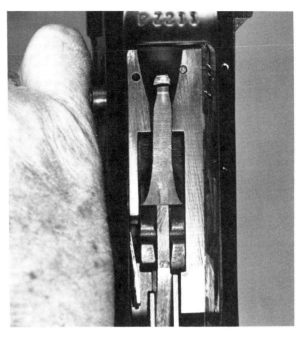

15–33. Locking-block latch must engage locking block and lock it in the down position as shown.

release of the locking-block occurs appreciably before this, the lock will drag on the barrel extension prior to actual locking up, causing sluggish operation.

Premature release of the locking-block is generally caused by a worn or incorrectly fitted (too-short) locking-block latch. In either case, the latch should be replaced. Actual release is caused by rotation of the front end of the link as it moves forward.

Inspection and Installation of Carrier and Carrier Latch

Remove the barrel assembly and place the receiver in the inverted position. Install the carrier

assembly and the carrier screws in their respective sides of the receiver.

A final inspection of the carrier latch should be made at this time. The carrier latch should hit approximately in the center of the protrusion from the rear section of the carrier assembly. If the latch rests too closely to the edge of the carrier, it may slip off the edge during operation, causing malfunction. If adjustment to the carrier latch is necessary, you will have to remove it.

If the carrier latch is installed with a screw (an older model) it may be removed without additional disassembly. If it is installed with a pin (newer models), you must remove the action spring and breechblock assembly before removing the carrier-latch retaining pin with a 3/32-inch punch.

Place the carrier latch in a vise, as shown in illustration 34. Using a crescent wrench, put a slight twist in the latch to move its engaging edge inward or outward so it contacts the protrusion on the aft section of the carrier assembly approximately in the center.

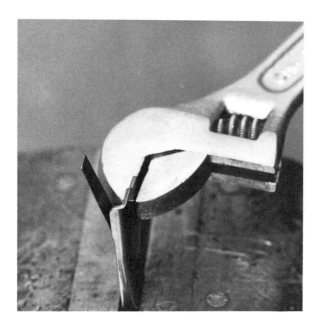

15–34. Use a crescent wrench to put a slight twist in the carrier latch *if necessary*, so it will contact the aft section of the carrier assembly as explained in text.

Reinstall the carrier latch, button, and retaining pin (or screw) and check again for proper installation and engagement with the carrier.

Installation of Trigger-plate Assembly

On older models, the carrier spring must be installed in the receiver on two pins before installation of the triggerplate assembly. This installation is shown in Fig. 15–35.

On newer models, the carrier spring is installed on the triggerplate assembly and the spring is oriented as shown in Fig. 15–36.

With the hammer cocked and the safety placed in the safe position, lower the triggerplate assembly into the receiver, making sure the

15–35. This view shows the location of the carrier-latch spring on older models.

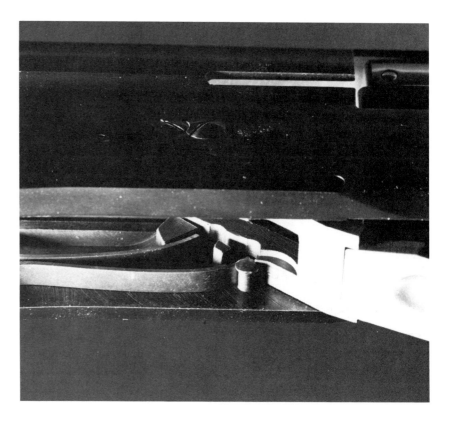

15–36. Carrier-latch spring correctly assembled to the trigger-plate group on new-style A-5.

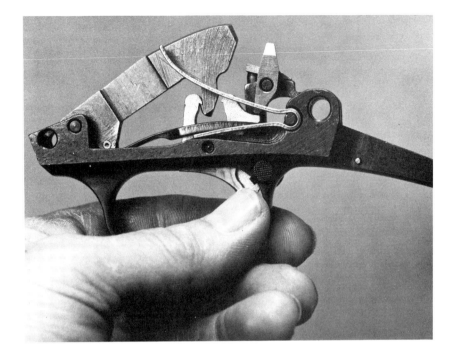

carrier spring (on the newer models) engages the end of the left leg of the carrier.

First install the forward triggerplate screw. While depressing the rear of the triggerplate assembly, retract the operating handle slightly and the triggerplate should drop down into position. Then install the rear triggerplate screw.

Final Assembly and Inspection

Manipulate the action of the gun to the locked open position. Press the carrier-latch button and allow the breechblock assembly to move forward very slowly. When the breechblock assembly is back in battery position, make sure the carrier comes back to its locked position under the carrier latch.

If the carrier remains in a depressed position, the carrier spring is too short at the front end, which rides on the left leg of the carrier, or else it does not have enough hook at the front end to draw the carrier back into position. If the carrier spring is too long at the front end, it will cause the gun to hang on the carrier dog too long and the action will work sluggishly. If it's too long, remove and place the spring in a vise, and trim off a small amount of metal with a mill file. Try the spring again in the gun to determine the proper length. If the carrier spring is too short, it will have to be replaced.

With the action closed, depress the forward end of the carrier with the index finger and observe that the carrier clears the carrier latch. The carrier latch at the same time should contact the protrusion on the rear portion of the carrier approximately in the center.

Depress the rear portion of the carrier until the carrier bottoms out of the carrier latch. The gap between the rear portion of the carrier and the triggerplate should measure approximately .020-inch. If an excessive gap exists here, the carrier latch or carrier should be replaced.

Install the recoil assembly, barrel, forearm, and magazine cap. With the action cocked and closed, push the safety to the off-safe position and pull the trigger to insure that the hammer falls.

Re-cock the action and check the clearance between the safety sear and link. To check, close the action and press forward on the upper arm of the safety sear. Do this with a long punch, placed through the opening in the back of the receiver. Insure that $1/16$-inch to $1/8$-inch of play exists. If no play is present, the link is trying to override the safety sear, and breakage may result. Remove the link and relieve the surface contacting the safety sear with a fine-cut pillar file.

If the hammer does not fall, use a long punch through the opening in the back of the receiver and push forward on the top arm of the safety sear that engages the link. While pushing forward on the safety sear, pull the trigger. If the hammer falls, the link is too short and is not disengaging the safety sear from the trigger. This means the link must be replaced.

Put the buttstock back on the gun and install the tang screw.

Feed a dummy cartridge into the magazine and see that it is retained by the forward-most surface of the locking-block latch. If it is not, the locking-block latch must be removed and the hole through the latch elongated to let it protrude sufficiently to retain the dummy cartridge.

Depress the carrier to see that it clears the base of the dummy cartridge being retained by the locking-block latch. If not, relieve the forward end of the carrier.

Cycle the dummy cartridge out of the gun. With the gun cocked and in battery position, place the safety in the safe position and verify that the gun will not fire by pulling the trigger as hard as you can using the index finger of both hands.

Check for proper tightness of all screws and install all lock screws.

Place the safety in the off-safe position and check for a trigger pull of four to five pounds.

Before firing the gun, check headspace with go and no-go headspace gauges made to SAAMI specifications.

Common Problems— Probable Causes and Corrections

Trigger Will Not Release Hammer

Improperly altered hammer or sear notches which will not release. *Replace hammer or sear.*

Loose mainspring screw. *Adjust or replace.*

Broken mainspring. *Replace.*

Link bent so it does not release safety sear. *Repair or replace link.*

Altered safety sear not engaging link properly. *Replace safety sear.*

Gun Misfires

Broken firing pin. *Replace.*

Excessive headspace and/or firing pin too short. *Replace firing pin if too short. If headspace is excessive, return firearm to factory service department for repair.*

Loose mainspring screw. *Adjust or replace.*

Gun Jams or Tries to Feed Two Shells Into Chamber at Once

Improperly adjusted or worn carrier latch. *Adjust; if worn, replace.*

Too much clearance between carrier latch and carrier. *Adjust.*

Action Will Not Stay Open on Last Shot When Using Heavy Loads

Improperly adjusted friction rings. *Adjust.*

Weak recoil spring. *Replace.*

Carrier latch out of adjustment. *Adjust; repair or replace if damaged.*

Operating handle slipping off carrier dog. *Adjust carrier dog.*

Fails to Extract Fired Shells From Chamber

Worn, broken, or improperly adjusted extractors. *Replace or adjust, as needed.*

Weak extractor spring. *Replace.*

Bulge in chamber. *Return to factory service department for repair.*

Jams and Fails to Eject

Dry or burred magazine tube. *Deburr; lubricate if needed.*

Bent magazine tube. *Repair or replace.*

Tight forearm interfering with barrel. *Adjust or repair.*

Extractors out of adjustment or broken. *Adjust; replace if broken.*

Carrier latch out of adjustment. *Adjust.*

Broken ejector. *Replace.*

Bent carrier. *Repair or replace.*

Weak extractor springs. *Replace.*

Worn carrier dog. *Replace.*

Weak recoil spring. *Replace.*

Reduction of recoil due to add-on choking device which tends to reduce recoil velocity. *Adjust recoil spring, friction ring, and friction piece to function with light loads.*

Extra-soft recoil pads (rare). *Replace.*

Not holding gun tightly to shoulder when firing (rare). *Correction in this instance involves shooter, not gun.*

Barrel extension rubbing in receiver. *Remove recoil spring and check for free movement of barrel.*

Barrel Will Not Fit on Receiver

Burrs in receiver. *Deburr.*

Bent magazine tube. *Repair or replace.*

Improper fit and alignment of barrel extension. *Adjust if possible. If not, repair or replace.*

Fails to Chamber Second Round

Improperly adjusted or worn carrier latch. *Adjust or replace, as needed.*

Improper clearance between carrier latch and carrier. *Adjust.*

Trigger Fails to Engage Hammer

Burrs in hammer and trigger-sear notches. *Deburr. Take great care to remove only burrs, altering no angles or dimensions.*

Loose mainspring screw. *Tighten.*

Broken mainspring. *Replace.*

Mainspring and hammer need polishing where they make contact. (Old style without hammer roller.)

U-portion of trigger bent. *Repair or replace.*

Broken hammer. *Replace.*

Bolt Fails to Lock in Rearward Position When Last Shell Is Fired

Worn or broken carrier. *Replace.*

Broken, weak, or missing carrier-latch spring. *Replace.*

Improperly functioning carrier latch. *Adjust, repair, or replace, as needed.*

Weak recoil spring. *Replace.*

Improper setting of friction rings. *Adjust.*

Worn carrier latch sliding off engaging surface of carrier. *Replace latch.*

Bolt Fails to Return to Battery Position

Weak or broken action spring. *Replace.*

Burrs in action-spring tube binding action-spring follower. *Deburr.*

Improperly seated link in action-spring follower. *Adjust.*

Jammed or broken carrier or carrier latch. *Adjust, repair, or replace, as needed.*

Broken locking-block latch. *Replace.*
Broken locking-block. *Replace.*
Carrier spring too long. *Replace.*

Carrier Does Not Return to Lower Position

Long, worn, broken, or improperly assembled carrier spring. *Replace (or adjust if improperly assembled).*

Improperly assembled carrier latch interfering with carrier. *Adjust.*

Shells Fail to Exit Magazine When Released

Broken, kinked, dented, or bent magazine tube. *Replace or, if possible, repair.*

Heavy grease in magazine tube. *Clean.*

Carrier latch out of adjustment or broken. *Adjust, repair, or replace, as needed.*

Improper adjustment of cartridge stop. *Adjust.*

Safety Sear Fails to Release Trigger When Bolt Is Locked

Damaged or altered sear. *Replace.*

Broken or bent link. *Replace or, if possible, repair.*

Forearm not allowing barrel to come far enough forward to let link release safety sear. *Adjust or repair, as needed.*

Hammer Does Not Release from Safety Notch

Burrs in safety notches on hammer or trigger. *Carefully deburr.*

Weak or broken trigger spring. *Replace.*

Hammer and trigger out of adjustment. *Adjust.*

Rusty mainspring and hammer. (Old models

without hammer roller.) *Replace.*

Mainspring screw loose. *Tighten.*

Safety Does Not Operate Properly

Burrs in web of trigger or in triggerplate. *Deburr.*

Broken or worn safety. *Replace.*

Broken or weak triggerspring. *Replace.*

Barrel Does Not Unlock from Breechbolt Assembly

Improper clearance between locking-block and barrel extension. *Adjust.*

Burrs on link where operating handle comes into contact with link. *Deburr.*

Gun Drops Shells Out of Loading Port When Fired

Improperly adjusted carrier latch. *Adjust.*

Broken or worn carrier latch. *Replace.*

Broken or worn carrier. *Replace.*

Shells Override Top of Locking-Block Latch and Jam Between Carrier and Breechbolt

Battered forearm where barrel-guide ring rests, allowing barrel to move too far forward out of receiver. *Replace or, if possible, repair forearm.*

Improperly adjusted carrier latch. *Adjust.*

Improper relation of carrier to carrier latch. *Adjust.*

Shells Jam in Action While Entering Chamber

Sharp edge or burrs at headspace seat of chamber. *Deburr if possible, or return firearm to factory service department for repair.*

Burrs in extractor slots. *Deburr.*

Extractor springs too strong. *Replace.*

Extractors not shaped properly or incorrectly adjusted. *Repair, adjust, or replace.*

Carrier latch scissoring off carrier. *Adjust.*

Improperly adjusted carrier latch. *Adjust.*

Gun Doubles or Fires Full Automatic

Trigger pull too tight. *Adjust.*

U-gap in trigger too wide and sears not engaging properly. *Replace trigger.*

Safety sear notches on hammer and trigger insufficiently engaged. *Adjust.*

Loose mainspring. *Adjust or replace.*

Note: In addition to the malfunctions listed, others can occur due to lack of lubrication. While repairing the firearm, check all parts for wear, burrs, deformities, and small cracks. If you are not certain about the amount of metal that has been worn away or the original shape of a part, it is well to compare it with a new factory part.

15–37. To remove a broken magazine tube, break it at a scored line, being careful not to damage the threads in the receiver.

Broken Magazine Tube

On rare occasions, a magazine tube is broken off flush with the receiver while attempting to align the barrel-guide ring or barrel extension. In this connection, remember that the magazine-cutoff spring screw must always be removed in order to unscrew the magazine tube. The broken section may be removed from the receiver by scoring the inside of the magazine tube in a straight line with a sharp chisel and hammer. Caution must be taken not to make the score line too deep and damage the threads of the receiver. Next, the section of the magazine tube can be broken at the score line with a cold chisel by lifting at one side of the score line as shown in Fig. 15–37 and working backward. The broken section can then be worked out and replacement made.

If replacement is made, after the new tube has been completely screwed into the receiver, drill through the magazine-cutoff spring-screw hole with a #38 bit. Make certain no burrs are left inside the magazine tube as they will interfere with the passage of shells. The magazine-cutoff screw acts as a set screw for the magazine tube.

Adjustment of Friction Rings

The "shock-absorber system" of the recoil-operated A-5 is extremely simple, yet it must be given some attention. Proper maintenance and adjustment will reduce recoil to a minimum. This contributes to pleasant shooting and protects the mechanism against excessive shock and wear, thus prolonging the life of the gun. Ejection and loading are automatically carried out by utilizing the forces delivered to the gun when the shell is fired. The friction-ring system regulates these forces.

For instance, the A-5 may fail to eject if you fire a light load with the friction rings set for heavy loads. On the other hand, if you fire a heavy load with the friction rings set for light loads, the gun will recoil unnecessarily hard and the mechanism will receive excessive shock.

It should be noted, however, that the weight of the shooter and the manner in which he holds the gun may require some variance from the recommended adjustment. For example, a lightweight individual or a shooter who holds the gun loosely may find that his gun will function better for him if adjusted for light loads while shooting a moderately heavy load such as a 3¼-dram-equivalent/1¼-ounce loading of a 12-gauge shell. It is always desirable to utilize the setting for heavy loads as long as the mechanism functions properly.

Warning: Never fire the gun with the bronze friction piece removed from its position rearward of the barrel-guide ring, as damage to the gun will result.

Lubrication of the Magazine Tube

Whether the friction ring is set for heavy or light loads, the amount and kind of oil on the magazine tube will, by varying the amount of friction, affect the amount of recoil. In general, the more oil is put on the magazine tube (or bronze friction piece), the easier this friction piece will slide on the tube; hence, a greater degree of recoil will be obtained.

If you are firing a light load and the gun fails to eject, adding oil to the magazine tube, in the region of the bronze friction piece, will sufficiently increase recoil for good ejection.

Oil that congeals in cold weather or deposits gummy residue may reduce recoil to the point where the gun will fail to eject. Use a high-quality lubricant. Occasionally clean the magazine tube and relubricate it. If temperatures of 10 to 30 degrees below freezing are likely to be encountered, be sure to utilize an oil that remains fluid in such temperatures.

There should be a film of oil on the magazine tube at all times, except when 12-gauge 2¾-inch, 1½-ounce magnum loads are being used in a 2¾-inch chamber gun. With this load, it is desirable to wipe the magazine tube almost dry. Function will not be affected and you will find these heavy loads much more comfortable to shoot.

Recommended Points of Lubrication During Reassembly

Excessive oil will cause an accumulation of dirt and unburned powder. During reassembly of the gun, the following lubrication procedures are recommended:

Place a drop or two of oil on each side of the receiver track.

Place a drop or two on each side of the breech-bolt assembly.

Place several drops on the action spring and work it back and forth before assembling the carrier.

Place a drop in the carrier-dog spring.

Place a drop in the safety-sear spring hole.

Place a drop where the hammer rides on the mainspring.

With the rings and recoil spring removed, place a light film of oil on the magazine tube.

16

Remington 700 Bolt-Action Rifle

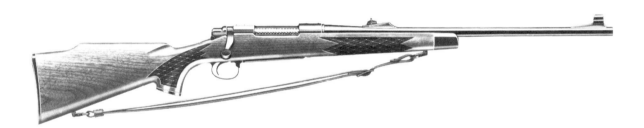

The Remington 700 series of centerfire bolt-action rifles has an enviable reputation for fine accuracy and extreme durability. Shooters especially like the fine trigger. Often, 700 actions are used as the basis for building extremely accurate benchrest rifles.

The following information, while dealing specifically with the Model 700, is applicable, in some instances, to earlier Remington rifles such as the 721, 722, or 725. Although the Remington Model Seven is built along much smaller and lighter lines, it is also quite similar to the 700 with respect to disassembly, maintenance, and reassembly.

Cycle of Operation

The operation of the 700 is, of course, typical of many bolt-action centerfire rifles. Pulling the bolt handle up and rearward until it is stopped will extract and eject a fired case and cock the firing pin. Pushing the bolt forward and down will strip a round from the magazine, feed it into the chamber, and lock the action, again readying the gun for firing.

As the bolt handle is raised, the locking lugs rotate in the receiver to a position that allows the

159

EXPLODED VIEW OF REMINGTON 700

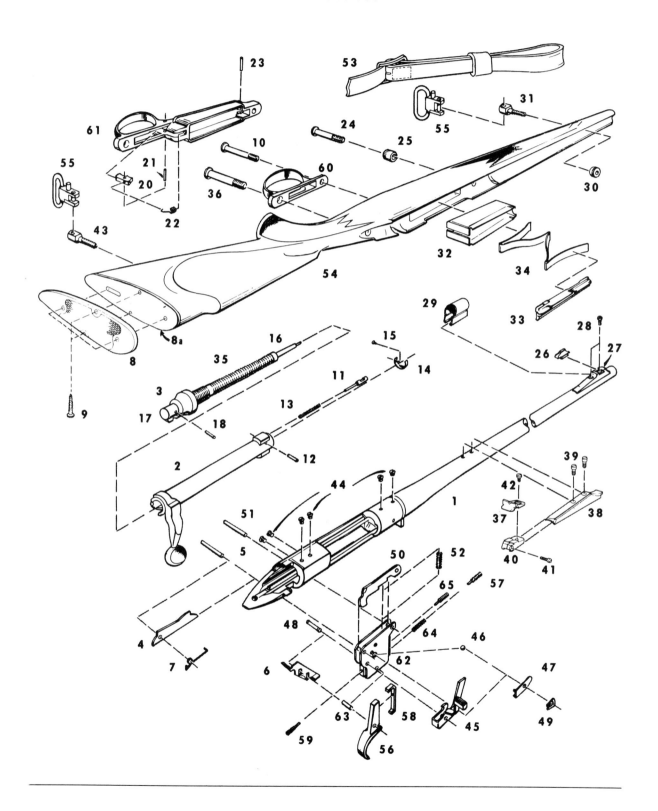

View No.	Part No.	Name of Part	View No.	Part No.	Name of Part	View No.	Part No.	Name of Part
1		barrel assembly	29	15363	front sight hood, BDL	47	15368	safety switch detent spring (R)
2		bolt assembly	30	15357	front swivel nut, BDL	48	17043	safety swtich pivot pin (R)
3	17012	bolt plug	31	15358	front swivel screw, BDL	49	17044	safety switch snap washer (R)
4	17013	bolt stop (R)		90957	grip cap, BDL (not shown)	50	15666	sear safety cam (R)
5	24475	bolt stop pin (R)		25380	grip cap screw	51	24476	sear pin (R)
6	15478	bolt stop release (R)		90958	grip cap spacer, BDL (not shown)	52	17047	sear spring (R)
7	15224	bolt stop spring (R)				53	30855	sling strap assembly, BDL
8	90953	buttplate	32	15284	magazine, ADL		26990	sling strap assembly and mountings complete
8a	90954	buttplate spacer, BDL		16430	magazine, BDL (not shown)	54	33366	stock assembly, ADL
9	25380	buttplate screw	33	90952	magazine follower		33371	stock assembly, BDL
10	15287	center guard screw, ADL		91017	magazine follower, BDL		18186	stock reinforcing screw (not shown)
11	17017	ejector		15940	magazine tab screw, ADL		16970	stock refinishing screw dowel (not shown)
12	17676	ejector pin	34	17028	magazine spring			
13	17019	ejector spring		15677	magazine spring, BDL	55	26555	swivel assembly, BDL (Q.D.)
14	91816	extractor	35	17029	mainspring	56	15280	trigger (R)
	15376	fastener, sling strap	36	26355	rear guard screw	57	17053	trigger adjusting screw (R)
16	22020	firing pin	37	32510	rear sight aperture		26345	trigger assembly (R)
17	22040	firing pin assembly	38	91595	rear sight base	58	19461	trigger connector (R)
18	17022	firing pin cross pin	39	28505	rear sight base screw (2)	59	91128	trigger engagement screw (R)
20	15291	floor plate latch, BDL	40	90905	rear sight slide	60	15281	trigger guard
21	16451	floor plate latch pin, BDL	41	90906	elevation screw	61	26376	trigger guard, BDL
22	16452	floor plate latch spring, BDL	42	90904	windage screw		26371	trigger guard assembly, BDL
23	16453	floor plate pivot pin, BDL	43	15358	rear swivel screw, BDL	62	26655	trigger housing assembly (R)
24	22035	front guard screw	44	17034	receiver plug screw	63	24477	trigger pin (R)
25	15161	front guard screw bushing, ADL	45	26585	safety switch assembly (R)	64	15400	trigger spring (R)
26	15373	front sight	46	23222	safety switch detent ball (R)	65	15481	trigger stop screw (R)
	15719	front sight (low)						
27	28510	front sight ramp						
	15635	front sight ramp, BDL						
28	28505	front sight ramp screw						

Note: Basic .30-06 part numbers are listed. For other calibers obtain the correct part number from the owner's manual.

(R) = restricted part, available only for factory installation.

---

bolt to be drawn rearward. The cocking of the firing mechanism is accomplished during the lifting of the bolt handle. A cam at the rear of the bolt forces the firing-pin assembly rearward, compressing the mainspring. The assembly is held in the cocked position by a notch—see Fig. 15–2—on the rear of the bolt body. This engagement is held until the bolt handle is lowered, upon the closing of the action. Then the firing pin is held in its cocked position by the sear.

Should the rifle's action be opened prior to firing, the sear's engagement will, upon lifting the bolt handle, be transferred to the bolt notch.

With the action closed and the safety lever in the forward (fire) position, the rifle is fired by pressing the trigger rearward. This moves the trigger connector forward, leaving the sear unsupported against the cocked firing-pin mechanism. The sear is then cammed downward by the pressure of the firing-pin spring forcing the

16–2. Notch engagement holds 700 bolt assembly in cocked position while bolt handle is up.

firing pin forward. As the sear nears the end of its downward travel, the firing pin ignites the cartridge.

The bolt handle is then raised, cocking the firing-pin assembly. As the bolt handle is turned upward, primary extraction begins. The bolt's extractor, which has a firm purchase on the cartridge rim, is moved slightly rearward with the bolt as it cams from its locking surfaces. During primary extraction, the bolt assembly moves rearward about ⅛-inch. The mechanical advantage of this initial extraction is about eight to one. The secondary extraction takes place as the bolt is pulled rearward and the extractor withdraws the case from the chamber.

A spring-loaded ejector in the bolt face presses forward and outward on the fired case as it is withdrawn from the chamber. This causes the right front edge of the cartridge to bear against the inside of the receiver as the bolt is drawn rearward. As the forward edge of the fired case clears the receiver and enters the ejection-port area, the pressure of the ejector rotates the

fired case to the right, frees it from the extractor's grip, and causes it to be ejected upward and outward. The rearward motion of the bolt is arrested by the bolt stop.

As the bolt is closed, the top edge of the rim of the uppermost cartridge in the magazine is engaged by the bottom front edge of the bolt. As the bolt is pushed forward, the cartridge is pushed forward. The cartridge frees itself from the magazine when it no longer is engaged by the magazine's ears, and is pushed into the chamber by the bolt. The bolt is locked with its rear lug surfaces bearing on mating receiver surfaces when the bolt handle is closed.

On the Remington 700 and all similar Remington models, the head of the cartridge is completely enclosed by the bolt head when a round is chambered. This provides great strength in the support of the cartridge.

As the bolt handle is turned down, the cartridge's forward motion is arrested by mating surfaces in the chamber. This causes the ejector to be compressed into the bolt face. Simultaneously, as the bolt is closed, the extractor snaps over the rim of the cartridge, obtaining a firm purchase on it.

Because the extractor does not grasp the cartridge until the bolt is locked into its final position, it is necessary to turn the bolt fully downward whenever working cartridges through the action, as when unloading ADL models or when checking feeding. If the bolt is drawn rearward before it is turned fully downward, the cartridge fed into the chamber will remain there even though the bolt is pulled rearward.

The safety switch is located at the right rear of the receiver. Rotating it rearward puts it in the safe position. Rotating it fully forward places the mechanism in the firing position. The safety can be engaged only when the action is cocked. The bolt handle can be opened when the rifle is on "safe," thereby adding to safety in manipulating the bolt when the rifle is loaded.

However, the bolt handle can be inadvertently unlocked when hunting. If it's in a partially lifted position when the trigger is pulled, the bolt will be forcefully rotated into the closed position. This prevents the gun from firing when it is not properly locked. However, it may or may not fire the cartridge, depending upon how much of the mainspring's stored energy is consumed in turning the bolt closed. This will be determined by the distance the bolt must rotate to properly lock the action.

The engagement of the safety when rotating rearward brings a cam into position beneath the sear-safety cam. This locks the cam against the firing pin and prevents normal firing.

On earlier Remingtons, an arm was moved into a slot to prevent the bolt from being opened when the safety was applied.

Bolt-Group Removal

With the safety switch in the forward (fire) position, lift the bolt handle up and draw the bolt rearward until it engages the bolt stop. Then press upward on the bolt-stop release, located in

the trigger guard directly in front of the trigger (Fig. 16–2). Holding the bolt-stop release in a depressed position, withdraw the bolt from the rifle's receiver.

Disassembly of Ejector Group From Bolt

If required, the ejector assembly is easily dismantled. The ejector and ejector spring are retained in the bolt face by a pin. Driving out the pin located in the bolt body (Fig. 16–4) will free the ejector and its spring. The ejector and spring are heavily compressed, so you must take care to prevent their forceful exit from the bolt, as the flying parts could cause injury or become lost. The ejection hole should be free from debris or burrs. The ejector should be clean and burr-free

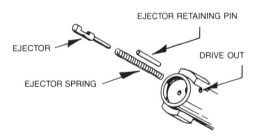

16–4. Removal of ejector, ejector spring, and ejector pin (*caution—see text*).

16–3. Pressing on the bolt-stop release (located in trigger guard) allows the bolt to be withdrawn from the receiver.

before replacing. The ejector must move freely in the bolt body for proper case ejection.

Reassembly is accomplished by placing the spring and ejector in the bolt and aligning the groove in the ejector with the pin hole. The ejector will need to be compressed into the bolt. Then drive in the retaining pin.

Extractor Removal and Replacement

The ejector pin, ejector spring, and ejector must be removed prior to removal of the extractor. Then drive the extractor rivet from the bolt, using an appropriate-size punch (Fig. 16–5). Dislodge and remove the loosened extractor from the bolt rim. A small screwdriver is convenient for this operation.

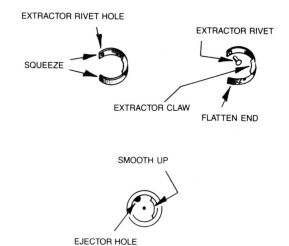

16–6. Replacement of extractor and extractor rivet.

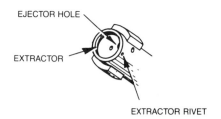

16–5. Removal of extractor and extractor rivet (caution—see text).

The extractor rivet will probably be damaged when being removed. Replace it with a new one when assembling the bolt.

Note: It is not necessary to remove any ejector or extractor parts unless these units are not functioning as intended. Normal cleaning can be accomplished with a toothbrush and solvent while these parts are assembled to the bolt body.

Adjust the replacement extractor for proper tension before assembly. To do this, squeeze the ends of the extractor together slightly (Fig. 16–6). Straighten its tail (flattened end) and then place the extractor inside the rim of the bolt face. Be sure the sloping area of the extractor claw is on the outside, the flattened side of the claw on the inside. Align the hole in the extractor with the rivet hole in the bolt. Insert the extractor rivet. *Note:* If the original extractor is used, the squeezing of its ends and straightening of its tail

(for proper tension) probably will be unnecessary.

Place support against the inside of the bolt rim and the head of the rivet. Then peen over the protruding end of the rivet. This will draw down the head on the rivet, tightening the extractor in the bolt. Smooth up the peening to prevent interference as the outside surface of the bolt head contacts the receiver. The outside surface of the rivet should blend with the bolt body (Fig. 16–6).

Check the extractor for proper tension with a fired case. It must grip firmly and hold the case in position when the bolt is held face downward. If the case is gripped too tightly (snaps free with difficulty), tape the extractor back under the bolt rim just a very small amount. Use a soft punch for this operation. Repeat this adjustment, if necessary, until the grip of the extractor is satisfactory.

If a fired case is gripped too lightly (falls away from the extractor when the bolt is held face downward), the extractor claw must be pulled from under the bolt rim to increase tension on the case. Disassembly may be required to correct the tension of the extractor. After tension is correct, smooth up the face of the claw, using a suitable stone, to match the bolt rim (Fig. 16–6).

Then reassemble the ejector group to the bolt.

Note: An early-design .222 Remington extractor was a snap-in unit requiring no rivet. This type may be disassembled and reassembled by simply inserting a pointed tweezer into the holes provided in the ends of the extractor. When the tweezer is positioned in the holes, compress its ends together and lift the extractor out or into place.

Removal and Disassembly of Firing-Pin Group

With the bolt cocked and firmly held in a padded vise, pull the firing-pin head (Fig. 16–7) rearward until a coin or washer can be inserted into the slot near the back edge of the firing-pin head. This is somewhat difficult, due to the need to compress the mainspring.

An alternative method is to grip the sear-engaging area of the firing-pin head using a vise with hard, smooth jaws. Care must be taken not to cause damage. Then pull forward on the bolt body and slip a coin or washer into the groove as it is exposed.

The entire firing-pin group can then be un-screwed from the bolt, but take care not to dislodge the coin or washer.

Since the mainspring is under heavy compression, disassembly of this unit is not recommended unless essential for the replacement of damaged parts. Suitable means must be employed to prevent the firing pin and/or firing-pin head from causing injury or damage due to sudden release.

Compress the mainspring by pushing forward on the bolt plug while holding the front end of the firing-pin securely against a stop. The coin or washer placed in position earlier will fall free and, with ample compression, the firing-pin cross pin will be exposed. Another set of hands will be required to drive out the cross pin as you maintain pressure on the bolt plug. When the cross pin has been driven free, remove the punch and slowly release the compression of the mainspring by allowing the bolt plug to move gradually rearward. See Fig. 16–8 for the relationship of these parts.

Complete firing-pin assemblies are interchangeable (firing pin, mainspring, bolt plug, firing-pin head, and firing-pin cross pin). However, the replacement of the firing pin requires drilling a hole in it with a #42 drill (.093-inch).

To do this, assemble the shank of the replacement firing pin into the firing-pin head. Be certain the recess in the firing-pin head is free of any debris or obstructions. Seat the shank of the replacement firing-pin firmly in the firing-pin

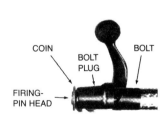

16–7. Removal of firing-pin group from bolt body (*caution—see text*).

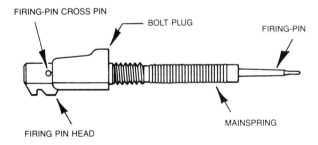

16–8. Disassembly of firing pin components (*caution—see text*).

head. While maintaining positive contact between the two parts, drill through the firing pin, entering and aligning the drill through the firing-pin head hole. This must be done exactingly. The drill should not remove any material from the hole on either side of the firing-pin head. If you have doubts, have an experienced professional do this part of the job.

Reassembly of the firing-pin group and the bolt is accomplished in reverse order. Be extra-careful with parts, as mainspring tension is applied to drive in the firing-pin cross pin. It will also be required to place a coin or washer as for disassembly, in order to screw the firing-pin assembly into the bolt body.

Removal of Rear-Sight Assembly

Remove the windage and elevation screws and slide the rear-sight aperture and slide from the rear-sight base. Remove the two screws from the base, which will then fall free of the barrel. Reassemble in reverse order.

Removal of Front-Sight Assembly

Many shooters remove the protective hood from the front sight, toss it into a drawer, and never see it again. Assuming it's still on the rifle and you wish to remove the front-sight assembly, pry apart the bottom ears of the hood slightly, until it can be slid forward off the sight base. Take care not to damage the metal finish.

To remove the sight blade, use a Williams Front Sight Pusher, moving the sight from left to right until it is free of its dovetail. Excess pounding on the front sight with a brass punch and mallet can cause damage. As noted in the chapter on hand tools, the Williams Front Sight Pusher eliminates this risk.

The front ramp is held in place by two screws. When removing rear and/or front sights, always place slug screws in the exposed threaded holes to prevent damage to the threads and to offset chances of rusting. All sights are reinstalled in reverse order.

Removal of Barreled Action From Stock

On BDL models, unscrew the trigger-guard's front and rear screws. Then open the floorplate and unscrew the third action screw. On ADL models, remove the forward action screw and two trigger-guard screws. Remove the trigger-guard or trigger-guard assembly, depending on the model. Lift away the stock.

On ADL models, the magazine spring and follower will be loose in the stock. On BDL models, they will be attached to the hinged floorplate and may be removed by sliding the spring away from its retaining grooves in the floorplate.

The magazine box in BDL models may remain in place (a friction fit) or may fall free from the action as the stock is removed. Take care not to allow a loose magazine to cause finish damage. On ADL models, the magazine will be secured to the action with one small screw.

Because the trigger-guard assembly (BDL and Classic models) is made of aluminum, it is suggested that no attempt be made to remove the floorplate assembly. The pivot pin is very tight, and if the trigger-guard is not supported perfectly, the guard can be damaged when the pin is driven out of place.

Note: Remington warns against any attempts

to work on the trigger. All trigger parts are available only with factory installation.

To reassemble all components, simply reverse the procedures described above.

Common Problems— Probable Causes and Corrections

Bolt Overrides Cartridges in Magazine

Magazine follower binds. *Adjust side angle on magazine box.*

Damaged follower spring. *Replace spring.*

Magazine spring caught under trigger guard. *Reposition spring.*

Tabs (ears) on follower bent. *Straighten tabs or replace follower.*

Cartridge Stems Chamber

Sharp or rough receiver rails. *Polish or file rails.*

Sharp edge, rear end of chamber. *Edge needs smoothing.*

Rough ramp in receiver. *Polish ramp.*

Magazine loose in receiver. *Adjust magazine box.*

Bolt Closes Hard Over Cartridges

Bolt interferes with shell rim. *Remove interference on bolt.*

Extractor interferes with shell rim. *Fit new extractor (grind relief behind claw of replacement extractor).*

Ejector binds or fails to retract far enough.

Free up or replace ejector.

Burr at ejector hole on bolt. *Deburr hole.*

Sharp corners on bolt lugs. *File radius on lug corners.*

Extractor rivet loose. *Tighten or replace rivet.*

Cartridge Fails to Extract

Tight or rough chamber. *Return to factory.*

Extractor broken or damaged. *Replace extractor.*

Not enough hook space on extractor. *Replace extractor.*

Height of claw not correct. *Replace extractor.*

Extractor stuck back in bolt recess. *Replace extractor.*

Cartridge Fails to Eject

Burr at ejector hole in bolt. *Deburr hole.*

Ejector binds or fails to retract far enough. *Free up or replace ejector.*

Extractor rivet loose. *Re-stake or replace rivet.*

Extractor drops shells. *Replace extractor.*

Gun Misfires

Short (damaged) firing-pin. *Replace firing pin.*

Firing pin binds. *Free up or replace firing pin.*

Short firing-pin protrusion. *Replace firing pin.*

Firing control out of adjustment. *Return firearm to factory.*

Faulty ammunition. *Test with different lot of ammo.*

Firing Pin Follows Down (Does Not Stay Cocked)

Trigger out of adjustment. *Return firearm to factory.*

Improper vertical engagement of sear and connector. *Return firearm to factory.*

Trigger does not retract. *Return firearm to factory.*

Corners on sear or connector rounded. *Return firearm to factory.*

Trigger binds on trigger guard. *File trigger guard.*

Not enough tension on weight screw (light pull). *Return firearm to factory.*

Bolt Opens Hard

See causes listed under *"Cartridge Fails to Extract."*

Upset extraction cam on bolt handle. *Smooth up cam surface.*

Burr at ejector hole in bolt. *Deburr hole.*

Blown or set-back primer in shell. *Return firearm to factory.*

Bolt Pulls Out of Action When Manipulated

Bolt stop or bolt release binds or is broken. *Return firearm to factory.*

Safety Switch Works Too Hard or Too Freely

Safety switch binds, or safety-switch snap washer is stretched out (switch works too freely). *Return firearm to factory.*

Bulged or Blown Cases

Oversized chamber. *Replace barrel—or replace barrel and receiver.*

Maximum headspace. (Ammunition may be at fault.) *Return firearm to factory for new bolt.*

Bolt Binds

Guard screws protrude into bolt track. *File ends of screws.*

Scope screws protrude into bolt track. *File ends of screws.*

Bolt-handle interference on stock. *Alter or replace stock.*

Step at rear of bolt lugs. *File to "blend."*

Rifle Does Not Group Well

Crown of barrel damaged. *Recrown.*

Fouling in bore. *Remove fouling (see Chapter 8 and 9).*

Oversize bore. *Return firearm to factory for new barrel.*

Improper bedding of barrel in stock. *Correct bedding or replace stock.*

Loose sight. *Tighten or replace.*

Note: For correction of all other problems except those of a minor nature, the rifle should be returned to the manufacturer's customer-service department.

17

Remington 1100 Semiautomatic Shotgun

The Remington Model 1100 is the most popular autoloading shotgun ever produced. There are many million in use, and they give superb service when properly maintained. The 1100 action is operated by exhausting a tiny amount of powder gases downward through two holes located in the barrel near the front of the fore-end. (Only one hole is used in three-inch Magnum guns.) The tapped gases move a series of parts to cycle the firearm's action.

The 1100 has been made in 12, 16, 20, 28, and .410 bore sizes. In 12- and 20-gauge models chambered for 2¾-inch shells, any shell of that length, from light target loads to short magnums, may be used without adjustment to the shotgun. The three-inch Magnum 12- and 20-gauge barrels will allow the shotgun to function properly with any three-inch shell or with 2¾-inch Magnum loads. The 28-gauge model accepts all 2¾-inch ammunition, while the .410

accepts both 2½- and three-inch ammunition.

There is a difference in parts, including barrels, between older 20-gauge guns (built on 12-gauge-size frames) and the newer 20-gauge Lightweight (LW) models. And three-inch Magnum parts are sometimes different from 2¾-inch models.

Cycle of Operation

Since the 1100 is gas-operated, the barrel does not move during cycling, and thus the 1100 avoids the sometimes annoying "double shuffle" of shotguns that are recoil-operated. The gas from the barrel enters the gas cylinder and accelerates a piston device in the fore-end. Excess gases, not needed to operate the piston, are vented. The pressure of the gases thrusts the piston rearward to push upon the action-bar sleeve, causing the action-bar assembly to move the breechblock rearward. This rearward movement of the action parts compresses the return spring (located in the buttstock). The release of the spring forces the bolt forward to feed a cartridge and close the action, ready for firing.

The functions and manipulations that operate the 1100 begin with the loading procedure. Withdraw the bolt until it is locked in its rearward position. Place the safety button in the safe position. Then drop a shell into the ejection port and press the carrier-release button, located just ahead of the trigger guard. This starts the bolt forward, and the cartridge in the ejection port is raised up into the loading position by the shell carrier. The cartridge is chambered, and the bolt is locked into battery position.

As many as four shells may then be loaded into the magazine (unless it is plugged to hold only two) by pushing them in through the loading port in front of the trigger guard. As you load the magazine, press the carrier-release button with the nose of each shell. This allows the cartridge carrier to move upward into the action, allowing

room for the shell to enter the receiver—see illustration 2—and then to be pushed into the magazine tube. Be sure the shell is pushed well into the magazine so the cartridge stop can snap into place behind it to secure it properly.

Pressing the cartridge latch with the shell nose, pushing the shell carrier up into the receiver, and pushing the shell into the magazine should be one fluid motion. The 1100 loads easily, and any fumbling merely indicates that the shooter is not familiar with the gun.

The 1100 is now ready to fire, once the safety button is pushed to the "fire" position (from right to left). When the trigger is pressed, its top section rotates forward, carrying the connector, in its ready position, forward against the sear. This pivots the sear out of engagement with the hammer. The hammer is then free to rotate forward under compression of its spring and plunger. As it rapidly moves forward it strikes the firing pin, which in turn moves forward to ignite the cartridge. The firing-pin spring is compressed as the pin moves forward and after ignition the spring's stored energy returns the firing pin to its retracted position.

Just before the firing pin reaches the primer, the upward motion of the hammer plunger engages the disconnector. This causes the disconnector to rotate so that its forward end is lowered from the rear of the left action bar and cams the left shell latch to release the next shell in the magazine. The rear section of the disconnector rises with the sear. Now the gun cannot be fired again until the breechblock cycles fully and the trigger is released to permit the disconnector to be seated again behind the left action bar, and the connector to make contact again with the sear.

The two-way performance of the disconnector is an important safety feature which demands that the breechbolt be fully locked and the trigger released before the sear can be released again for succeeding shots to be fired.

As the bolt moves rearward after firing, the unlocking, extraction, ejection, and cocking cycles are accomplished. Unlocking occurs with the initial rearward movement of the action-bar sleeve, causing the slide block to move to the rear of the bolt. As the slide block moves, it cams the locking block away from the mating shoulder of the barrel extension. This unlocks the action and cams the firing pin fully rearward, preventing it from protruding from the bolt face.

Extraction occurs when further travel of the action bar moves the bolt rearward. The extractor's purchase on the shell rim holds the shell against the bolt face, pulling it from the chamber.

As the bolt moves rearward, it forces the hammer to rotate downward, compressing its coiling mainspring and causing its mating notch to engage the sear. Pressure of the sear spring locks the sear in this position.

Ejection occurs when the shell hits the ejector, located on the left rear side of the barrel. This pivots the shell off the extractor and it escapes through the ejection port.

The rearward motion of the action-bar assembly and sleeve carries the breechbolt and locking lug until the motion is terminated with full compression of the action spring. The action-bar assembly then begins its forward movement, carrying with it the breechbolt and locking block. The entire unit moves forward only a small distance before it is intercepted and stopped by the carrier dog, attached to the rear of the carrier. The carrier dog engages a notch on the bottom of the action bar.

The shell that was released from the magazine under spring pressure moves swiftly rearward while the interceptor latch prevents another shell from escaping the magazine. The shell carrier remains in its bottom (normal) position, held by the carrier latch, until the head of the shell, moving rearward, hits the carrier latch, causing it to pivot out of engagement and release the carrier (Fig. 17–2).

The carrier is then forced upward by the carrier dog, which simultaneously frees the action-bar assembly, action-bar sleeve, bolt, and locking lug to move forward under pressure of the compressed mainspring.

As the action closes, the upraised carrier holds the shell in position so that the advancing bolt face contacts the rear of the shell rim, pushing the shell forward into the chamber. The carrier

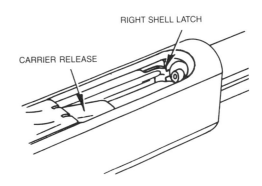

17–2. Carrier release and right shell-latch locations in bottom receiver opening.

dog is released from pressure by the passing action-bar assembly and is forced upward by the carrier dog follower and spring. This movement pivots the carrier downward into its normal depressed position. The disconnector, relieved from pressure by the left action bar, releases the depressed interceptor latch, enabling it to rotate. This allows the shell it was retaining in the magazine to move rearward slightly until its rim contacts the feeding latch, arresting the shell's motion. This shell is then held in place until the next feeding cycle.

As the bolt completes its forward travel and stops, the travel of the slide block beneath the bolt continues—camming the locking block into the recoil shoulder of the barrel. The locking block, when fully engaged by the recoil shoulder, locks the bolt face securely against the chambered shell, and it is held in this position by the slide block as it reaches its full forward position.

When the locking block is fully rotated into position, a passageway through the bolt aligns to allow for proper protrusion of the firing pin (when struck by the hammer) to ignite the chambered shell. All forward motion is halted when the slide block comes to rest within and against the front section of the bolt.

When the action is thus fully locked, the disconnector clears the end of the left action bar. The spring-actuated connector is then released

EXPLODED VIEW OF REMINGTON 1100

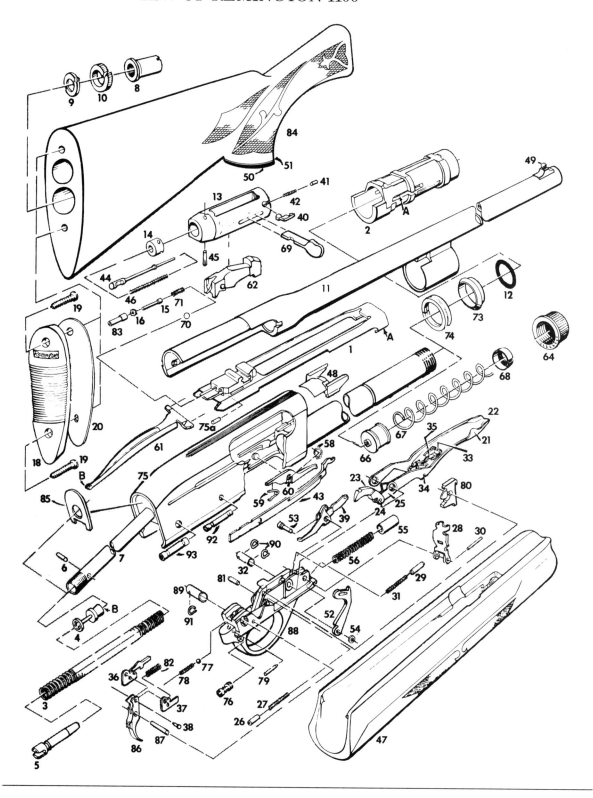

View No.	Part No.	Name of Part
1	33950	action bar assembly
2	15241	action bar sleeve
3	15252	action spring
4	15171	action spring follower
5	15440	action spring plug
6	15441	action spring plug pin
7	15443	action spring tube
8	15442	action spring tube nut
9	15498	action spring tube nut washer
10	15499	action spring tube nut lock washer
11		barrel assembly
	NOTE:	Please list choke needed.
12	15899	barrel seal
13	15738	breech bolt
	26865	breech bolt assembly
14	15172	breech bolt buffer
15	91199	breech bolt return plunger
16	15711	breech bolt return plunger retaining pin
18	20616	butt plate
19	25410	butt plate screw
20	15387	butt plate spacer
21	15628	carrier
22	26875	carrier assembly, 12-gauge
23	15480	carrier dog
24	18781	carrier bog pin
25	18760	carrier dog washer
26	17416	carrier dog follower
27	17415	carrier dog follower spring
28	15257	carrier latch
29	15703	carrier latch follower
30	16345	carrier latch pin
31	16966	carrier latch spring
32	90295	carrier pivot tube
33	16347	carrier release (action release)
34	16983	carrier release pin
35	16327	carrier release spring
36	17419	connector, left (R)
37	17551	connector, right (R)
38	17420	connector pin (R)
39	92060	disconnector
40	16176	extractor
41	17432	extractor plunger
42	17433	extractor spring
43	26630	feed latch
44	17436	firing pin
45	18623	firing pin retaining pin
46	15702	firing pin retractor spring
47	26870	fore-end assembly, 12-gauge
48	91658	fore-end support
49	27730	front sight - for vent rib use No. 18796
	27725	front sight base, 12-gauge

View No.	Part No.	Name of Part
50	15388	grip cap
	15390	grip cap inlay
	15757	grip cap screw
51	15389	grip cap spacer
52	15249	hammer
53	16600	hammer pin
54	15809	hammer pin washer
55	17465	hammer plunger
56	19014	hammer spring
58	15398	interceptor latch retainer
59	15383	interceptor latch spring
60	26635	interceptor latch
61	26075	link
62	26640	locking block assembly
	15855	locking block retainer
64	15239	magazine cap
	91078	magazine cap detent
	15892	magazine cap detent spring
66	32225	magazine follower
	18097	magazine plug (3-shot)
67	15382	magazine spring
68	91657	magazine spring retainer
69	91197	operating handle
70	23222	operating handle detent ball
71	91200	operating handle detent spring
73	15384	piston
74	15385	piston seal
75	26080	receiver assembly (R)
75a	17676	return plunger retaining pin
76	25115	safety switch
77	23223	safety switch detent ball
78	17514	safety switch spring
79	17515	safety switch spring retaining pin
80	18750	sear
81	17463	sear pin
82	17518	sear pin
83	91198	slide block buffer
84	34770	stock assembly
85	19993	stock bearing plate
86	25370	trigger (R)
	20610	trigger assembly (R)
87	17533	trigger pin
88	26235	trigger plate, R.H.
	26236	trigger plate, L.H. (for R.H. gun)
	27300	trigger plate assembly, R.H.
	27301	trigger plate assembly, L.H. (for R.H. gun)
89	17541	trigger plate pin bushing
90	17539	trigger plate pin detent spring, front (need 2)
91	17540	trigger plate pin detent spring, rear
92	20601	trigger plate pin, front
93	20606	trigger plate pin, rear

(R) = restricted part, available only for factory installation.

Note: Parts are listed for 12-gauge field-model 1100s. For other gauges or models, refer to the owner's manual or contact Remington.

and drops into position to connect the notch on the sear. When this is completed, the action-bar sleeve pushes the piston and piston seal into a forward position against the barrel seal in the gas cylinder. The shotgun is now ready to begin its operating cycle anew when the trigger is once again pulled. But before this can occur the trigger must be released from its rearward position (from the last firing). When the trigger is released, it moves forward, rotating its top half rearward. The gun is now ready to fire.

After the last shell has been fed from the magazine and fired, the cycle of operation differs so as to retain the bolt in its rearward, open-action position. This occurs because when a shell is not fed from the magazine to strike the carrier latch, the carrier latch cannot be actuated with the carrier. Therefore, locked in its down position, the carrier dog remains engaged with the action-barrel assembly, locking the gun in the open position.

If the gun is not once again loaded, the action can be closed by depressing the carrier release.

To unload the shotgun without firing a shell, place the safety in the "on" position and then pull the operating handle fully rearward. The chambered shell will be extracted and ejected. The bolt will then lock in the rearward position. Depressing the carrier release will feed another shell and close the bolt. Repeat the process until the last shell has been ejected.

Removal of Fore-end Assembly and Barrel

Unscrew the magazine cap and slide the fore-end assembly forward (Fig. 17–3). No further disassembly of the fore-end unit is suggested. If parts need replacement, replace the entire unit.

With the action closed, grasp the barrel above the gas cylinder and pull forward to remove it from the receiver and the magazine tube. You will open the action before removing the barrel seal and piston, but always take care not to let the action slam closed while the barrel is disengaged. Close it gently or you may damage the shotgun.

No attempt should be made to remove the ejector or front-sight base from the barrel. These are factory-assembled and brazed or silver-soldered to the barrel. Factory replacement of these parts is urged.

17–3. Removal of fore-end assembly. Simply pull fore-end forward after removing magazine cap.

17-4. Removal of barrel. After removing fore-end cap, barrel may be pulled free of receiver.

Removal of Barrel Seal and Piston

With the action opened, grasp the barrel seal, piston and piston seal (as a unit) and slide them forward off the magazine. Use a quick but smooth motion.

Removal of Operating Handle

Gently close the action, easing the bolt forward. Then grip the operating handle and, applying adequate pressure, pull it outward from the bolt. The operating handle is held in place with a detent-and-plunger arrangement. It will resist movement until sufficient pressure is applied to "snap" it free.

Removal of Action-Bar Assembly, Bolt Assembly, and Action-Sleeve Unit

Depress the carrier release and push the carrier up into the receiver. This will allow access to the right shell latch (Fig. 17–2). Press the right shell latch until the action bar moves forward with an audible click. Grasp the action-bar sleeve and slide the entire unit forward off the magazine tube (Fig. 17–5). Remove the breechbolt from the action bar by simply lifting upward.

Action-Bar Unit Disassembly

It is not usually necessary to remove the action-bar sleeve or disassemble the unit itself. The

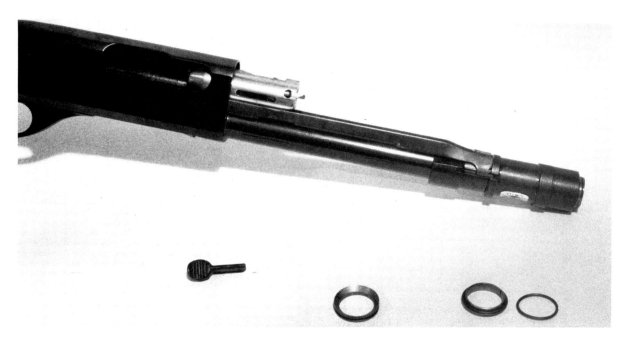

17–5. Removal of bolt assembly, action bar, and action-sleeve unit. After removing the operating handle, pull the entire unit forward and off the magazine tube. Remove breechbolt by lifting upward.

action bar can be bent during disassembly or reassembly. If the sleeve must be removed insert a screwdriver behind the action bar in the slot (either side) on the sleeve (Fig. 17–6). Gently pry the action bar from the slot.

The slide block is brazed to the action bar, and no disassembly should be attempted. Ditto for the brazed-on link-retaining block.

The operating-handle plunger can be removed if necessary. Depress the plunger and hold it downward. Slide the unit sideways out of the slot in the slide block. Take care not to lose the plunger or its spring.

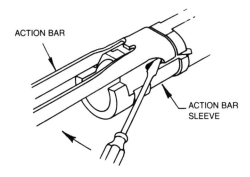

17–6. Action-bar sleeve can be removed using screwdriver to pry the bar from the slot (*caution—see text*).

Slide-Block Buffer System and Related Parts

The Slide-block buffer, breech bolt-return plunger, plunger-retaining ring, spring and return plunger-retaining pin are all designed to absorb stress within the breechbolt when the action is opened after firing. These parts should not be disassembled except for replacement of worn or damaged components.

To disassemble, drive out the return plunger-retaining pin from right to left. Grasp the plunger tightly and pull it from the slide block. Examine the parts carefully to determine if any damage was caused by disassembly.

Note: There is a newer style of operating-handle detent and slide-block buffer system. With these, proceed as previously described until the plunger has been pulled free of the slide block. Then tip the rear of the action bars down to allow the detent spring and ball to slide from the rear of the slide block. Do not disassemble the new-style units unless absolutely necessary for the installation of replacement parts.

Breechbolt Disassembly

Drive out the firing-pin retaining pin located at the rear of the bolt (Fig 17–7). Drive it from top to bottom. Pull the breechbolt buffer, firing pin, and retractor spring from the bolt. Remove the locking-block assembly.

The extractor can be removed by forcing the extractor plunger rearward in the bolt until the extractor claw can be pivoted inward toward the bolt face. The rear of the extractor can then be forced upward past the plunger and removed from the bolt. Slowly release tension on the plunger, taking care not to allow the plunger or its spring to escape under pressure. Remove the extractor plunger and spring.

17–7. Firing-pin retaining pin is removed by driving it from top to bottom.

Disassembly of Magazine Components and Triggerplate Unit

Pry out the retainer from the end of the magazine. Use caution to prevent it from flying free, as it is under spring tension. Ditto for the magazine plug (if any). Then slide out the magazine spring and follower. A retainer or magazine plug that is allowed to fly out can cause personal injury (Fig. 17–8).

The triggerplate group (with all of its many parts) is easily removed. Push out the front and rear retaining pins and withdraw the plate assembly from the receiver (Fig. 17–9).

Note: Do not allow the hammer to snap forward on the disassembled triggerplate unit. Hold the hammer with thumb pressure and gently allow it to move forward. This will prevent damage to forward components of the assembly.

All of the fire-control components are re-

17–9. Remove front and rear retaining pins to allow removal of the triggerplate group.

17–8. Removal of magazine-spring retainer, spring, and follower. This should be done carefully to prevent spring and retainer from flying free and causing injury.

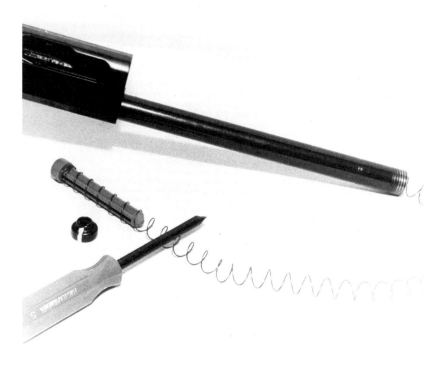

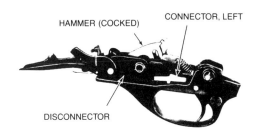

17–9A. Triggerplate group.

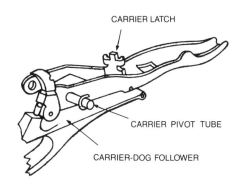

17–10. Carrier disassembly and parts location.

moved from the gun as a unit when the trigger-plate group is taken out. No further disassembly of this group is required for routine maintenance. Pressurized solvents and degreasers can be used to clean this assembly, and further take-down is not suggested unless needed to repair or replace worn or damaged parts.

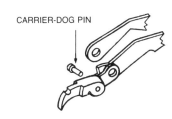

17–11. Carrier-dog and pin removal.

Disassembly of Carrier Group

Slip a triggerplate-pin detent spring (either one) from the end of the carrier pivot tube. Hold the carrier-dog follower down to prevent it from popping free of the plate (Fig. 17–10). Push out the carrier pivot tube. Pull the carrier latch rearward and disassemble it from the triggerplate.

Drive the carrier-dog pin (Fig. 17–11) to the inside of the carrier and out of place, and disassemble the parts (carrier dog and washer).

To remove the carrier spring, disengage the bent front end of the spring from the carrier and push it rearward (Fig. 17–12).

The carrier release is disassembled by driving out the carrier-release pin (Fig. 17–13). The pin is swaged at both ends to tighten it to the carrier, so it will be necessary to use a replacement pin when reassembling the gun.

To disassemble the carrier latch, carrier-latch

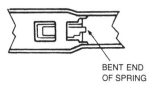

17–12. Carrier-spring location

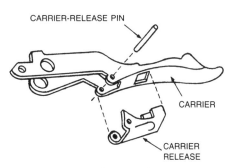

17–13. Carrier-release disassembly.

follower, and spring, press the carrier-latch follower down and hold it in place to prevent it from popping loose. Push out the carrier-latch pin and slowly release the latch from the triggerplate. Pull the carrier latch and spring from the plate.

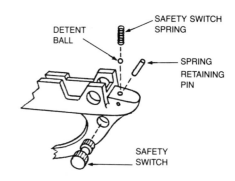

17–14. Safety switch disassembly.

Hammer, Plunger, Hammer Spring, Sear, and Trigger Assembly

It is urged that these parts not be disassembled at home. Doing so requires that the staked end of the hammer pin be ground down to the surface of the hammer-pin washer. Reassembly requires extreme caution to insure that a malfunction of the gun will not occur. Any disassembly of these parts should be done by a trained, experienced gunsmith or at the factory. All the trigger-group parts are available only for factory installation.

Safety-Switch Disassembly

Remove the retaining pin by pushing from left to right—see Fig. 17–14. Notice that the pin is tapered, and be certain to properly orient it during assembly.

As the pin is withdrawn, hold a forefinger over the spring hole in the top of the triggerplate to prevent the safety-switch spring from popping free. Remove the spring and detent ball from the triggerplate. Then push out the safety switch.

Buttstock Removal

Unscrew the buttplate (or recoil-pad) screws and remove the buttplate and spacer. Insert a long, heavy screwdriver into the rear of the stock and unscrew the action-spring tube nut. Remove the nut and washers. Detach the stock from the action by pulling it rearward.

Action-Spring Components Disassembly

Push in on the action-spring plug by inserting a suitable tool such as a narrow punch or Phillips screwdriver to relieve tension on the action-spring plug pin. Push out the pin and then slowly relieve tension on the action spring and plunger. Do this carefully, as they are under considerable tension.

To disassemble the link from the action-spring follower, use a long-nosed plier and squeeze the tails of the link together directly in front of the follower which retains them. With the tails compressed, pull the link forward and out of the receiver with a lifting and twisting motion. The follower can then be removed from the action-spring housing by letting it fall free.

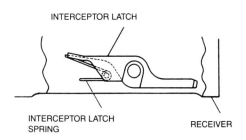

17–15. Interceptor-latch disassembly (*caution: don't remove interceptor latch spring—see text*).

Components Staked, Brazed or Welded to Receiver

The interceptor-latch spring is staked into the receiver and should not be removed. If the spring is faulty, have an experienced gunsmith replace it unless you are sure of your ability to perform this task.

The action-spring tube, magazine-tube assembly, barrel lock, and interceptor-latch stud are all brazed or welded to the receiver. No attempt at disassembly should be made. If any of these parts need replacing, return the shotgun to the factory.

Interceptor Latch and Shell Latch

The interceptor latch is mounted on a stud in the lower left wall of the receiver. To remove it, spread the tabs on the interceptor-latch retainer, then lift and remove it from the stud. Disengage the interceptor-latch spring from the groove in the latch and disassemble the latch from the receiver (Fig. 17–15).

Because the shell latch is staked into position, it is suggested that this component not be disassembled unless necessary for replacement. Then, because staking will be required, it may be best to let a professional handle the job unless you feel confident about your ability to do it.

It should be noted that the shell latch occasionally works loose and will slide forward or rearward when the shotgun is disassembled. If the triggerplate-pin hole in the receiver does not align with the hole in the shell latch (Fig. 17–16) the shell latch should be properly aligned and positively re-staked in position.

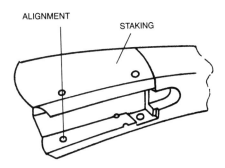

17–16. Shell-latch alignment and restaking.

Fore-End Support Assembly

The fore-end support assembly may be removed from the action-bar assembly if necessary. Proceed by wedging a screwdriver blade between the fore-end support assembly and the left (wide) action bar. Pry the support outward and down, away from the bar until it can be lifted free.

General Reassembly Procedures

For the most part, reassembly of the Remington 1100 is accomplished in reverse order of disassembly procedures. However, some special procedures need to be followed, and these will be noted.

Fore-End Support Installation

Before assembly, check the sides of the fore-end support to make sure they are straight and not spread apart. If necessary, squeeze inward to straighten them. With the pointed ends facing forward and the block facing up, hook the right side of the support over the right (narrow) action bar. Squeeze the bars inward and press upward on the support until it snaps over the bars (Fig. 17–17).

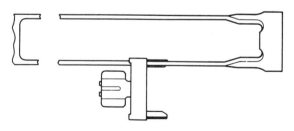

17–17. Fore-end support assembly.

Interceptor-Latch Installation

Place the interceptor latch over the mounting stud so that the recess on the latch faces up and the hook is forward. Depress the top of the latch spring and fit it into the groove in the bottom rear of the latch. Push the latch down against the wall of the receiver. Be sure the small letters on the tab of the latch retainer are facing upward. Then spread the tabs and place the retainer over the stud and into the recess in the latch. The retainer should snap into the groove in the stud.

Link Assembly

Hold the long tails of the link with a needle-nosed plier so that the curved tails face toward the bottom of the receiver. Insert the tails into the conical recess in the action-spring follower and release the grip on the tails.

Buttstock Assembly

Be certain the flat steel stock-bearing plate is positioned against the receiver. After slipping the buttstock into place and lightly tightening the buttstock nut (action-opening tube nut), align the edges of the stock with the edges of the receiver. Then carefully tighten the stock nut. Don't forget to place the nut washer and lock washer on the action-spring tube before placing the nut on the tube. The lock washer goes onto the tube between the nut and flat washer.

Carrier-Group Assembly

When reassembling the carrier dog and carrier-dog washer assembly, it is necessary to restake the small end of the carrier-dog pin so as to tighten the pin to the carrier.

It is also necessary to position the carrier dog over the follower, making sure the prong on the carrier enters the hole in the carrier latch. Then align the carrier, carrier-dog washer, and trigger-plate holes. After inserting the trigger-pin bushing, insert the detent spring.

Assembly of Triggerplate Group to Receiver

Dip the carrier into the receiver while guiding the disconnector past the receiver rail. Then lift the carrier slightly and settle the rear of the triggerplate into the receiver. Slide the entire unit rearward in the receiver until the retaining-pin holes of the triggerplate align with the corresponding holes in the receiver.

Breechbolt-Group Assembly

Make certain the extractor reseats properly on the shoulder of the extractor cut in the bolt. The claw of a replaced extractor should be tightened on the rim of a dummy cartridge to insure a proper purchase. Make this adjustment by removing metal from the pad at the mid-section of the extractor.

Be careful that the firing-pin retaining pin is tapped flush with the bottom of the bolt. If the tightening ridges on the retaining pin are worn, replace the pin.

Whenever a replacement buffer is required, it will need to be drilled. Do this by inserting the buffer completely into the bolt and, while holding it in position, drill through the bolt and buffer with a #24 drill. Take care not to remove any material from the bolt.

Operating-handle Detent and Buffer System—New Style

Insure that the return plunger-retaining pin is driven in from left to right. When in place, the pin must be flush with the left side of the slide block. Check that the breechbolt return plunger works freely. *Note:* When a replacement slide buffer is used, it must be drilled through with a .078-inch drill. Use a slide block as a drill jig.

Assembly of Action-Bar Group and Bolt Group

Insert one side of the action bar into the sleeve as in Fig. 17–6. Tap the other side downward until the action bar slips into its groove. Do not bend or twist the action bars.

Place the breechbolt unit over the slide block at the rear of the action bar. Slide the entire unit over the magazine tube. Move it rearward into the receiver until the action bars contact the right shell latch. At this point, the unit will be an inch or so into the receiver. While holding the gun in a vertical position, depress the carrier release, which will allow access to depress the right shell latch (Fig. 17–2) until the entire bolt and action-bar unit can be moved rearward into the receiver.

If the carrier rises up and interferes, reach through the ejection port and push it downward. Before the barrel is inserted, the entire bolt group needs to be locked in the rearward position (open action).

Piston Seal, Piston, and Barrel Seal

The piston seal is slipped over the magazine tube first, followed by the piston. The barrel seal (O-ring) is put onto the magazine tube next. Be careful not to damage the O-ring when installing it. Slide all three pieces rearward on the tube until the O-ring drops into the channel cut for it around the magazine tube.

Common Problems— Probable Causes and Corrections

Gun Fails to Be Loaded

Magazine follower, spring, or tube defective; prevents cartridge from leaving magazine with sufficient velocity. *Replace follower or spring. Have factory replace magazine tube if required.*

Carrier release fails to release carrier latch. *Replace or adjust prong contacting latch.*

Carrier latch jams carrier release. *Replace latch and/or its spring.*

Gun Fails to Feed Shell from Magazine

Shell latch does not slip off shell properly. *Adjust or replace latch.*

Shell-latch stop surface rough or damaged. *Smooth up or replace.*

Carrier sits too high, holding shells in magazine. *Adjust or replace carrier. Check carrier latch and carrier-dog follower spring.*

Magazine spring damaged. *Replace.*

Magazine double feeds—shell latch failing. *Replace or adjust latch.*

Broken interceptor-latch spring. *Replace.*

Broken or worn interceptor. *Replace.*

Gun Fails to Feed Shell up on Carrier

Carrier latch defective, jamming carrier release. *Replace latch spring.*

Carrier release defective, jamming carrier movement. *Replace carrier release or adjust carrier prong to contact carrier latch.*

Carrier jams, shell latch binding carrier. *Adjust latch to free carrier.*

Carrier action defective or sluggish. *Replace carrier. Check carrier's pivot-tube-and-slide-to-carrier-dog contact.*

Extractor too tight—shell feeds under claw too hard. *Replace extractor*, or *relieve claw tension*, or *smooth up claw's inside radius.*

Action Fails to Close

Action bar bent, jamming action. *Replace or straighten.*

Carrier movement impeded and jamming. *Replace carrier. (See causes and corrections for "Gun Fails to Feed Shell up on Carrier.")*

Action spring defective. *Replace.*

Piston assembly dirty, defective. *Clean, and check movement.*

Gun Fails to Lock When Closed

Too little headspace. *Return firearm to factory.*

Locking block binds (or missing). *Check assembly, free up locking block.*

Defective or mutilated shell rim. *Remove shell.*

Action binds. *Free up—check slide movement, action bar.*

Rough chamber. *Have factory polish chamber or replace barrel.*

Extractor or extractor slot in barrel damaged. *Replace extractor or repair slot.*

Gun Fails to Fire

Firing pin damaged, too short, or bent. (Light firing-pin blow indicates these problems.) *Free up or replace firing pin. It should protrude from bolt face 0.030-inch to 0.060-inch.*

Right connector not seated against sear. *Clean assembly or have factory replace sear and/or connector.*

Disconnector binds connector, cannot slide down. *Free up or replace disconnector.*

Disconnector (bent tail) assembled above connector. *Reassemble Correctly—below connector.*

Hammer fails to cock. *Check engagement of hammer and sear notch. Check spring and replace if necessary.*

Trigger binds. *Free up or have factory replace trigger.*

Caution: Do not open action immediately after a misfire; a wait of approximately two minutes is recommended.

Gun Fails to Extract

Extractor damaged. *Replace.*

Extractor claw loose on shell rim. *File extractor's mid-section.*

Extractor slot in barrel damaged. *File slot for proper fitting.*

Extractor spring and/or plunger defective. *Replace spring and/or plunger.*

Chamber of barrel rough. *Have factory polish chamber or replace barrel.*

Action Fails to Open

Action binds. *Free up action bars. (See causes and corrections for "Action Fails to Close.")*

Piston assembly defective. *Clean or replace piston and/or O-ring.*

Gas holes in barrel-guide ring mutilated. *Check for proper hole size—see table of gas-orifice sizes at end of this chapter.*

Gun fails to open when using light loads. *Replace piston with new split-piston design.*

Gun Fails to Eject

Ejector defective or damaged. *Return to factory for replacement.*

Action binds, slow timing. *Free up. (See causes and corrections for "Action Fails to Open.")*

Extractor loose on shell or defective. *Tighten by filing extractor's middle pad. Check extractor and spring, and replace if damaged.*

Carrier feeds up too fast and interferes with ejecting shell. *Adjust shell latch—or replace carrier or latch.*

Rough chamber. *Have factory polish chamber or replace barrel.*

Gun fails to open on light loads. *Replace split-design piston.*

Action Fails to Lock Open

Carrier latch or spring defective. *Replace latch and/or spring.*

Action binds. *Free up. (See causes and corrections for "Action Fails to Open.")*

Carrier-dog-to-slide engagement faulty. *Adjust engagement, replacing either part if necessary.*

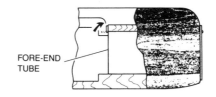

17–18. Fore-end tube assembly.

Avoid Gas-Cylinder Damage

Any damage to the gas cylinder producing an "out-of-round" condition may cause piston parts to be inoperable. The gas cylinder is brazed to the underside of the mid-section of the barrel. Within it are the piston, piston seal, and barrel seal. To operate properly, these parts must slide freely upon the end of the magazine tube. Make certain that any barrel-holding devices do not damage the gas cylinder.

Recent Variation—Fore-End Tube, Fore-End Support, Interceptor Latch

In 1975, some components of the Remington Model 1100 were redesigned to improve function and/or durability. These improvements can be added to most 1100s by following the instructions now given.

The new-style fore-end tube parts are made of heavier materials and the series of tabs used to hold the fore-end tube in position have been replaced by a single tab. To install the new tube make sure the hole in the front of the fore-end is large enough to accept it. If necessary, the hole diameter should be increased to 1.093-inch (+/- 0.005-inch). Then, with the small tab facing upward, insert the fore-end tube group into the fore-end. Bend the tab upward (Fig. 17–18) and flush against the fore-end wall.

To install the new-style fore-end support group, remove the action-bar assembly. Then remove the original fore-end support (as described earlier). With the pointed ends facing forward and the inside of the radius facing upward, place the new fore-end support assembly over the center of the right (narrow) action bar (Fig. 17–17).

Rotate the fore-end support assembly clockwise 180 degrees, press inward on the left (wide) action bar and snap the support over the bar. Replace the action-bar assembly and the barrel.

If the barrel assembles tightly or the vent rib does not align with the receiver mating, remove a very small amount of material from the top of the barrel support to align the barrel and achieve a snug fit—see Fig. 17–19.

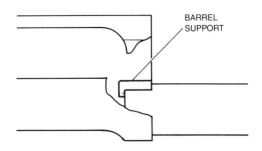

17–19. Barrel-support location.

To fit extra handle barrels that assemble excessively tight, remove a very small amount of material from the bottom of the breech end of the barrel until you achieve a snug fit.

The new interceptor latch has a skirt added to shroud the loop on the latch spring. Remove the old parts. The loop of the spring should fit be-

---

GAS-ORIFICE SIZES FOR REMINGTON MODEL 1100 SHOTGUNS

Gauge & Barrel Length	Number of Orifices	Orifice Diameter & Drill Size
12 ga. 2¾"; 34" full trap	2	.079"/No. 47
12 ga. 2¾"; 30", 28", 26", 22"	2	.079"/No. 47
12 ga. 2¾"; skeet	2	.086"/No. 44
12 ga. 2¾"; skeet w/compensator	2	.086"/No. 44
12 ga. 3"; 30" (magnum)	1	.073"/No. 49
12 ga. 3"; 34" (duck & goose)	1	.073"/No. 49
16 ga. 2¾"; 28", 26"	2	.076"/No. 48
20 ga. 2¾"; 28", 26", 22"	2	.076"/No. 48
20 ga. 3"; 28" (magnum)	1	.076"/No. 48
20 ga. 2¾"; 26" w/compensator	2	.086"/No. 44
20 ga. 2¾"; 28", 26" (lightweight)	2	.067"/No. 51
20 ga. 3"; 28" (LW magnum)	1	.064"/No. 52
28 ga. 2¾"; reg & skeet	2	.067"/No. 51
.410 ga. 3"; reg	1	.067"/No. 51
.410 ga. 2¾"; skeet	2	.060"/No. 53
20 ga. 3"; (magnum LT20)	1	.064"/No. 52
20 ga. 2¾"; (LT20s)	2	.064"/No. 52
20 ga. 2¾"; (LT skeet)	2	.067"/No. 51

---

tween the inside wall of the receiver and the skirt on the interceptor latch. Place the latch over the stud, with the recess side facing upward and the hook facing forward. Depress the top of the spring and fit it into the groove in the bottom rear of the latch. Press the latch downward against the receiver wall. Make sure the small letters on the tab of the latch-retainer are facing upward. Then spread the tabs and place the retainer over the stud and into the recess in the latch. The retainer should snap into the groove in the stud (Fig. 17–15).

18

Remington 870 Pump-Action Shotgun

The Remington 870 pump shotgun has outsold all other models. During the 35 years I have used 870s, not one has ever failed in the field. This Remington has been made in 12, 16, 20, 28, and .410 gauges. And it has been offered in both standard and magnum-length chambers, as well as in right- and left-hand models.

Cycle of Operation

With the shotgun's action cocked and open, place the safety switch in the safe position by pushing in on its left end. Then drop a shell into the ejection port and push the operating slide fully forward. This chambers the cartridge and locks the shotgun in the battery position. The magazine is loaded by pushing up on the shell carrier, through the bottom receiver opening, with a shell's nose and moving the shell forward into the magazine until it is positively latched into place. Repeat until the magazine is fully loaded.

When the cross-bolt safety is in the "off" position and the trigger is pulled, the top portion of the trigger rotates forward, carrying the connector forward against the sear. This pivots the sear out of engagement with the hammer. The released hammer, under compression of the hammer spring, pivots forward and strikes the firing pin. The firing pin then moves forward, compressing its retractor spring, and ignites the primer of the chambered shotshell. The firing pin is then pushed to the rear by the firing-pin retractor spring.

Just before the firing pin is struck by the hammer, the hammer plunger, in its upward movement, engages the action-bar lock. Downward movement of the front of the action-bar lock is restrained if the fore-end is held tightly rearward until pressure against it is briefly released. This occurs involuntarily as the shotgun recoils rearward. When the action bar is freed, the forward end of the action-bar lock is lowered from its position at the rear of the left action bar, and the rear section rises and lifts the connector from contact with the sear.

The twofold guardian performance of the action-bar lock is a safety feature that disconnects the trigger assembly and sear until a shell is fully seated in the chamber and the breech is fully locked.

After the gun is fired, pulling the slide handle rearward unlocks the action, extracts and ejects the fired case, cocks the hammer, and starts the feeding cycle.

The initial rearward movement of the fore-end carries the slide to the rear of the breechblock. As it travels, the slide cams the locking block from the recoil shoulder of the barrel, freeing the bolt for rearward movement, and the firing pin is cammed rearward and locked there.

As the bolt moves rearward, the fired case is extracted from the chamber. The extractor, powered by its springs, is pivoted to hold the fired case firmly against the bolt face. The rim of the fired case then strikes the ejector-spring shoulder, causing the case to pivot so that it is ejected through the receiver port.

Just before ejection is completed, the rearward motion of the bolt moves the hammer downward, compressing its coil spring, and it engages the sear. Pressure of the sear spring locks the sear in a notched position against the cocked hammer.

The final motion forces the entire slide and breechblock group to the most rearward position in the receiver. At this point, the left action bar is free to cam the left shell latch, releasing the next shell from the magazine. The shell is pushed from the magazine by the compressed magazine spring, and comes to rest on the carrier. As the shell is moved onto the carrier, the right shell latch is cammed into position by the right action bar to retain the next shell in the magazine.

When forward motion of the bolt is started by the closing stroke ("pump"), the carrier dog attached to the rear of the carrier is engaged by the returning slide. This pivots the carrier upward, placing the new shell in front of the bolt. The advancing bolt depresses the ejector spring into its channel while simultaneously forcing the loaded cartridge forward into the chamber.

The carrier dog, released from the pressure of the passing slide, is forced upward by the carrier-dog follower and its compressed spring, and the carrier pivots downward. The right shell latch is released and the left shell latch, no longer being cammed out of the way, intercepts the shell in the magazine—preventing its escape. The shell is held in this position until the next feeding cycle begins.

As a shell is loaded into the chamber and the action closes the bolt against the shell, the travel of the slide within the bolt continues and cams the locking block into position in the recoil shoulder of the barrel. The locking block secures the breechbolt firmly against the chambered shell. When the locking block is fully positioned, the passageway through the bolt is opened to allow the firing pin the necessary freedom of movement to travel forward to strike the primer.

The fore-end return motion is arrested as the slide comes to rest against the front section of the bolt. The fully locked position enables the action-bar lock to clear the end of the left action bar. The suspended connector is then released by spring pressure and dropped to a ready position to begin the firing cycle anew.

Barrel Removal

After making certain the chamber and magazine are unloaded, move the fore-end (slide handle) halfway back. If the shotgun is cocked, it will be

EXPLODED VIEW OF REMINGTON 870

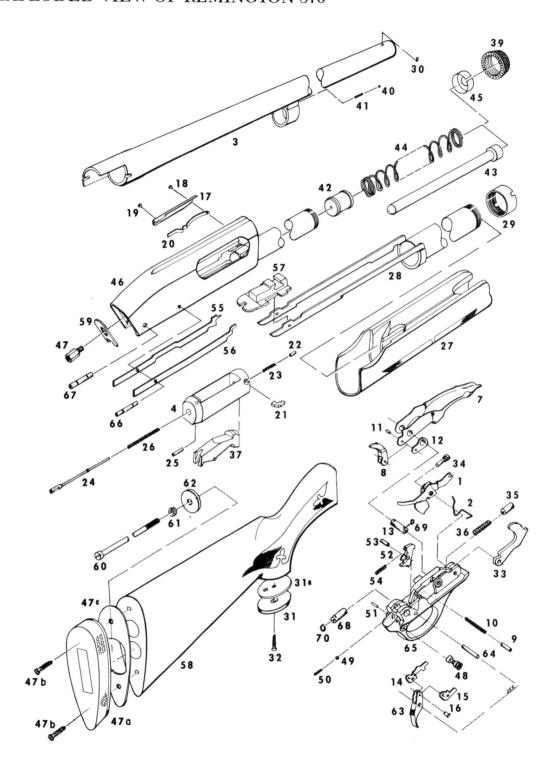

View No.	Part No.	Name of Part
1	18849	Action Bar Lock
2	19622	Action Bar Lock Spring
		Note: All barrels (same gauge) interchangeable without adjustment. Also give choke needed.
3		Barrel Assembly
4	18545	Breech Bolt, 12-ga.
	20015	Breech Bolt, 16-ga.
	20016	Breech Bolt, 20-ga.
	22860	Breech Bolt Assembly, Complete, 12-ga.
	22861	Breech Bolt Assembly, Complete, 16-ga.
	22862	Breech Bolt Assembly, Complete, 20-ga.
7	18584	Carrier
	20060	Carrier Assembly
8	15480	Carrier Dog
9	17416	Carrier Dog Follower
10	17415	Carrier Dog Follower Spring
11	18781	Carrier Dog Pin
12	18760	Carrier Dog Washer
13	17417	Carrier Pivot Tube
14	17419	Connector, Left (R)
15	17551	Connector, Right (R)
16	17420	Connector Pin (R)
17	25431	Ejector, 12-ga.
	24446	Ejector, 16-ga.
	24447	Ejector, 20-ga.
18	18646	Ejector Rivet, Front
19	18647	Ejector Rivet, Rear
20	18648	Ejector Spring
21	16176	Extractor
22	17432	Extractor Plunger
23	17433	Extractor Spring
24	17436	Firing Pin
25	18623	Firing Pin Retaining Pin
26	17437	Firing Pin Retractor Spring
	20088	Fore-end (Wood only) 12-ga.
	20089	Fore-end (wood only) 16-20 ga.
27	34785	Fore-end Assembly, 12-ga
	34786	Fore-end Assembly, 16-20 ga.
28	20065	Fore-end Tube Assembly
29	18634	Fore-end Tube Nut
30	18673	Front Sight (plain barrel)
31	18015	Grip Cap
	14943	Grip Cap Spacer
32	91634	Grip Cap Screw
33	18749	Hammer
34	16600	Hammer Pin
	15809	Hammer Pin Washer
35	17465	Hammer Plunger
36	19014	Hammer Spring

View No.	Part No.	Name of Part
37	22325	Locking Block Assembly
	24075	Locking Block Assembly, (oversize)
39	25375	Magazine Cap
40	17451	Magazine Cap Detent
41	16791	Magazine Cap Detent Spring
42	32350	Magazine Follower
43	18097	Magazine Plug, 3-shot, wood
44	19479	Magazine Spring
45	91657	Magazine Spring Retainer
46	20030	Receiver Assembly, 12-ga. (R)
	20031	Receiver Assembly, 16-ga. (R)
	20032	Receiver Assembly, 20-ga. (R)
47	18551	Receiver Stud
47a	14705	Recoil Pad
47b	25410	Recoil Pad Screw
	14944	Recoil Pad Spacer
48	25115	Safety Switch
49	23223	Safety Switch Detent Ball
50	17514	Safety Switch Spring
51	17515	Safety Switch Spring Retaining Pin
52	18750	Sear
53	17463	Sear Pin
54	17518	Sear Spring
55	20040	Shell Latch, Left, 12-ga.
	20041	Shell Latch, Left, 16-ga.
	20042	Shell Latch, Left, 20-ga.
56	20048	Shell Latch, Right, 12-ga.
	20046	Shell Latch, Right, 16-ga.
	20047	Shell Latch, Right, 20-ga.
57	14543	Slide
58	34800	Stock Assembly
59	19993	Stock Bearing Plate
60	18571	Stock Bolt
61	18572	Stock Bolt Lock Washer
62	18573	Stock Bolt Washer
63	25370	Trigger (R)
	20610	Trigger Assembly (R)
64	17533	Trigger Pin
65	25035	Trigger Plate, R.H. (right hand safety)
	25036	Trigger Plate, L.H. (for R.H. Gun)
	22985	Trigger Plate Assembly, R.H.
	22986	Trigger Plate Assembly,(L.H. Safe), for R.H. Gun
66	20601	Trigger Plate Pin, Front
67	20606	Trigger Plate Pin, Rear
68	17541	Trigger Plate Pin Bushing
69	17539	Trigger Plate Pin Detent Spring, Front
70	17540	Trigger Plate Pin Detent Spring, Rear

(R) = restricted part, available only for factory installation.

necessary to press in the action-bar lock (Fig. 18–2) before the fore-end can be moved rearward. With the fore-end correctly positioned, unscrew the magazine cap and slide the barrel forward out of the receiver. Do not slam the action forward after the barrel has been removed, as the action bar will then bind on the shell latch.

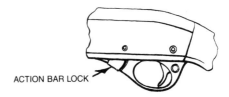

18–2. Action-bar lock is located at front of trigger guard on left side.

Removal of Fore-end Unit

Press in the front end of the left shell latch by reaching up into the receiver through the loading port. With the left shell latch compressed, pull the fore-end gently forward off of the magazine tube.

The breechbolt assembly, locking block, and slide will be simultaneously withdrawn from the receiver (Fig. 18–6). As these are simply sitting in grooves on the action bar, they will fall away. Take care not to drop them on any surface that could damage them.

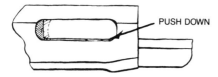

18–3. Push down on the bolt when disassembling the shotgun if it binds on the bottom of the ejection port.

The slide may catch on the bottom of the ejection port if the triggerplate assembly is in the shotgun. Push the bolt assembly downward to relieve this condition (Fig. 18–3).

Removal of Magazine Spring, Retainer, and Follower

Carefully pry out the magazine-spring retainer, using a screwdriver. Do not damage the end of the magazine and keep a hand cupped over its end. The magazine spring and retainer can escape with some velocity due to the compression of the magazine spring, and flying parts can be lost or cause injury. After the magazine spring has been removed, point the magazine tube downward and allow the magazine follower to slide out.

Stock Removal

There is seldom a reason to remove the buttstock but it can be easily accomplished. Loosen the top buttplate screw and remove the bottom buttplate screw. Swing the buttplate to the side and insert a long, heavy screwdriver into the buttstock hole, engaging the slot of the stock bolt. Remove the bolt and the stock will come away from the receiver.

Removal of Triggerplate Group

Push out the front and rear triggerplate pins. Lift the rear end of the triggerplate group from the receiver and slide the assembly rearward, tilting it clockwise to clear the action-bar lock from the receiver.

Normally, no further disassembly of the Model 870 is necessary. The entire triggerplate can be adequately cleaned with pressurized solvents or by immersion in solvent combined with agitation. Residual solvents can be removed after cleaning with a pressurized degreasing and solvent-removing compound.

Triggerplate-Component Disassembly

Disengage the hammer by holding it in the cocked position while the trigger is pulled. Then allow the hammer to move slowly forward. Do not allow the hammer to snap forward under spring tension, as damage to parts could result.

Push out the carrier pivot tube from the left side, with the front triggerplate-detent spring attached. Remove the carrier assembly, carrier-dog follower, and carrier-dog follower spring.

The hammer plunger can then be compressed and the hammer pin driven out. Remove the hammer, action-bar lock, hammer plunger, and hammer spring.

Push out the triggerplate-pin bushing from the right side with the rear triggerplate-pin detent spring attached. Remove the sear spring, drive out the sear pin from the right side, and lift out the sear. Push out the safety-switch spring-retaining pin, and remove the safety-switch spring, retainer, and safety switch.

Disassembly of Carrier Group and Breechbolt Group

First file off the peened metal from the carrier-dog pin and then drive it out from the peened side. Remove the carrier dog and carrier-dog washer.

Using an appropriate-size punch, drive out the firing-pin retaining pin from the top side of the bolt. Release the firing pin slowly until all spring tension is relieved. Then remove the firing pin and its retractor spring.

Force the extractor plunger rearward in the bolt with a small-bladed screwdriver and roll the

DRIVE REARWARD HERE

18–4. Installation and removal of extractor.

extractor forward out of the extractor slot. Then remove the extractor plunger and spring (Fig. 18–5).

Shell Latches

Both the shell latches are peened into place in the receiver and should not be removed unless necessary. A loose shell latch can often be re-peened without removal. When peening, place the triggerplate-group retaining pin through the receiver and shell latch to keep the shell latch properly located (see Fig. 18–8).

To remove a shell latch, secure the action in a suitably padded vise with the bottom side up. Insert a heavy drift punch into the hole in the latch (but not so as to contact the receiver) and drive the latch rearward (Fig. 18–4). The same procedure is used for either the left or right shell latch. This removal will wipe away the peened metal that held the latch(es) in place. Proper and adequate staking will be required when replacing the shell latch(es).

EXTRACTOR

EXTRACTOR PLUNGER

18–5. Removal of the shell latch.

General Reassembly Procedures

Reassembly of the Model 870 is for the most part a reversal of the disassembly order. However, a few procedures require special attention or extra steps. These are as follows.

Buttstock Assembly

Don't forget to place the flat steel stock-bearing plate between the stock and receiver when replacing the buttstock. The stock washer goes onto the stock bolt with its projections forward (against the stock).

Magazine-Tube Assembly

If the gun is to be used for hunting and must conform to regulations limiting its shell capacity to three rounds, do not forget to install the magazine plugs. The standard plug is wood or plastic, but there is also a Vari-Weight steel plug that increases the gun's weight and thus reduces perceived recoil. If a standard plus is used, the magazine-spring retainer is placed in the magazine with its rimmed end down. It should be tapped into place, flush with the front end of the tube.

If the Vari-Weight steel plug is used, the magazine-spring retainer is not installed. The magazine tube must have a hole drilled in it, appropriately sized and located to accept the Vari-Weight retaining screw.

Extractor Assembly

Place the extractor spring in the hole at the rear of the extractor slot. Insert the small end of the extractor plunger into the spring. Holding the extractor by the claw, place its rear end into the extractor seat and force the extractor rearward against the plunger and spring. Do not let the extractor spring and plunger fly out. See Fig. 18–5 for the correct starting position to snap the extractor into place. The extractor plunger must snap over the rear shoulder of the extractor.

Firing-Pin Assembly

Position the firing-pin retractor spring on the front end of the firing pin, push the parts into the hole at the rear of the bolt, and position the firing-pin retractor spring in the hole at the front end of the bolt. Push the tip of the firing pin into the same hole. While maintaining compression on the retractor spring, align the clearance cut on the firing pin with the firing-pin retaining pin hole (in rear of bolt). Drive in the retaining pin from the bottom of the bolt until it is flush with the bolt's bottom surface.

Assembly of Fore-end Unit, Slide, Bolt, and Locking Block

Place the bolt (with the locking block assembled to it) and the slide on the action bars in the correct position (Fig. 18–6). This is best accomplished after installing the fore-end unit over the magazine tube. Gently insert the action bars,

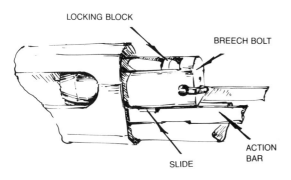

18–6. Parts orientation for installing the breechbolt group and operating bar with fore-end.

slide, and bolt into the receiver until the unit contacts the right shell latch. Depress the front end of the right shell latch (to clear the action bar) and move the assembly rearward until it contacts the front end of the left shell latch. Depress the front end of the left shell latch and move the assembly rearward.

Shell Latches

If the shell latches have been removed, the left latch can be identified by the bend in it (to clear the action-bar lock). This bend is located in the

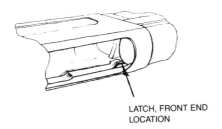

18–7. Front ends of shell latches must be positioned between the receiver and magazine tube.

middle of the latch. Be sure to assemble shell latches in the proper groove.

The front ends of the latch must be positioned between the receiver and the magazine tube (Fig. 18-7). Before staking a latch in position, use the front triggerplate pin, placed through the receiver and shell latch, to precisely align the latch. Be certain the front end of the shell latch is properly located before staking it into position (Fig. 18–8).

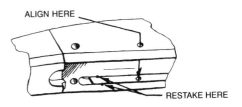

18–8. Restaking shell latch.

Triggerplate Components, Carrier Assembly, and Barrel

The triggerplate components are assembled in reverse order to takedown, but it may be necessary to restake the right side of the triggerplate to tighten the hammer pin. The projection on the rear of the action-bar lock must be assembled under the left connector (Fig. 18–9).

For carrier reassembly, it will be necessary to restake the small outside end of the carrier-dog pin to hold the pin in position.

The hammer should be cocked and the safety switch should be in the "on" position before installing the fire-control unit—that is, the triggerplate group. Also, the slide handle should be in its rearmost position, thus placing the bolt unit fully rearward in the receiver.

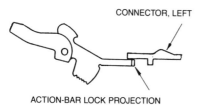

CONNECTOR, LEFT

ACTION-BAR LOCK PROJECTION

18–9. Correct assembly of action-bar lock and left connector. Projection fits *under* connector.

Insert the triggerplate unit into the receiver, tilting the assembly clockwise to clear the action-bar lock.

Use particular care when assembling the triggerplate unit to the receiver. Any deformation of the action-bar lock will prevent proper engagement with the end of the action bar. Align the pin holes properly before inserting rear and front pins.

Also remember that the action should be opened about halfway when mounting the barrel to the receiver.

Fitting of New Action-Bar Lock

A damaged action-bar lock can be replaced, but when installing the new one it is important to

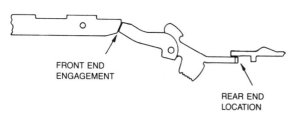

FRONT END
ENGAGEMENT

REAR END
LOCATION

18–10. Correct engagement of action bar and action-bar bolt when gun is in locked position.

check that its rear end is correctly positioned under the left connector. The front end of the action-bar lock must have full engagement with the action bar (Fig. 18–10) when the shotgun is in the locked position.

Fore-end Replacement

A special spanner or screwdriver will be needed to remove the tube nut from the front of the fore-end. When replacing the tube nut, be sure to locate the fore-end centrally between the action bars. Use care to avoid splitting the fore-end wood when replacing the nut.

Extractor Replacement

A damaged or broken extractor can be replaced, but the shell may feed up under the new extractor with difficulty. If so, the lower corner of the extractor claw will need to be rounded (Fig. 18–11).

ROUND LOWER
CORNER

LOWER
PAD

18–11. Lower corner of a replaced extractor can be rounded if shell feeds up and under the extractor with difficulty. The extractor's lower pad may be rounded slightly to help with this problem.

Parts Requiring Factory Service or Advanced Gunsmithing

The trigger, connectors, and connector pins—in fact, all trigger-related problems—require factory service. The shotgun or the complete triggerplate unit should be returned to the factory.

It is not advisable for the home gunsmith to replace the ejector and ejector spring, either. Reassembly of the rivets that hold these parts in place will result in the need to reblue the receiver.

Common Problems— Probable Causes and Corrections

Shell Cannot Be Loaded into Magazine

Carrier allows shell to load too low and thus hit rim of magazine entrance. *Install new carrier dog.*

Shell latches improperly positioned. *Check that front ends of both shell latches are between magazine tube and receiver—(see Fig. 18–7).*

Gun Fails to Feed as Forearm Moves Rearward

Action bar binding or hindered. *Check for deformation of action-bar notches, which con-* tact shell latches. Repair, if possible, or return to factory.

Shell latches not moving freely or engaging correctly. *Check that front end of latch has maximum engagement of approximately ¹⁄₁₆-inch over shell head. Latches should be free of deformity.*

Magazine spring and follower not moving freely. *If spring is weak, replace. Also check for dents in magazine tube, which can hinder movement of follower.*

Carrier not dropping low enough (to allow shell to pass onto it) or dropping too low (below loading port). *If carrier tip is bent, repair or replace. Check for burrs on rails and remove if required.*

Gun Fails to Lift Shell into Chambering Position or Balks as Cartridge Starts to Chamber

Action bar movement must be free. (*See causes and corrections for "Gun Fails to Feed as Forearm Moves Rearward."*)

Shell latches hindered in retaining next shell in magazine. (*See causes and corrections for "Gun Fails to Feed as Forearm Moves Rearward."*)

Carrier dog and carrier-dog follower spring not working smoothly. *Check for secure, correct fit in notch of slide to prevent shell from hanging in bottom of chamber. If necessary, replace carrier dog and/or carrier-dog follower spring.*

Extractor claw not functioning properly. If claw has been altered or if sharp edge that grips shell is worn or rounded, extractor must be replaced. *Only one extractor alteration is recommended for hard feeding of shell rim up under extractor: Carefully round lower corner of extractor (Fig. 18–11). If still more clearance is necessary, remove material from lower pad of extractor, but remember that too much clear-*

ance will allow shell to drop from grip of claw prior to ejection.

Gun Fails to Close Fully and Lock Up

Action bars not moving freely. *(See causes and corrections for "Gun Fails to Feed. . . .")*

Chamber rough. *Check for pits, rust, possible deformation in area of chamber where shell rim seats. Locking block must be fully seated in its recess in barrel extension. If chamber is damaged, new barrel may be needed.*

Extractor's passage into corresponding barrel slot hindered. *If necessary, chamfer front lower corner of extractor.*

Gun Fails to Fire

Firing pin broken, short, or binding in bolt. *Replace firing pin. Locking block not fully in position, so firing pin cannot contact primer. Reassemble with locking block properly positioned.*

Slide not fully forward in breechbolt and positioned under locking block. *Fore-end may simply need to be manipulated—moved forward—more positively.*

Action-bar lock not free to allow full engagement with left connector in trigger assembly. *Check for correct installation of action-bar lock, and for burrs or damage. Repair or replace if necessary.*

Hammer malfunctioning. *Notch on rear of hammer must be free of deformation and capable of full engagement with corresponding sear notch. Replace hammer if necessary (Fig. 18–12).*

Sear malfunctioning. *Notch on front of sear must be free of deformation and capable of full*

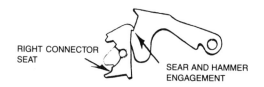

18–12. Hammer notch must be free of deformation and capable of full engagement with the corresponding sear notch.

engagement with hammer notch. Replace sear if necessary.

Trigger malfunctioning. *End of right connector, when cocking hammer, must be capable of seating fully into notch on rear of sear. Failure to seat may be caused by faulty triggerplate-pin bushing. Return triggerplate assembly or complete shotgun to factory for repair.*

Hammer spring weak. *Replace.*

Gun Fails to Extract, or Action Opens Hard

Faulty extractor movement in bolt and/or in barrel slot. *Extractor claw must have full purchase on shell rim. Replace extractor if claw is deformed or altered.*

Locking area of barrel extension must be rough or deformed. *Check area where extension joins barrel for excessive metal or recess which could hinder extraction (Fig. 18–13). Smooth up area to correct condition.*

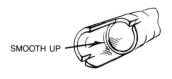

18–13. Smooth up any excessive metal in this area.

Deformation of barrel where the shell's rim seats, in throat, or at extractor slot, and/or rusting and pitting of chamber. *Smoothing of minor deformation at breech end of barrel may be possible, or new barrel may be required.*

Action bar not moving freely. *Check especially for deformation of shell-latch notches. Repair or replace.*

Action-bar lock not functioning freely. *Check for sufficient clearance between it and action bar to assist unlocking under recoil.*

Firing-pin retaining pin not staked firmly flush with bottom of bolt to prevent it dropping into patch of slide. (*See instructions for firing-pin assembly.*)

Gun Fails to Eject

Ejector not tight on its rivets; binding movement of ejector spring. *Return shotgun to factory for necessary replacement.*

Extractor not moving freely or its claw not gripping rim of fired shell firmly. *Check for deformation of claw. If necessary, tighten grip of claw by removing very small amount of material from middle pad of extractor. (Removal of too much material will cause shell to feed up under claw with difficulty.)*

Shell latches lacking full working engagement to keep next shell in magazine until fired case has been ejected. *Check for proper installation of latches, and repair or replace if necessary.*

Barrel Out of Line

Magazine tube sprung. *Bend carefully to re-align barrel.*

Safety Binds

Return firearm to factory.

Slide Binds on Rear of Ejection Port

Slide slightly misaligned. This is caused by occasional twisting motion on action bars by shooter when extracting shell. *To correct, chamfer rear corner of slide to clear ejection port.*

Action Jammed Forward with Barrel Removed

This condition is caused by attempting to remove fore-end unit without depressing right shell latch or by closing action too forcefully when barrel is removed. *If damage has occurred to action bars or right shell latch, replace fore-end tube assembly and/or right shell latch.*

19

Winchester 94 Lever-action Rifle

The Winchester Model 94 began its career about a century ago. Other than cosmetic changes and slight model variations, the 94s manufactured until 1963 were surprisingly alike, with a great many interchangeable parts. However, in 1964 a major revamping was undertaken, beginning with serial number 2,700,000. This included a number of part modifications as well as some dimensional changes. Because the so-called "post-'64" models were poorly accepted, additional changes were made during the 1970s and '80s. Thus, it is imperative to establish the era of manufacture for any 94 you will be working on and which part numbers apply. Because of the many variations, an exploded view is not shown. Check with the factory for an exploded view applicable to your gun.

Some parts for older models may no longer be available from the manufacturer—for instance, heavy locking blocks for renewing headspace tolerances on older firearms. In many cases, the factory can supply alternate parts that can be adapted, and dealers such as Gun Parts Corp. and others have large quantities of older-style parts.

The 94 is a trouble-free rifle requiring only minimal repair or service and it is an easy rifle to work on. Many of the parts and their movements can be viewed through the top of the receiver; hence, difficulties are usually easy to diagnose.

The only frequent repair is limited to the first post-'64 models, which employed a sheet-metal carrier that was easily damaged if subjected to even slightly abnormal stress. This sheet-metal

19–2. Almost all of the 94's working mechanism can be viewed and inspected from the top of the opened action.

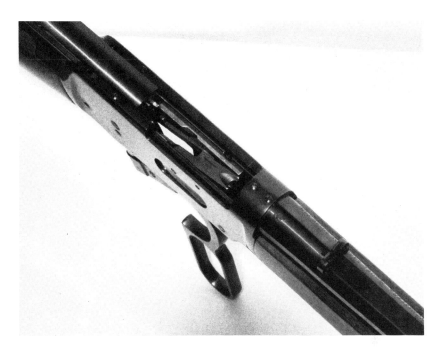

carrier should be routinely replaced with the later machined steel (from a casting) part. This will eliminate difficult feeding from magazine to chamber.

Cycle of Operation

The 94 is, of course, a classic lever-action with tubular magazine. The cartridges are loaded into the right side of the receiver, through the loading gate and into the magazine. When the lever is pulled downward, it draws the locking lug down away from the locked position at the rear of the bolt. Once the locking lug (which contains a firing-pin striker) has cleared the bolt, the continuing downward lever motion forces the bolt rearward. As the bolt moves rearward, it compresses the hammer into the cocked position. As the lever nears the lowest point of its travel, a cartridge is raised on the carrier into the feeding position. When the lever is raised to the closed position, the bolt moves forward, chambering a fresh round. As the cartridge is chambered, the carrier is lowered into the bottom of the receiver. As it reaches this point, a cartridge is released from the magazine and escapes partially onto the carrier. When the lever is again cycled and the bolt begins to move rearward, this cartridge can then escape fully onto the carrier and be raised up to the feeding position.

When the trigger is pressed, it causes the sear to release the hammer which, under compression of its spring, is driven forward against the firing-pin striker in the locking lug. The striker then moves against the firing pin which, in turn, ignites the primer.

Extraction is achieved by a single claw mounted on the bolt, and ejection is accomplished by the spring-loaded ejector which is also mounted to the bolt.

A protrusion on the front end of the link serves as a cartridge stop to prevent rounds from escaping from the magazine except when the gun is closed. At that time, only one cartridge will move partially from the magazine.

The following description of takedown deals with current Model 94s, made during the late 1980s.

19–3. Removing the screw from the rear of the top tang allows buttstock to be pulled rearward off receiver.

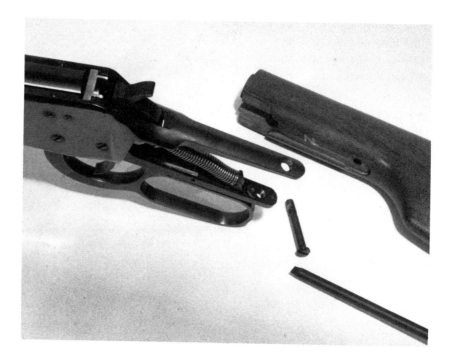

Buttstock Removal

A single screw, located at the rear of the top tang, holds the buttstock to the rifle. After the screw is removed (Fig. 19–3), slide the buttstock rearward and away from the receiver. If it sticks, jar the stock loose by slapping it with a cupped hand, striking rearward.

Removal of Lower Tang Group

The lower tang group includes the mainspring, hammer, hammer-retaining roll pin, trigger, sear, trigger stop, and related parts. With the buttstock removed, it will be noted that the entire group pivots on a single screw. This screw is removed from the lower left rear of the re-ceiver and the tang group is slid away (Fig. 19–4).

Once removed, the group may easily be dis-assembled into component parts. Start by cup-ping a hand around the tang and mainspring to capture the spring securely. Then uncock the hammer (the trigger stop will first need to be pushed inward) by depressing the trigger and allowing the hammer to move slowly forward. Now slowly pivot the hammer forward until the spring and its strut jump free. The hammer-retaining pin can then be removed and, in turn, the hammer. A drift pin holds the trigger and sear in position. They can be removed after drift-ing out the pin.

Another pin holds the trigger stop and the combination trigger and trigger-stop pin in posi-tion. Drift the pin free and then the parts can be easily removed.

Reassembly is accomplished in reverse order except that the hammer (main) spring will need to be compressed on its strut and a slave pin or drift punch must be inserted (from the top side) into the hole in the strut to keep the spring compressed (Fig. 19–5). After the hammer, ham-mer strut, and mainspring are in place, pull the slave pin or drift punch free.

19-4. Removing screw from the lower-rear, left-action side allows tang group to be slid away from receiver.

19-5. A pin punch can be used to compress the hammer spring on its strut when reassembling the tang group.

19-6. Removing the locking block.

Locking-Block Removal

Lower the lever to its bottom position. Then grasp the locking block and pull it rearward, free of the link. The lever may have to be moved slightly upward before the locking block will pull free (Fig. 19-6). Should it be necessary to re- move or replace the firing-pin striker, drive the retaining roll pin free from the locking block and the striker will fall free of the rear side of the locking block. Reassemble in reverse order.

Removal of Bolt Assembly

Remove the large-headed screw located on the left side of the receiver at the front top edge. Then, with the lever held in the closed position, insert a pin punch in the hole located at the top forward section on the right side of the receiver (Fig. 19–7). Tap the pin punch lightly and a retaining pin will punch out of the hole left open by the removal of the large-headed screw.

Now remove the link-retaining screw from the forward bottom edge of the receiver's left side (Fig. 19–7). Withdraw the lever and link from the bottom of the receiver, pivot the cartridge carrier so that it points straight downward out of the receiver bottom, and pull the bolt free of the receiver.

Reassembly is accomplished in reverse order. Note that the finger-lever pin is started from the left side of the receiver with its beveled end entering first.

19–7. After removing the large-headed screw from the left side of the action, use a pin punch to drive out the link/bolt assembly pin.

Lever and Link Disassembly

It is seldom necessary to separate these parts, but to do so, drive out the retaining pin and the two will separate (Fig. 19–8). The friction stud and spring, which lock the lever in the closed position, can be removed from the link by driving out the retaining pin. Take care not to lose these small parts as they will jump free when the drift punch is pulled out. Cup your hand over the parts to capture them as you pull the punch free. Reassembly is accomplished in reverse order.

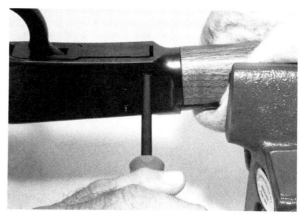

19–8. Removing the link-retaining pin will allow the lever and link to be withdrawn from the receiver.

Bolt and Cartridge-Carrier Disassembly

At this point, the firing pin can be slid from the rear of the bolt (Fig. 19–9). Further bolt disassembly is seldom warranted. However, the ejector can be removed by driving out the roll

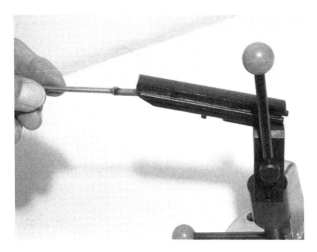

19–9. Firing pin is withdrawn from rear of bolt.

Loading-Gate Removal

Disassembly is not suggested, as a special tool is required for assembly. If necessary, however, remove the remaining large-headed screw from the right side of the receiver to free the loading gate. Reassembly will require holding the loading gate in position and compressing it. This can be accomplished with a screwdriver bent into an L-shape, which is pressed against the loading gate from inside the receiver.

pin that holds it in place. It is under heavy spring pressure, so care must be taken to prevent losing parts. Drive the roll pin out from left to right. Because this pin is riveted on the right end, it will be necessary to replace it before assembly. Do remember to rivet it in place. The extractor may be removed by unscrewing the retaining screw. Reassemble in reverse order.

Remove the remaining large-headed screw from the left side of the receiver and withdraw the cartridge carrier (Fig. 19–10).

Removal of Cartridge Guides and Carrier Spring

Disassembly is seldom required—and not recommended, as these parts are nettlesome to reassemble. The cartridge guides are held in position by two small-headed screws (one for each guide) located on each side of the receiver. They are somewhat difficult to tighten securely

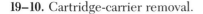

19–10. Cartridge-carrier removal.

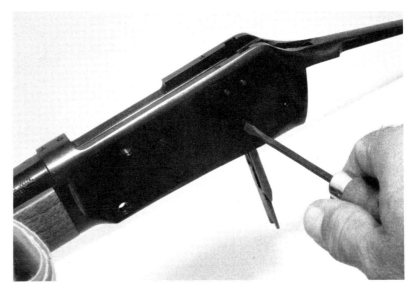

and require a very exact screwdriver fit. The cartridge-carrier spring can be removed by carefully inserting a screwdriver through the loading-gate opening (with gate removed). Replacing the spring requires patience and dexterity.

Action Reassembly

When pushing the bolt into the receiver, with the firing pin in place, be sure the cut in the firing pin aligns with the pin hole in the bolt. Also, the cartridge carrier should be swung upward against the bolt when assembling the finger lever and link. Insert the link screw before attempting to insert the finger-lever pin.

Use a drift punch, inserted into the right side of the receiver, to align the pin hole in the bolt, firing pin, and finger lever before starting the pin in from the left side. The pin will start with finger pressure and go into place easily. If it does not, the parts are not properly aligned. A bit of patience is required—and no force. Some manipulation of the finger lever will be required.

Removal of Magazine Tube, Barrel Bands, and Fore-end

Disassembly of these parts is straightforward, but reassembly alignment of barrel bands can sometimes be nettlesome, so disassembly is suggested only if necessary.

Start by removing the magazine-cap screw from the front bottom edge of the magazine tube. Be careful not to let the magazine cap and spring fly free as the screw is removed. Tip the muzzle down and allow the magazine follower to fall free of the magazine.

Next remove the two barrel-band screws and pull the magazine forward and free of the gun. The barrel bands may now be removed. It's a good idea to coat the barrel liberally with oil before sliding the barrel bands free. This will prevent a tight band from scratching the barrel's finish. The front band will need to be rotated 180 degrees in order to clear any front-sight ramp.

Reassembly is accomplished in reverse order. The fore-end may need to be tapped into posi-

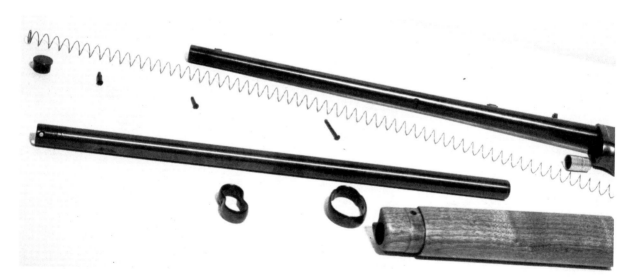

19–11. Magazine-tube components disassembled.

tion. Place a block of soft wood over the end of the fore-end and tap it lightly with a small hammer. Do so carefully so as not to damage it. The rear barrel band may have to be driven carefully into place to align it and the fore-end screw hole. Do so carefully. Many fore-ends are damaged in a moment of carelessness when tapping the rear barrel band into place. Using a soft wood dowel and a light mallet will help prevent such damage.

Make no attempt to force the barrel-band screw into place. Properly align the hole and everything will go together easily. That's all there is to disassembly and reassembly of the 94.

Common Problems— Probable Causes and Corrections

Gun Balks on Loading

Loading gate binding on shell head. *Replace loading gate.*

Gun Fails to Feed

Bent magazine tube. *Replace it and/or magazine spring as required. If carrier does not operate unless gun is forcefully opened, replace carrier and carrier spring.*

Gun Double-Feeds or Fails to Cam Cartridge Back into Magazine

Link-stop lug upset or worn. *Replace link. Also replace cartridge carrier if it is sheet-metal type. Replace loading gate as well to prevent recurrence of link damage.*

Shells Do Not Rise High Enough to Chamber

Loose, broken, or blunt carrier spring, or dull point on carrier. *Replace parts as required. Loose cartridge-guide screws can also cause problem. Tighten.*

Action Binds on Closing

Insufficient clearance for extractor. *Inspect cartridge rims for nicks or burrs. Also be sure extractor aligns with matching cut barrel. Ejector binding in breechbolt can also cause problem. Replace or refit extractor.*

Gun Fails to Fire

Broken or binding firing pin or weak mainspring. *Replace part.*

Miscellaneous Problems

Winchester 94 problems are most often self-explanatory when the firearm is examined closely. There are no difficult-to-solve problems. Those involving headspace or barrel require factory service.

Earlier Model 94s

The current 94s are without doubt the easiest on which to work. Early models had a number of variations that required modifications in disassembly and reassembly procedures. It is impossible to cover all of these variations, but they include cartridge-guide screws that mount from the inside of the receiver; a drift pin instead of a screw to hold the link in position (this variation used a set screw to keep the pin in place); flat hammer springs; a hammer with stirrup; lower tang dovetailed to the receiver. Before working on a pre-1980 94, you should know what version you have and how it may differ. For a complete parts list of Model 94 variations, contact U.S.R.A.C.

The style of the 94s covered in foregoing disassembly and reassembly procedure can be easily recognized in that no provision for a half-cock safety notch is provided on the hammer. Instead, the hammer has only two basic positions—fully cocked and at rest. For a carrying safety, the hammer is left in the at-rest position. In this position, it is withdrawn from contact with the firing-pin striker, and it cannot be moved forward unless the lever is held fully closed and the trigger depressed.

1987 WINCHESTER 94 LEVER-ACTION RIFLE, STANDARD VERSION PARTS (FOR .30-30 CARBINE)

Part No.	Name of Part	Part No.	Name of Part	Part No.	Name of Part
94120005	Barrel, Carbine(30-30 Win.), 20″ Standard	2594X	Firing Pin	11994X	Magazine Plug Screw - Standard
94120020	Breech Bolt	4094X	Firing Pin Striker		
94120025	Breech Bolt Complete, comprising bolt with extractor and screws, firing pin, ejector, ejector spring and ejector stop pin	4194X	Firing Pin Striker Stop Pin	11294X	Magazine Spring- Standard
		8194X	Forearm - Standard	13394X	Magazine Tube - Standard
		6194X	Friction Stud	13894X	Magazine Tube Complete - Standard comprising: magazine tube with magazine follower, magazine plug, magazine plug screw and magazine spring
		6094X	Friction Stud Spring		
		6394X	Friction Stud Stop Pin		
		8594X	Front Band - Standard		
3394X	Buttstock Complete - Standard	38594USA	Front Band Screw		
694X	Buttplate - Standard	94120421	Hammer and Sear R		
9112	Buttplate/Pad Screws (2 required)	4394X	Hammer Bushing	15194X	Rear Band - Standard
		3494X	Hammer Screw - Standard	15294X	Rear Band Screw
94070035	Carrier	94120450	Hammer Spring	94120100	Receiver - Standard R
1394X	Carrier Screw	94120470	Hammer Spring Guide Rod	94120421	Sear and Hammer R
1494X	Carrier Spring	94070082	Hammer Spur Assembly	94	Sight Assembly, Rear - Standard
1594X	Carrier Spring Screw	4994X	Link Complete - Standard comprising: link with friction stud, friction stud spring and friction stud stop pin		
1794X	Cartridge Guide L.H. - Standard			94A	Sight Binding Screw, Rear (2 required)
1694X	Cartridge Guide R.H. - Standard			94B	Sight Blade, Rear
1894X	Cartridge Guide Screw (2 required)	5094X	Locking Bolt - Standard	3281	Sight Cover, Front
		5194X	Locking Bolt Complete - Standard comprising: locking bolt with firing pin striker and firing pin striker pin	3C	Sight Elevator, Rear - Standard
94070050	Ejector			103F	Sight, Front - (.360″ High) - Standard
94070051	Ejector Complete comprising: ejector with spring and ejector stop pin			12970C	Sight Plug Screw, Telescope (4 required)
		10494X	Lower Tang		
		94121040	Lower Tang Complete comprising: R lower tang with hammer, hammer bushing, hammer spring, hammer spring guide rod, sear, trigger with hammer block assembly, trigger pin, trigger stop, trigger stop pin, trigger stop spring and trigger spring		
2394X	Ejector Spring			6994X	Spring Cover
94070055	Ejector Stop Pin			7094X	Spring Cover Screw
94070060	Extractor			94120770	Trigger with Hammer Block Assembly
94070065	Extractor Retaining Screw (2 required)			7794AX	Trigger/Sear Pin
16994X	Finger Lever			94120773	Trigger Spring
2994AX	Finger Lever Link Pin			7594X	Trigger Stop
3494X	Finger Lever Link Screw	5794X	Magazine Follower	33270	Trigger Stop Pin
2894X	Finger Lever Pin	11394X	Magazine Plug - Standard	7494X	Trigger Stop Spring
2994X	Finger Lever Pin Stop Screw			16494X	Upper Tang Screw

Note: Part numbers vary by caliber, barrel length, model, etc. Check with U.S.R.A.C. before ordering parts other than for standard .30-30 Carbine

(R) = restricted part, available only for factory installation.

20

Savage 110 Bolt-action Rifle

The Savage 110 bolt-action rifle has been offered in a number of variations. The popular Model 110E is the most common. The basic 110 rifle has also been sold under private labels using different names and model designations. These include:

Company	Brand Name	Model No.
Canadian Industries, Ltd.	CIL	950, 950-D, 950-C
Colter & Company	Westpoint	410
Talo	Golden West	710DL
Western Auto Supply	Revelation	250D, 250
Gamble		
Skogmo, Inc.	Hiawatha	510

The information contained in this chapter generally applies to all Savage rifles in the 110 series, as well as the five brands listed above.

It should be pointed out that Savage Arms does not sell parts or repair rifles. Instead, the company contracts with Savage Services Corporation (33 Lockhouse Rd., Westfield, MA 01085) to provide service and parts. Savage also has a nationwide network of parts distributors which is listed in the appendix. Refer to these under parts. As indicated in the appendix listing, some of these distributors handle obsolete Savage parts.

Savage 110 receivers vary somewhat. Models 110ED, 110D, and 110C differ from older models in that the earlier receivers are not machined to accept the 110C-style trigger or the later-style

EXPLODED VIEW OF SAVAGE 110ED, 110D, 110C

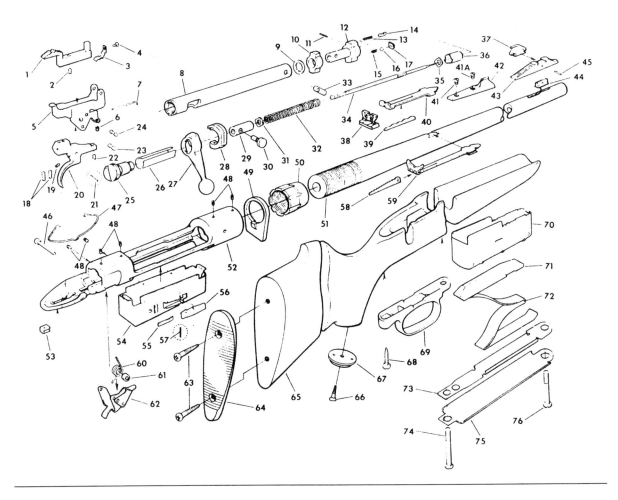

Key No.	Part No.	Name of Part	Key No.	Part No.	Name of Part
1	113-192	Safety	17	113-59	Extractor
2	110-593	Trigger Pull Adjusting Screw	18	113-870	Trigger Travel Adjusting Screw
3	113-776	Safety Detent Spring	19	113-869	Trigger Pin Retaining Screw
4	99-444	Safety Detent Spring	20	113-279	Trigger
5	113-280	Trigger Bracket	21	113-563	Trigger Spring Pin
6	113-593	Trigger Pull Adjusting Screw	22	113-593	Trigger Engagement Adjusting Screw
7	113-871	Trigger Pull Adjusting Spring	23	110-285	Trigger Pin
8	113-16	Bolt body (specify caliber, left or right)	24	110-590	Safety Bearing Pin
9	110-582	Front Baffle Friction Washer	25	110-583	Bolt Assembly Screw
10	110-581	Front Baffle	26	110-587	Cocking Piece Sleeve
11	113-55	Ejector Retaining Pin	27	113-17	Bolt Handle (specify left or right)
12	113-19	Bolt Head R	28	113-584	Rear Baffle (specify left or right)
		Bolt Head Assembly Complete R	29	110-34	Cocking Piece
		(113-734) (Specify caliber, left or right hand)	30	110-36	Cocking Piece Pin (specify left or right)
13	340-56	Ejector Spring	31	110-588	Cocking Piece Lock Washer
14	113-53	Ejector	32	110-166	Mainspring (specify caliber)
15	110-284	Extractor Spring	33	110-20	Bolt Head Retaining Pin
16	76-178	Steel Ball	34	113-77	Firing Pin (specify caliber)

Key No.	Part No.	Name of Part
35	110-586	Firing Pin Stop Nut Washer
36	110-585	Firing Pin Stop Nut
37	99-218	Front Sight
38	110P-229	Rear Sight (folding)
39	110-233	Rear Sight Step
40	3-229	Rear Sight
41	325-227	Front Sight Screw (short)
41A	325-226	Front Sight Screw (long)
42	342-218	Front Sight
43	110-219	Front Sight & Base Assembly
44	110-607	Front Sight Dovetail Black
45	110-599	Front Sight Pin
46	110-206	Sear Pin
47	110-154	Magazine Retainer Spring
48	99R-289	Dummy Screw
49	110-176	Recoil Lug R
50	110-10	Barrel Lock Nut R
51	113-1	Barrel (specify caliber) R
	113M-1	Barrel (magnum) R
52	113-2	Receiver (specify caliber) R
53	110-604	Trigger Pull Adjusting Screw Cover
54	113-293	Magazine Guide (specify caliber)
55	113-486	Magazine Latch Spring
56	113-495	Magazine Latch
57	113-484	Magazine Latch Pin
58	110-233	Rear Sight Step
59	110-229	Rear Sight Step
60	113-209	Sear Spring
61	110-439	Sear Bushing
62	113-205	Sear
63	94-32	Buttplate Screw
	110-60	Recoil Pad Screw
64	110-5	Buttplate
	775-5	Buttplate
	110-314	Recoil Pad
65	114MC-708	Stock Complete (specify caliber) (Model 110) (specify right or left hand)
	114M-708	Stock with Recoil Pad (Model 110D, Magnum Only) (specify caliber, right or left hand)
	114E-708	Stock Complete (Model 110ED) (specify caliber)
	114EM-708 Stock with Recoil Pad	
	114P-708	Stock Complete (Model 110DP-110DPE) (specify caliber, right or left hand)
66	99-423	Pistol Grip Screw
67	110M-422	Pistol Grip Cap
68	110-311	Trigger Guard Screw
69	110-99	Trigger Guard
70	110D-142	Magazine Box (specify caliber)
71	113-143	Magazine Follower
72	110-156	Magazine Spring
73	110-625	Floor Plate Insert
74	110-85	Floor Plate Screw, Rear
75	110-84	Floor Plate
76	110-594	Floor Plate Screw, Front

Model 110C Parts That Are Different From Other 110 Parts

Key No.	Part No.	Name of Part
77	113-857	Magazine Latch Button
78	113-420	Escutcheon
79	113-708	Stock Complete (Model 110C) (specify caliber, right or left)
80	113-84	Floor Plate (specify caliber)
81	113-735	Magazine Assembly (specify caliber)
82	113-99	Trigger Guard
83	113-868	Magazine Ejector Spring

(R) = restricted part, available only for factory installation.

Model 110C: Parts that are different from other 110 parts.

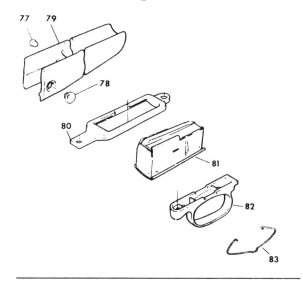

magazines. Also, models with the suffix C or D are equipped with a new-style sliding extractor and integral ejector. Newer models do not have a recessed chamber to accept the bolt head as do earlier models.

Design and Cycle of Operation

Designed by Nicholas Brewer and introduced in 1958, the original Model 110 incorporated construction features that were then new, but essentially those novel aspects of design were in no way a departure from the traditional Mauser-type turnbolt action utilizing a bolt with forward dual-opposed locking lugs and a staggered-column box magazine. Brewer was an expert with regard to tooling, machining, and manufacture in general. His innovations resulted in a very strong action that could be produced very economically (utilizing more but simpler parts than previous designs).

In addition, the design lent itself easily to the manufacture of a left-handed version. In the early 1960s, the company also endeared itself to amateur and professional gunsmiths by making available separate barreled actions. Both short and long actions have been offered.

Brewer's original bolt was guided only by its locking lugs, and sometimes too much play developed in the raceway—the bolt's travel was "sloppy," as shooters say, and had to be worked carefully to avoid jamming. This was corrected in 1972 by broaching a groove inside the receiver to form a guide system with a tongue protruding from a baffle lug.

Despite its unique design features, the Savage 110 employs a cycle of operation that typifies bolt-actions—essentially similar to other descendants of the Mauser. The characteristic bolt-action cycle was described for the Remington Model 700 and need not be repeated here.

Bolt Removal and Disassembly

Raise the bolt handle and draw the bolt fully rearward. Then, while simultaneously depressing the bolt release, at the right rear side of the action and pulling the trigger (Fig. 20–2), withdraw the bolt to the rear. This maneuver is best accomplished by using the thumb to depress the bolt stop and the middle finger to pull the trigger. Withdraw the bolt, using the other hand.

To disassemble the bolt, unscrew the assembly screw from the rear of the bolt (Fig. 20–3). The cocking-piece sleeve attached to the screw will be withdrawn with the screw. Slide off the bolt handle and rear baffle. The cocking pin can now be withdrawn from the rear side of the bolt body. This is the large-headed pin that enters the bolt perpendicularly in front of the rear baffle. The firing-pin assembly can now be withdrawn.

20–2. To withdraw the bolt from the receiver, bolt release must be depressed while simultaneously pulling the trigger.

20–3. Removing the assembly screw from the rear of the bolt along with cocking-piece sleeve.

Next, push out the bolt-head retaining pin, located behind the front baffle. The bolt head, front baffle, and friction washer can now be removed from the front end of the bolt.

When reassembling the bolt be sure the friction washer is placed in position before the front baffle. The chamfered side of the baffle faces the front of the bolt.

Disassembly of the striker-and-mainspring unit is not recommended unless it is necessary to replace a broken firing pin or mainspring. To disassemble, unscrew the cocking piece (the tubular piece at the back of the spring) and then remove the cocking-piece lock washer (Fig. 20–4). The mainspring will be free to escape as the cocking piece is unscrewed, so use caution to prevent lost parts. The firing pin-stop nut's lock washer is then disengaged and the firing pin-stop nut removed. The disassembled bolt is shown in Fig. 20–5.

Reassembly is accomplished in reverse order. When reassembling the firing-pin stop nut to the firing pin, adjust it so there is 0.055-inch to 0.065-inch protrusion of the firing pin through the bolt head. This distance must be carefully measured. When the adjustment is right, en-

20–4. Removing the cocking piece and its lock washer.

20–5. Disassembled bolt looks like this.

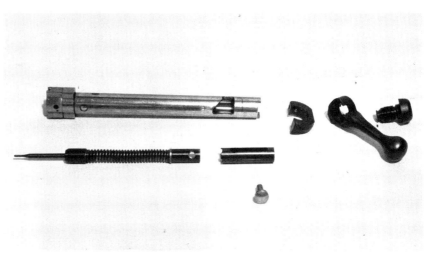

gage the nut with the firing-pin stop nut lock washer to secure its position. Then double check the amount of firing-pin protrusion from the bolt head.

When the cocking piece is installed, it must be adjusted so the hole for the cocking-piece pin will have 0.005-inch to 0.015-inch clearance in relation to the bottom of the cam cut in the bolt body, with the firing pin in the forward position. This hole will have to be in line with one of the protrusions on the cocking-piece lock washer.

The bolt must be cocked before it can be reinserted into the receiver. Do this by forcing the cocking-piece pin up the cam surface until it rests in the cocked notch. Be sure the bolt is firmly held in a well-padded vise before doing this.

The ejector and extractor should not be removed from the bolt unless absolutely necessary. The extractor can be removed simply by sliding it out of the slot in the bolt head. Take care to allow for the capture of the steel ball and spring, which will snap out as the extractor is slid away.

The ejector, also under heavy spring tension, is held in place by a pin. Driving out the pin and then removing the drift punch will allow the ejector and spring to escape the bolt. It is impossible to cover all versions of the 110. However, whether these parts are bolt-mounted or located in the magazine latch, disassembly is seldom necessary on these variations. The previous description applies to rifles with serial numbers above 100,000.

Removal of Stock

Remove the front action screw and rear action screw (front trigger-guard screw). The stock will then separate from the barreled action, with the magazine spring and follower falling loose. The magazine guide is staked into position on the receiver. It is suggested that the magazine box

not be disassembled from the receiver. It is also suggested that the trigger, bolt release, and safety parts not be disassembled.

Trigger-Pull Adjustment

Be sure the rifle is unloaded and cocked. Referring to the trigger diagram (Fig. 20–6), turn in the adjustment screw (key No. 1) on the front end of the trigger until the sear releases. Stop turning immediately upon its release. Then back up the screw exactly one-half turn outward to give the minimum 0.015-inch sear engagement. This step alone is often all that is necessary to provide a desirable trigger pull.

Recock the action and move the safety rearward to the on position. If the safety will not move, back out the screw at the rearmost part of the trigger (key No. 2) until the safety will go on. This screw should be carefully adjusted to allow the safety to slide freely, yet also for no movement of the trigger if it is pulled while the safety is on.

Slide the safety forward and pull the trigger to uncock the action. Then adjust the screw immediately behind the trigger (key No. 3) so that the trigger has a minimum of movement when

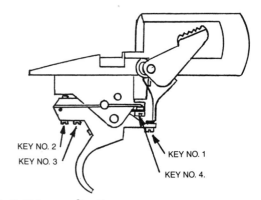

KEY NO. 2
KEY NO. 3
KEY NO. 1
KEY NO. 4.

20–6. Trigger-adjusting screws.

pulled. Test this by cocking the rifle and pulling the trigger. If the gun will not fire, trigger travel is insufficient. Correct this by turning the screw outward a half-turn at a time. Then check the cocking of the rifle. If the sear binds on the trigger and the rifle will not cock, adjust by backing out the screw (key No. 3) a half-turn at a time.

Weight of pull may now be adjusted by using the screw located at the right outside trigger position. This is the screw against which the long piano-wire spring is positioned.

Note: Savage literature suggests a four-pound minimum pull.

Turning in the screw (key No. 4) will increase trigger-pull weight, while backing it out will decrease trigger-pull weight. The screw must be turned to allow the spring to rest in one of the two notches provided—in other words, in half-turn increments.

After all screws have been properly adjusted, lock each into position by placing a drop of nail polish over each screw. Allow the nail polish to dry completely before use.

Reassembly Procedures

When reassembling the rifle, be sure the correct end of the follower is positioned forward. The high step of the follower should be on the left side of the receiver.

If the bolt will not open after reassembly, the front action screw has gone too deep and is binding on the locking lug. Remove the screw and shorten as necessary, but do not damage its threads when doing so.

Note: The bolt stop also serves as a cocking indicator. When the bolt stop is in its high position, the rifle is cocked. When the rifle is fired, the bolt stop drops to its lowest position, approximately flush with the stock.

Common Problems— Probable Causes and Corrections

As noted earlier, the design of the 110 incorporates features (new and unusual in 1958 but now more common) for ease of production and strength of the action, but this rifle operates essentially like any Mauser-type bolt-action. Common bolt-action problems, their causes and corrections, were covered in the chapter on the Remington Model 700. It is unlikely that you will encounter any malfunctions or other problems peculiar to the Savage Model 110. Broken, worn, or damaged parts should be repaired or replaced as in other bolt-action rifles.

21

Marlin 336 Lever-action Rifle

The Marlin 336 has been popular since the late 1890s as a woods carbine in caliber .30-30 Winchester and, to a lesser extent, in .35 Remington. It has also been chambered for a number of other cartridges such as .32 Winchester Special, .45-70 Government, and .444 Marlin. It has been offered as a carbine, full-length rifle, a shorter-than-normal carbine, and in deluxe and "plain-Jane" versions (the Glenfield line). In some instances the 336 designation has not been applied, although the gun had a 336 action.

Most of the variations have been cosmetic, though several mechanical or parts changes have occurred. This discussion will center on current models which, in addition to the normal half-cock hammer safety, now incorporate a cross-bolt, through-the-receiver safety.

Cycle of Operation

The Marlin 336 is a typical exposed-hammer, lever-action rifle. Cartridges are inserted through the loading port on the right side of the receiver, and the nose of each cartridge pushes the round in front of it (lying half in the receiver and half in the magazine) fully forward into the magazine tube.

As the lever is lowered, the cartridge lying only partially in the magazine escapes so that it lies fully on the cartridge carrier. The remaining cartridges are locked in the magazine by the cartridge carrier.

Also as the lever is lowered, the bolt is moved rearward, cocking the hammer. Simultaneously, any shell or empty case in the chamber is withdrawn by the bolt-mounted extractor. As the bolt clears the receiver-mounted ejector, the ejector enters a cut in the bolt and is held tightly against it by the ejector spring. When the cartridge strikes the ejector, it is pivoted and thrown through the port on the right side of the receiver.

As the lever is closed, the cartridge carrier rises up and places a new cartridge in front of the bolt. As the lever-closing stroke is continued, the bolt is moved forward, pushing the cartridge into the chamber. During the final closing movement of the lever, the bolt is locked into place by the locking block as it cams into the bolt's lower rear half. The cartridge carrier then drops to its lowest position and another round partially escapes the magazine. Its rearward travel is arrested by the loaded gate, readying the gun for the next manipulation of the lever.

21–2. To disassemble the 336, first remove the lever pivot screw, then pull the lever back and down, away from the receiver.

Removal of Finger Lever, Bolt Assembly, and Ejector

The Marlin is simplicity in design and disassembly. With the lever partially open, begin disassembly by removing the lever pivot and retaining screw located in the lower receiver tang protrusion, at the front end of the lever. Then pull back and down on the lever, pulling it away from the rifle (Fig. 21–2).

With the rifle lying on its left side, withdraw the bolt assembly from the rear of the receiver. The hammer may have to be compressed slightly with a thumb to accomplish this step. It will be necessary to have lowered the lever far enough to disengage the locking block to allow for bolt withdrawal (Fig. 21–3).

The ejector, in a recess in the right side of the receiver, can be lifted out with a needle-nosed plier or tweezer. Or, you can simply roll the

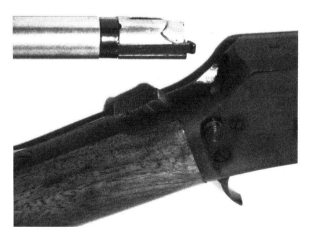

21–3. Bolt is withdrawn directly from the receiver. Keep receiver on left side to prevent loss of ejector.

EXPLODED VIEW OF MARLIN 336

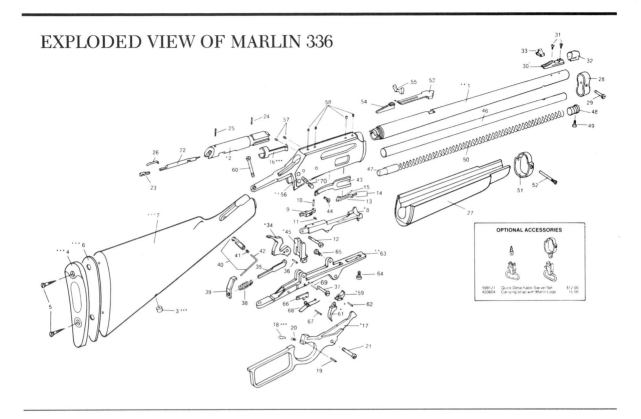

View No.	Part No.	Name of Part	View No.	Part No.	Name of Part
1	101340	Barrel R	28	301233	Front Band
2	101686	Breech Bolt, caliber 30-30	29	301291	Front Band Screw
	501686	Breech Bolt Assembly (consisting of Parts 2, 16 and	30	220539	Front Sight Base
		22 through 26) (Not shown)	31	320190	Front Sight Base Screw (2)
3	320101	Bullseye	32	320245	Front Sight Hood
4	320202	Buttplate with Spacer	33	330644	Front Sight Insert
5	320590	Buttplate screw (2)		520539	Front Sight Complete (Consisting of above 4 parts)
6	320103	Buttplate Spacer	34	101273	Hammer
7	501016	Buttstock Complete	35	320174	Hammer Strut
8	101161	Carrier	36	401397	Hammer Strut Pin
9	201063	Carrier Rocker	37	301090	Hammer Screw
10	401062	Carrier Rocker Pin	38	420294	Hammer Spring (mainspring)
11	401094	Carrier Rocker Spring	39	320175	Hammer Spring Adjusting Plate
	501161	Carrier Assembly, cal. 30-30 (consisting of above	40	520377	Hammer Spur Complete
		4 parts) (Not shown)	41	420193	Hammer Spur Screw
12	301190	Carrier Screw	42	420204	Hammer Spur Wrench
13	201168	Ejector	43	101594	Loading Spring
14	501168	Ejector With Spring	44	301091	Loading Spring Screw
15	401294	Ejector Spring	45	101081	Locking Bolt
16	301169	Extractor	46	201022	Magazine Tube
17	501370	Finger Lever	47	301024	Magazine Tube Follower
18	201071	Finger Lever Plunger	48	301225	Magazine Tube Plug
19	301197	Finger Lever Plunger Pin	49	301092	Magazine Tube Plug Screw
20	401196	Finger Lever Plunger Spring	50	401395	Magazine Tube Spring
21	301192	Finger Lever Screw	51	201521	Rear Band
22	401299	Firing Pin, Front	52	301590	Rear Band Screw
23	401199	Firing Pint, Rear		501342	Rear Sight, Complete
24	420299	Firing Pin Retaining Pin, Front	53	520241	Rear Sight Base
25	420299	Firing Pin Retaining Pin, Rear	54	320242	Rear Sight Elevator
26	401295	Firing Pin Spring	55	201342	Rear Sight Folding Leaf
27	101227	Forearm	56	101760	Receiver R

View No.	Part No.	Name of Part
57	320690	Receiver Sight Dummy Screw (2)
58	320493	Scope Mount Dummy Screw (2)
59	201051	Sear
60	320391	Tang Screw
61	201143	Trigger
62	401097	Trigger and Sear Pin
63	501258	Trigger Guard Plate R
64	301390	Trigger Guard Plate Screw

View No.	Part No.	Name of Part
65	301490	Trigger Guard Plate Support Screw
66	301859	Trigger Safety Block
67	320397	Trigger Safety Block Pin
68	401095	Trigger Safety Block Spring
69	401099	Trigger Guard Plate Latch Pin
70	599183	Safety Button Assembly R

(R) = restricted part, available only for factory installation.

receiver over onto its right side and shake the ejector out of the receiver after it falls from its notch (Fig 21–4).

Note: When replacing the ejector, the pinlike protrusion goes into the corresponding receiving hole. The pin protrusion is positioned so that it is at the rear, and the spring faces forward and is fully contained in the receiver groove. It may be necessary to hold the ejector in place until the bolt has been started past it.

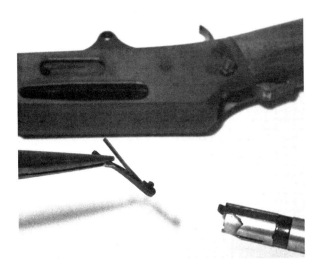

21–4. Lift the ejector from the receiver.

Buttstock Removal

Remove the large screw from the end of the upper rear tang. Then pull the buttstock away from the receiver. If the stock does not slide easily to the rear, a few rearward slaps with a cupped hand over the stock comb will accomplish the task (Fig. 21–5).

Hammer Removal

With the buttstock removed, slide the hammer-spring retainer out of the left side of the receiver; the top portion must clear the receiver first—then slide out the bottom portion. It will be necessary to compress the hammer spring

21–5. Buttstock is removed by drawing it rearward after its retaining screw has been removed.

21–6. Removing the hammer-spring retainer.

slightly while sliding out the bottom end of the retainer. Do so by manipulating the top end of the retainer forward (Fig. 21–6).

Then remove the hammer screw (located just below the cross-bolt safety on the right side of the receiver). To slip the hammer from the top back end of the receiver, depress the trigger, allowing the hammer to pivot forward. To depress the trigger, push the trigger stop pin, located behind the trigger, into the lower tang. When the hammer is fully pivoted forward, pull up on it and it will clear the receiver easily (Fig. 21–7).

Removal of Lower Tang, Locking Block, and Carrier

Remove the retaining screw at the bottom front edge of the receiver. Next, remove the retaining screw at the bottom edge of the receiver's left side.

The lower tang may now be removed by pulling downward on its rear end. If it is tight, hit the front edge of the finger-lever retaining-pin protrusion with a light leather mallet. Use a few light blows to move the tang rearward about ¼-inch. Then pull down on the rear end of the tang and pull it away from the receiver (Fig. 21–8). When reassembling the rifle, it may be necessary to use light taps of a leather mallet to align the lower tang with its retaining-screw holes.

Now lift the locking block from the rear end of the receiver, pulling it out of the receiver bottom (Fig. 21–9). Note that its hook, which engages a corresponding hook on the finger lever, faces the

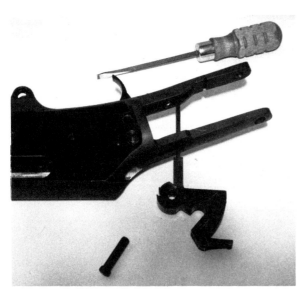

21–7. Hammer removal.

21–8. Lower tang removal.

21–9. Locking-block removal.

rear of the rifle. The locking block must be so installed when reassembling the rifle.

The cartridge carrier may be withdrawn by removing the retaining screw on the right side of the receiver directly in front of the cross-bolt safety (Fig 21–10).

Removal of Cross-Bolt Safety

The cross-bolt safety does not usually need to be removed except for repair or replacement. It is retained in the receiver by a set screw on the left rear edge of the receiver. Do not lose the spring and detent when disassembling.

21–10. Removing retaining screw on right side of receiver to withdraw cartridge carrier.

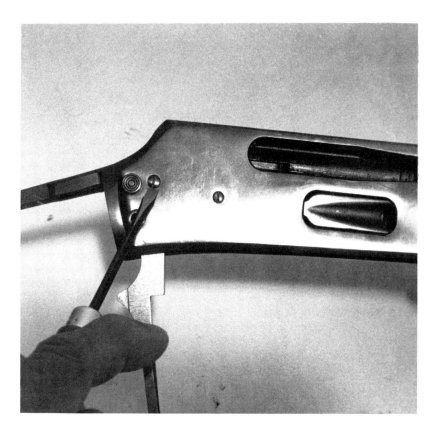

Removal of Loading Gate

The loading gate is held in place by the only remaining screw on the right side of the receiver. However, it is suggested that the loading gate not be removed unless necessary, as it can be quite difficult to replace.

To install it again requires its compression against the inside of the receiver while its screw hole is aligned. This is best accomplished with an offset (right-angle) screwdriver blade pressed firmly against the inside edge of the loading gate. Naturally, the gun must be firmly held in a padded vise during this operation.

Removal of Magazine Tube and Fore-end

As with all similar rifles, removal of the magazine tube is not recommended due to the difficulty sometimes encountered when aligning the barrel-band screw holes for reassembly. However, disassembly may be necessary from time to time. Start by removing the magazine-tube cap from the forward end the tube. The cap is under spring pressure and will fly free as the screw is withdrawn if you do not capture it. Cup your hand over the cap as the screw is withdrawn.

Set the cap aside and withdraw the magazine spring. Then point the barrel downward and

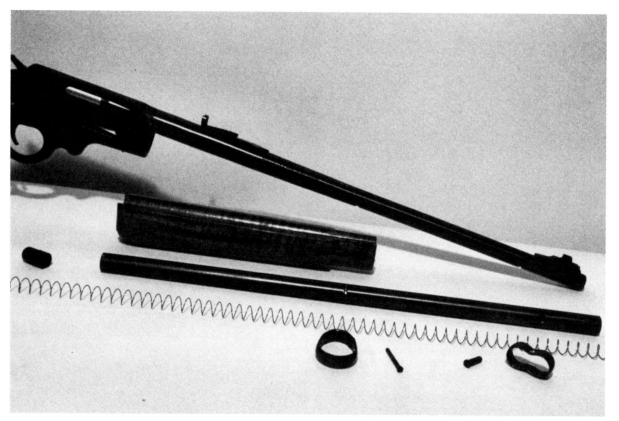

21–11. Magazine-tube assembly.

allow the magazine follower to slide free of the magazine tube.

Now remove both barrel-band screws. Both the barrel and magazine should be liberally oiled to prevent scratching the finish before proceeding.

The magazine tube can now be pulled free. Rotate the front band 180 degrees to clear the front-sight ramp (if required) and slide the front barrel band free of the rifle. The rear band can now be removed. It may require a few light taps with a mallet and wood dowel to get it started.

The fore-end can then be pulled free (Fig. 21–11). *Note:* The fore-end may fit the receiver tightly and care should be taken not to break it. When reinstalling the fore-end, it may have to be tapped into place. Place a soft piece of wood across its front end and tap lightly with a mallet.

The rear barrel band may also have to be tapped into place to align the screw holes. Many folks have stripped the threads of barrel bands and screws by attempting to force a screw into alignment. Avoid grief by insuring that the barrel-band holes are properly aligned (check with a tight-fitting punch) before attempting to install the screw.

Reassembly

Reassembly is accomplished in reverse order. No special problems will be encountered except as already noted and as follows:

When sliding the bolt into the receiver, be sure the gun is in an upright position and the locking lug and carrier are in their down positions or they will interfere with bolt entry. Keep the ejector in place and align the corresponding bolt cut with the ejector.

The bolt must not be pushed fully into the receiver. When it is two-thirds of the way in, stop and position the finger lever in the receiver so that its tip, which goes into the bolt groove, is properly aligned. Also insure that the finger-lever screw is put into place securely. When this

has been done, the action will work smoothly and is properly assembled.

Earlier models will not have the cross-bolt safety and some may require minor modification of procedures. Go slowly and you will have no problems.

Bolt Disassembly

It may be necessary to replace the extractor, firing pin, firing pin striker, or spring. To do so will require disassembly of the bolt.

The extractor can be pried from its groove with a screwdriver. When reassembling, be sure its collar is not bent beyond being contained in the groove. If it is, replace the extractor. Assembly is accomplished by simply pressing the collar over the corresponding bolt groove.

The firing-pin striker is removed by driving out its roll-pin retainer (top to bottom). Then slide the striker rearward, taking care not to lose its spring. When reinstalling the striker, the roll pin should be driven slightly below flush with the bottom of the bolt.

The firing pin is removed by driving out its retaining pin (located under the extractor collar). The pin can then be removed from the rear of the bolt. Be sure the finger-lever groove and pinhole areas are properly aligned during reassembly.

Trigger Spring, Trigger Stop, Sear, and Trigger Removal from Lower Tang

It is not often necessary to disassemble these parts. If need be, drive the top and spring-re-

21–12. Trigger group properly assembled.

taining pin from the tang, taking great care not to lose the spring or trigger stop. Carefully note the position of the spring before disassembly. Its long end must rest on the right rear top of the sear when assembled. Also, the spring lies flat on the bottom of the tang recess.

To remove the sear and trigger, drive out the retaining pin. The forward pin does not require removal. It serves only as a catch for the lever-locking plunger located in the finger lever (Fig. 21–12).

Common Problems— Probable Causes and Corrections

Marlin 336s are among the easiest firearms to repair. There is little to do in the way of actual parts repair. Any malfunctions are likely to be caused by improper assembly; burrs, bends, or dents; or worn or broken components. Most repairs are simply a matter of parts replacement.

22

Marlin 70 Semiautomatic Rimfire Rifle

There are more semiautomatic .22 rimfire rifles in use than perhaps any other kind of sporting firearm, and the Marlin Model 70 is among the most popular.

The Marlin 70 is a non-takedown semiautomatic rimfire rifle designed to function with .22 LR ammunition, both high-speed and standard-velocity types. Its clip magazine allows seven shots to feed smoothly. The action has a hold-open feature on the bolt (pull the operating handle fully rearward and press it in). The bolt does not automatically stay open on the last shot.

Most Model 70s provide a very high level of accuracy and require only a minimum of maintenance. The action parts should be cleaned every 250 rounds or so, depending on the brand and type of ammunition used.

Cycle of Operation

Like other rimfire semiautomatic rifles (and a few low-powered centerfire pistols), the Marlin Model 70 employs the blowback system of operation. The functioning cycle has some similarities to gas operation and to recoil operation. However, the barrel does not move (as in recoil-operated firearms) and there is no mechanical lockup of barrel and breechblock. Locking is accomplished by inertia—the tendency of a body at rest to remain at rest or that of a body in motion to remain in motion.

Many shooters have difficulty understanding how this principle is applied to the functioning of

EXPLODED VIEW OF MARLIN 70

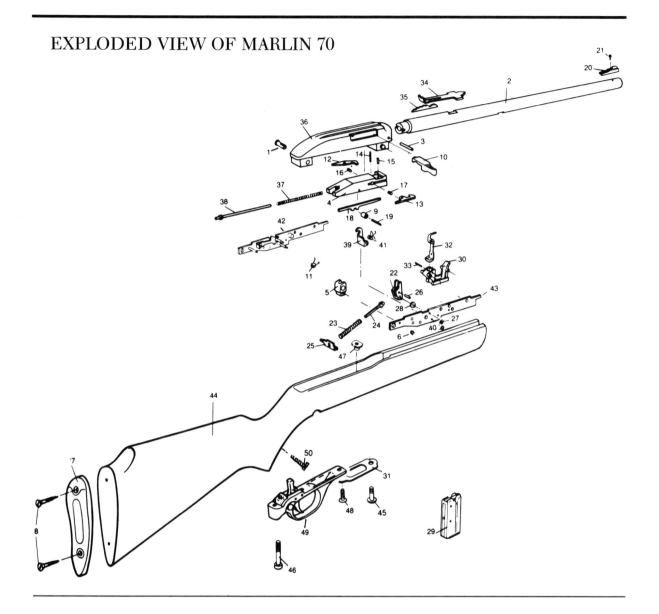

View No.	Part No.	Name of Part	View No.	Part No.	Name of Part
1	407997	Assembly Post	16	407895	Extractor Spring, Left Hand
2	107420	Barrel R	17	407895	Extractor Spring, Right Hand
3	307897	Barrel Retaining Pin	18	407299	Firing Pin
	507086	Breech Bolt Complete (not shown)	19	407198	Firing Pin Retaining Pin
4	107086	Breech Bolt	20	330144	Front Sight
5	407082	Buffer	21	420593	Front Sight Screw
6	407178	Buffer Pin Ring	22	207173	Hammer
7	320102	Buttplate	23	407094	Hammer Spring
8	320590	Buttplate screw(2)	24	407179	Hammer Strut
9	307188	Cartridge Lifter Roller	25	307075	Hammer Strut Bridge
10	207050	Charging Handle	26	407199	Hammer Strut Pin
11	407196	Disconnector Spring		507173	Hammer Complete (consisting of above 5 parts)
12	320269	Extractor, Left Hand	27	407178	Hammer Pin Ring
13	320369	Extractor, Right Hand	28	420176	Hammer Space
14	420798	Extractor Pin, Left Hand	29	407346	Magazine Complete (7-shot)
15	407097	Extractor Pin, Right Hand	30	207349	Magazine Guide

View No.	Part No.	Name of Part	View No.	Part No.	Name of Part
31	307347	Magazine Guard Plate	42	207164	Sideplate, Left Hand
32	307348	Magazine Latch & Ejector	43	307563	Sideplate, Right Hand
33	320797	Magazine Latch Pin		507363	Sideplate Assembly Complete (not shown)
	520641	Rear Sight Complete (includes 34 & 35)	44	507514	Stock
34	220641	Rear Sight Base	45	307192	Takedown Screw, Front
35	320942	Rear Sight Elevator	46	307392	Takedown Screw, Rear
36	507160	Receiver R	47	307391	Trigger Guard Nut, Front
37	307496	Recoil Spring	48	307690	Trigger Guard Screw, Front
38	307071	Recoil Spring Guide	49	507258	Trigger Guard Complete (not shown)
39	407051	Sear	50	320791	Stock Reinforcement Screw
40	407178	Sear Pin Ring			
41	407795	Sear Spring	(R)		= restricted part, available only for factory installation.

a firearm. The late Bob Wallack, a knowledge-able gunsmith and ballistics authority, offered this very clear, simple explanation:

Visualize a table on which there is a row of books standing upright. Now move the book at the right end a little farther to the right, away from the others, and place your hands in the opening you've made. If you move your hands apart with equal pressure in both directions, the single book will fly across the table, while the long row will only move slightly as you continue the pressure. Imagine that the single book is a bullet and the long row is a heavy, sliding breechblock; for the force of your hands, substitute the propellent gas generated by a powder charge. Inertia keeps the action from opening until the bullet is out, but by the time the bullet is well started, the breechblock will begin to move. The rearward force of the gas amounts, of course, to recoil—but since the barrel doesn't move as it does in the recoil method of operation, this system is called blowback. As in other systems, extraction, ejection, and cocking are accomplished as the bolt goes back after unlocking, and a fresh cartridge is chambered as the bolt comes forward again and the action is locked.

No complex "power train" of gas vents, pistons, and related parts is needed (as in the Remington 1100 autoloading shotgun, for instance) because the force of expanding gases simply works in both directions within the barrel— forward and rearward behind the bullet to fire the projectile and move the action. Why isn't this simple system used in higher-powered arms? Because the force generated by high-powered cartridges would require a very massive breechblock to resist sliding back (opening) until the bullet cleared the barrel. A .30-06, for example, would need a 16-pound breechblock.

The operation of the Model 70 is very simple. When the trigger is pulled the sear pivots away and allows the hammer to hit the firing pin and initiate the ignition sequence. As just described, the bolt is forced rearward when the forces of the expanding gases expand against the head of the cartridge. The cartridge is withdrawn from the chamber by the extractor as the bolt moves rearward. In turn, the ejector strikes the cartridge rim, forcing the case from the purchase of the extractor and causing it to be expelled from the action.

When the recoil spring is fully compressed, it drives the bolt forward, which in turn strips a cartridge from the magazine and then chambers it, readying the gun for firing.

Stock Removal

After making sure the firearm is unloaded and removing the magazine, turn out the front action screw. This is the large-headed screw in front of the magazine opening at the bottom of the stock.

22–2. Begin disassembly by separating the barrel and receiver from the stock and trigger group. This is accomplished by removing the two action screws.

22–3. To remove action assembly, withdraw action-assembly post and then lift the rear end of action assembly away from the receiver.

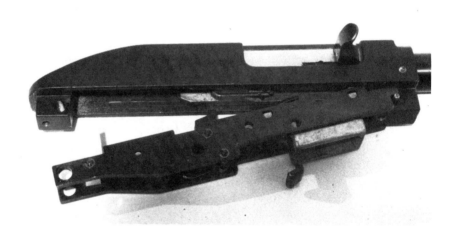

22–4. Removal of bolt and related parts from the bottom of the receiver.

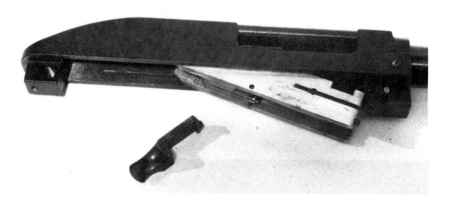

Then take out the rear action screw, located in the back end of the trigger guard. Do not remove the X-slot screw that goes into the pistol grip (behind the rear action screw). This is a non-functional part of the Model 70 and never needs removal.

Separate the stock and trigger group from the barreled action. It may be necessary to "snap past" the magazine-release lever by pulling upward and forward on the barrel as the unit is pivoted to the rear.

Removal of Action Assembly

With the barreled action held upside-down, press in on the assembly post, pushing the slotted end into the action assembly and withdrawing it from the other side. Now grasp the rear end of the action assembly, lifting it upward and away from the receiver. Further disassembly of this unit is not advised. Marlin strongly suggests that repairs to the action assembly be undertaken only by trained gunsmiths.

Removal of Bolt, Bolt Handle, and Action Spring

With the bottom of the receiver in an upward position and the barrel held in padded vise jaws, pull the operating handle about a half-inch rearward. While holding the handle in this position, lift the front end of the bolt upward to bring it out of the receiver's bottom. As you do this, the bolt handle will free itself of the bolt. Pull it out of the receiver.

By slightly compressing the action spring (recoil spring) with the bolt, you will be able to lift the bolt free of the rifle, removing it and the action spring, as well as the spring guide.

Removal of Trigger Guard and Trigger

Remove the screw in front of the trigger guard and you can separate the entire trigger unit from the rifle. Do not lose the small metal escutcheon to which the screw secures.

No further disassembly should be undertaken. The Marlin 70 can now receive the thorough cleaning which is required with all semi-auto rifles to insure reliability. Use pressurized solvents and cleaning fluids as well as an old toothbrush to rid all parts of firing byproducts and other residue or foreign material.

22–5. Removal of trigger group.

Reassembly

Reassembly is accomplished in reverse order. Be sure the small escutcheon used with the trigger group retaining screw is positioned so that its protrusion enters into the screw hole. Also be sure it does not infringe upon the magazine mortise.

Be sure to insert the recoil spring into the corresponding hole in the bolt. Then insert the long end of the spring guide into the spring. Do not bend this spring during assembly. Use one hand to start the spring guide into the hole in the receiver. Then carefully compress the spring by pushing the bolt rearward over it while guiding the spring into the bolt. When it's properly compressed, rotate the bolt into the receiver so that it is held in position by the front end of the receiver. Swing the bolt in only far enough for the operating-handle cut to be fully visible through the side opening of the receiver.

Place the bolt handle in the notch and, using a screwdriver, press the bolt rearward, allowing it to enter the receiver fully. Maintain the bolt handle's position in the bolt while performing this maneuver. Operate the bolt back and forth once or twice to insure that it has been properly reinstalled.

When installing the action screws, start both screws loosely to insure correct alignment. Then tighten the front action screw and snug up the rear screw—but not too tightly.

Common Problems— Probable Causes and Corrections

The Model 70 is, of course, subject to broken parts, or to failure due to burrs or normal wear. Most problems will be related to weak firing-pin blows. These can be caused by a short firing pin or a weak hammer spring. Replacement of the offending part will usually correct the problem.

Keep in mind that bent clip lips can cause problems in feeding and even ejection. Replace any clip which shows signs of bent or worn material at the cartridge-retaining lips.

Frequent cleaning and proper lubrication will otherwise keep most Model 70s going for a long, useful life.

PART 4

ADVANCED TECHNIQUES

23

Installing Interchangeable Choke Tubes

Chokes are a constant source of controversy among shooters and gunsmiths alike. There are a great many opinions as to what degree of constriction below bore diameter should be used to obtain specific pattern density, plus disagreement as to which pattern density relates to which choke designation.

This confusion exists partly because few manufacturers build shotgun bores or chokes to dimensions identical to those of other manufacturers, despite the fact that dimension specifications have been supplied—at least for cylinder, improved cylinder and full choke—by the Sporting Arms and Ammunition Manufacturers Institute (SAAMI). These SAAMI specifications are shown in an accompanying table. Pattern density is computed by counting the number of pellets striking within a 30-inch circle at a distance of 40 yards and comparing that number with the total number of pellets in the load. The only exception is that sometimes a skeet choke is tested using a 30-inch circle at 25 yards (in which case a 50 percent pattern density is desired).

Pattern percentages and choke constrictions are not absolute numbers. For a given choke designation, one shotgun manufacturer may

SAAMI PATTERN-PERCENTAGE CHOKE DESIGNATIONS

Choke Designation	Pellet Percentage
(% of total shot charge striking 30″ circle at 40 yds.)	
Cylinder	40
Skeet	45
Improved Cylinder	50
Modified	60
Improved Modified	65
Full	70

SAAMI CHOKE-DIAMETER SPECIFICATIONS

Choke[1]	10 ga.	12 ga.	16 ga.	20 ga.
Cylinder[2]	.775″–.780″	.725″–.730″	.670″–.675″	.615″–.620″
Improved Cylinder	N.A.	.724″–.726″	.664″–.666″	.609″–.611″
Full	.740″–.745″	.694″–.699″	.640″–.645″	.590″–.595″

[1]Chokes not listed are interpreted by the individual manufacturer.
[2]Cylinder is equal to bore diameter—no constriction.

elect a different degree of constriction or a different pattern percentage than another manufacturer. Further complications arise due to variations in the ammunition used to test pattern density. A change in ammunition can cause a notable change in choke performance.

For example, lead-shot hardness plays an important role in pattern density. Harder shot (shot with a higher antimony content) will pattern more densely than softer shot. Hard shot may have a 3 percent or higher antimony content, while soft shot often has 0.5 percent or less. The reason for the difference in pattern density is that the harder shot undergoes less deformation in its passage through forcing cone, bore, and choke, thus emerging from the muzzle rounder than soft shot. It is therefore less likely to veer from its course. Air resistance on the irregular surface of deformed pellets causes random and increased dispersion.

Velocity also plays an important role in pattern density. The faster the shot is accelerated through the bore, the greater the individual pellet deformation will be. Thus, lower velocity means denser patterns, while higher velocity means less pattern density. Other aerodynamic factors also contribute to a minor degree.

Shot size also plays a role. Usually, small pellets will pattern more densely than larger pellets. Density can be affected by the use of plated shot, too. Plated pellets (usually copper or nickel) have increased surface tension. Because of this, they are less deformed during acceleration to the muzzle and will pattern more densely than unplated shot. Still another variable is the use of a granulated polyethylene buffering mixed with the shot in some shells. Buffered pellets are better protected from deformation during acceleration and will pattern more densely than unbuffered shot charges.

Before evaluating a specific choke's performance, it is necessary to establish a performance reference to a specific type of ammunition. Many shooters have decided that the extra-hard shot and lower velocity levels of light target loads (2¾-dram equivalent) are ideal for pattern testing. Shot size #7½ seems to be favored in these target loads, as there are fewer pellet holes to count compared to #8 or 9 shot. And, at least in 12- and 20-gauges, the charge weight of shot used (1⅛ and ⅞-ounce, respectively) seems to provide ideal pattern density. Heavier shot charges seldom pattern as densely. This is all satisfactory, except for the waterfowler, who seldom uses shot sizes smaller than #4, always uses very heavy shot charges, and has to learn the pellet sizes and characteristics of steel shot rather than lead.

It is, therefore, important to analyze choke performance with the type of ammunition normally used. Except for testing with steel-shot waterfowl loads, select ammunition that has hard pellets (high antimony content) and a small shot size, plated and buffered if applicable.

How to Pattern a Gun and Load

A minimum of 10 patterns is needed to obtain a meaningful average. Gross errors in choke performance can be made if the target pellet count is figured as a percentage of an assumed total pellet count taken from a table based on average loads. It is vital to weigh the shot charges from 10 rounds of the ammunition to be used for pattern testing. From these 10 rounds, a useful average shot-charge weight can be determined. Then weigh 10 pellets simultaneously to determine the average pellet weight. Dividing this average pellet weight into the average shot charge weight will give you the actual—not merely assumed—average total pellet count. This count can be used to calculate pattern density pretty reliably, usually within plus or minus 5 percent. But a 10 percent up or down error can sometimes result.

Because aiming errors are possible at 40 yards, and with a shotgun they can be substantial, always draw the 30-inch pattern circle after the shot has been fired, positioning it to include the maximum number of pellets. Only when all this has been done will a true evaluation of a choke's performance be possible.

With a fixed-choke gun, pattern density can be decreased by carefully polishing the choke's diameter over its full length. This is a difficult task and requires very exacting equipment to maintain choke concentricity and uniformity. And when the job is done, if an ammunition change is introduced, pattern results can be notably different than expected.

The density of a pattern can be increased by altering the forcing-cone dimensions to reduce velocity or by increasing the bore diameter immediately before the choke. Again, the difficulty of the task is considerable. And again, the result will be right only for the same ammo used for the testing during adjustment.

Because of the great variations caused by different ammunition, the most practical solution to the choke problem is to be able to vary the amount of choke in the barrel. In the past, this was accomplished by installing appendages on the end of the barrel, containing collets that could be increased or decreased in diameter. Or, in some instances, fixed-choke tubes could be removed and replaced with others of different dimensions. Such choking devices were heavy, often ugly, and changed the gun's balance. They altered the shotgun's point of impact, too, because they placed the front sight considerably higher than normal due to their large diameters.

Constrictions Available with Screw-in Chokes

Fortunately, today's interchangeable choke tubes are simply screwed directly into the barrel with no adverse effect on weight, balance, appearance, or point of impact. The tubes are quite thin and do not require any excessive thickness of the barrel, either at the muzzle or over its entire length. A shotgun fitted with such tubes can be adjusted to fire pattern densities of any desired degree if tube selections include sufficient ranges of constriction. The shooter or gunsmith can choose a tube system with as many as 10 potential changes (the Tru-Choke system).

The practical maximum amount of choking has proved to be 0.045-inch. More constriction causes patterns to become erratic and can even be potentially dangerous, especially with steel-shot loads. This amount of total choking allows for a total of 10 steps in a practical and proven series of 0.005-inch increments. An accompanying table shows the designations given to each of these constrictions.

Choke changes of less than 0.005-inch do not,

in practice, produce a measurable change in pattern density. Thus, the table of chokes, fairly shows all of the choke variations that are practical. It also lists the traditional choke nomenclature as well as the designations in popular use today. In some instances, it may be necessary to increase or decrease choking by two "chokes" (.010-inch) to achieve any meaningful pattern differences.

Altering most fixed-choked shotgun barrels to accept screw-in chokes is not difficult and does not require special machinery. It is an alteration that most home gunsmiths can accomplish. The only tools required are a few bore pilots, a re-

Interchangeable choke tubes can give the shooter a choice of up to 10 different borings to modify patterns according to specific shooting requirements.

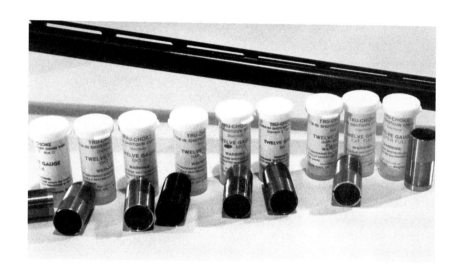

THE 10-CHOKE INTERCHANGEABLE TUBE SYSTEM
(as adopted by Tru-Choke)

Choke Nomenclature	Traditional Nomenclature	10-ga.	12-ga.	20-ga.	Approx. Pattern Density[1]
cylinder	cylinder (all)[2]	.775"	.730"	.620"	40
skeet I	12-ga. improved cylinder[2]	.770"	.725"	.615"	45
improved cylinder	20-ga. improved cylinder[2]	.765"	.720"	.610"	50
skeet II		.760"	.715"	.605"	55
modified		.755"	.710"	.600"	60
improved modified		.750"	.705"	.595"	65
full	20-ga. full[2]	.745"	.700"	.590"	70
trap	12-ga. full[2]	N.A.	.695"	N.A.	75[3]
extra full	10-ga. full[2]	.740"	.690"	.585"	80[3]
super full		.730"	.685"	.575"	85[3]

[1]Actual pattern density can vary substantially, depending on ammunition used. See text for details.
[2]A tolerance of +0.005" applies to traditional choking based on SAAMI specifications.
[3]Pattern density with these very tight percentages can be erratic, especially with pellet sizes of #3 or larger.

amer, tap, brace, long screwdriver, vernier, and vise. No heat or soldering is required and no special jigs are needed. Rib-equipped barrels do not need any special alteration, and no swelling of the barrel is required.

Barrels Suitable for Choke-Tube Conversion

Some preliminary barrel-thickness measurements need to be made to insure the safety and practicality of altering the barrel to accept screw-in choke tubes. The Tru-choke system was chosen for our instructions because of the wide range of tubes available, and the ease of purchasing the necessary pilots, reamer, and tap from the manufacturer (Trulock Tool Company). Other choke-tube systems are installed in a similar manner.

Not every barrel is suitable for alteration to accept screw-in chokes. Fortunately, most are. Barrels with internal bore diameters that are outside of normal tolerances should not be adapted to a screw-in choke. Oversized bores will result in a step up occurring at the junction of the choke tube and bore. This can be ruinous to barrel and choke—indeed, even a hazard to user and bystanders.

No attempt should ever be made to install screw-in chokes in any shotgun whose bore diameter exceeds 0.785-inch for 10-gauge, 0.735-inch for 12-gauge, 0.680-inch for 16-gauge, and 0.625-inch for 20-gauge. *Never!*

For the finest possible results, shooters and gunsmiths should limit themselves to barrels measuring 0.005-inch less than just stated for each gauge.

You must also be certain that a minimum barrel-wall thickness will be maintained after reaming. The absolute minimum for *all* gauges is a wall thickness of 0.010-inch at the thinnest portion of the barrel. This will insure ample strength when combined with an appropriate choke tube and proper installation. Under no circumstances should barrels with less than the following outside diameters (at the muzzle) be considered for adapting the screw-in chokes: 0.900-inch for 10-gauge, 0.825-inch for 12-gauge, 0.770-inch for 16-gauge, and 0.700-inch for 20-gauge.

The instructions in this book will pertain to single-barreled guns. Many modern double-barreled guns can be altered for screw-in chokes, but I don't recommend the job as a practical home-gunsmithing project. With two barrels, even a tiny misalignment can cause substantially different points of impact at hunting ranges.

Because a barrel's bore is seldom concentric with its outside diameter, the thickness of the barrel wall, at its thinnest point, is crucial. Measure the outside barrel diameter (as an example, a 12-gauge barrel may measure 0.830-inch). Then measure the inside diameter of the barrel (example: 0.700-inch). Subtracting the inside diameter from the outside diameter, and dividing the result by two, will give you the average bar-

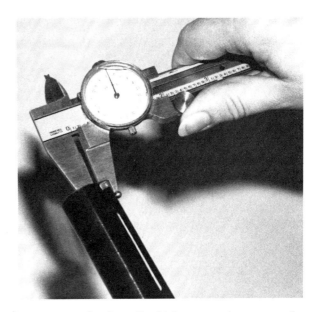

Measuring the barrel's thickness to determine the thinnest wall. This is important in deciding if a barrel is suitable for a screw-in choke alteration.

Any barrel to be converted to screw-in chokes must be straight at least over its last 15 inches of length.

rel-wall thickness. Example: 0.830″ − 0.700″ = 0.130″/2 = 0.065″. Now measure the actual barrel thickness at the 12, 3, 6, and 9 o'clock positions. Measurements might typically be 0.061, 0.064, 0.067, and 0.065. Using these measurements, we see that the barrel is thinnest at the 12 o'clock position (0.061-inch) and is 0.004-inch smaller than the average wall thickness.

Next, consider the reamer diameter, which in the case of a 12-gauge is 0.797-inch (The 10-gauge reamer is 0.867-inch and then 20 is 0.677-inch.) The reamer diameter, when subtracted from the barrel outside diameter of 0.830-inch and divided by two, gives us an actual wall thickness of 0.0165-inch. Then subtract 0.004 for the non-concentric bore and the result is the thickness of the barrel at its thinnest point *after choke installation*. In this example it would be 0.0165″ − 0.004″ = 0.0125″. The minimum wall thickness should always be 0.010-inch to insure a safe and satisfactory installation (regardless of gauge). Thus, the barrel in this example is satisfactory for alteration to accept the screw-in choke tubes.

Be absolutely certain that the barrel is straight for a maximum of 15 inches from the muzzle. This can be accomplished by placing a 15-inch straight edge against the outside of the barrel at the 12, 3, 6, and 9 o'clock position. A bent barrel is not suitable for screw-in choke alteration.

Tools for Choke-Tube Installation

Having determined that the barrel is suitable for the necessary gunsmithing, you need to gather the necessary tools:

1 Pilot of a diameter appropriate to the bore.
2 A vernier caliper to take accurate measurements.
3 A sturdy bench vise to hold the barrel.
4 Appropriate vise jaws or jaw padding.
5 A quantity of high-sulphur-content cutting oil.
6 A good brace.
7 The appropriate reamer for the gauge.
8 The appropriate tap for the gauge.
9 35-inch-long screwdriver.

If you have purchased the choke-installation kit from the manufacturer, you will have items 1, 7, 8, and 9 on the foregoing list of required tools. The pilot (item 1) is provided in five or six different sizes, in 0.002-inch increments, to insure a proper fit for any barrel of normal tolerances.

Additionally, a bore caliper will be useful for measuring bore diameter.

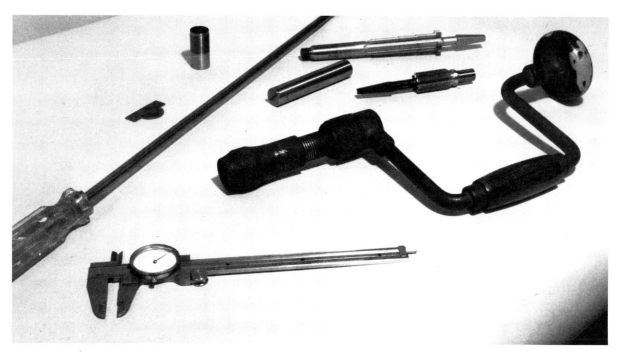

Tools needed for choke installation include a brace, reamer, tap, long screwdriver, and verniers.

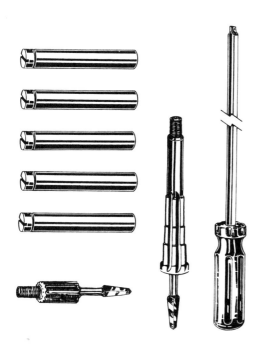

Assemble the pilot and reamer with a suitably long screwdriver.

Conversion Procedures

Having satisfied all the dimensional requirements mentioned, secure the barrel to be altered in the vise. A set of leather-faced wood jaw blocks, with an appropriate barrel channel, will insure that the barrel is not crushed or marred. Both barrel and vise must be secured so that there will be absolutely no movement.

Obviously, if the barrel is not equipped with a rib, it can be shortened to any desired length beforehand. Ribbed barrels should be left at their original length.

Slip the appropriate pilot into the barrel from the chamber end. Its slotted end should be toward the chamber. The proper pilot size is less than 0.002-inch under bore diameter. "Slop" of 0.002-inch or more in pilot fit will defeat the purpose of the pilot, to keep bore and choke tube concentric and straight. Move the pilot forward in the barrel until it touches the internal choke taper (if any). Using the long screwdriver, care-

Leave a bit of play between brace chuck and reamer to allow the reamer to "float." This will keep everything centered during the work.

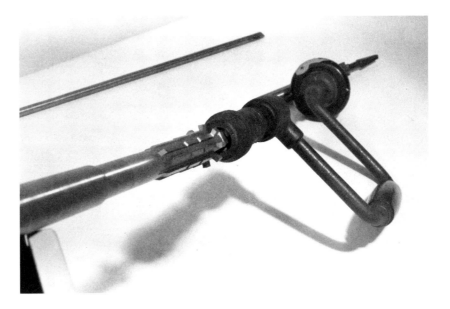

fully assemble the pilot and reamer. Be certain the mating surfaces of both pilot and reamer are clean. These units are designed to align properly with a minimum of torque. Do not overtighten the threads. Hand pressure on the screwdriver while hand-holding the reamer shank is all that is required.

Be sure the vise holds the barrel in a comfortable working position. Then close the brace over the reamer shank, but leave a bit of play. This will allow the reamer and chuck junction to float, enabling the reamer to follow the pilot without stress and helping to avoid misalignment by the operator.

Push the reamer gently to the front of the bore, lubricate it generously with cutting oil, and using moderate end pressure, begin to turn the reamer clockwise, starting the cut. Do not, under any circumstances, turn the reamer counterclockwise—not even a tiny bit. Such manipulation can ruin the reamer.

Flush the chips away with cutting oil. Keep the reamer turning, slowly, as you continue cutting. Ream in this manner until the stop portion of the reamer is between 0.060-inch and 0.075-inch from the muzzle. This will completely remove the original choking and open the barrel to the correct diameter for threading. When this position has been reached, remove the reamer and pilot from the barrel. Thoroughly clean all traces of metal chips from the bore.

Remove the pilot from the reamer and assemble it to the tap. Be certain that both mating surfaces are absolutely clean.

Thoroughly lubricate the tap and slowly start it into the bore, rotating it no more than four revolutions. Squirt plenty of cutting oil into the bore, as far as possible, and then make another four revolutions. Continue squirting oil and turning the tap a maximum of four revolutions until the tap first meets notably increased resistance. This resistance is caused by the end of the tap striking the necked down section of the bore. Reverse the tap and back it out slowly.

Again clean the barrel, removing all chips and grit. Reassemble the pilot to the reamer and very gently ream in until you feel the reamer stop its cutting action and begin to turn freely. Use care not to damage the freshly cut threads. This operation sharpens the step against which the choke tube will rest. Remove the reamer/pilot and once more clean the barrel, removing all traces of chips, grit, and cutting oil.

Screw in a choke tube, finger-tight, and then use the choke-tube installation wrench to gently snug it up. Never overtighten the tube.

Ream carefully and never, repeat *never*, rotate the reamer counterclockwise.

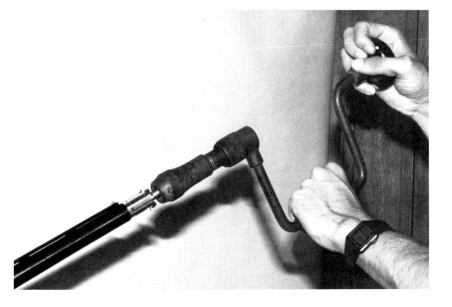

After cleaning barrel of all chips and gut, thread the reamed barrel carefully.

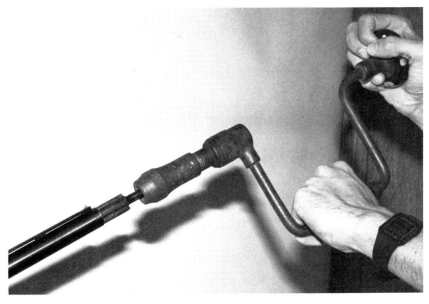

After threading, make a final and very careful ream, bringing the internal shoulder to a sharp step.

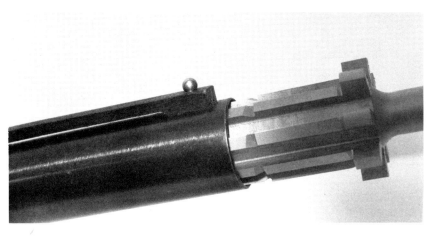

After you've cleaned away all chips from inside the barrel, it is ready to receive the choke tube.

Check the bore/choke-tube junction, using a good light from both ends. There should be a slight step down from bore to the back edge of the choke tube.

In some instances, it may be necessary to chase the threads with the tap once again, before the choke tube will screw in without undue resistance. If so, be certain not to damage the final reaming operation which leaves a true 90 degree step in the barrel against which the choke tube seats.

As in all gunsmithing tasks, the quality of the job depends on how well it is thought out beforehand and how slowly and carefully the work proceeds.

Naturally, the reamer and tap must be kept sharp. Any attempts to do the job with dull tools may end with a ruined barrel. While some local machine ships can properly sharpen reamers and taps, I prefer to return mine to the manufacturer for such work.

With screw-in chokes, the shooter has the advantage of being able to fine-tune his pattern to meet specific requirements for a specific lot of ammunition. When testing the gun, remember that a minimum of 10 patterns are needed to give a fair estimation of average pattern density.

Also, keep in mind that with very large shot sizes (#1, B, BB, BBB, T, F), a choke tube with somewhat less constriction may well deliver a denser pattern than a tube with slightly more constriction. Moreover, steel pellets tend to pattern very densely. Seldom is there reason to use a choke tighter than modified with steel shot. Certainly it is counterproductive to use a choke tighter than improved modified with steel pellets.

Barrel conversion for interchangeable choke tubes, like any gunsmithing task, should be first attempted on an easily replaced, inexpensive barrel. A careful craftsman should encounter no difficulties, but it's better to be safe than sorry. After a few installations, you can easily pay for the tooling by doing several choke-tube conversions for friends. After you gain initial experience, the job shouldn't take more than 40 minutes or so.

24

Repairing Stock Breaks and Splits

Wood is more fragile than you might suppose. Sooner or later, anyone who spends much time working on firearms will be faced with a broken stock. Stock breaks usually occur in the wrist/pistol-grip area. However, broken-off stock toes are not uncommon, nor are general cracks and splits.

If the broken stock has been subjected to years of abuse in the form of oil draining from the action, it will be impossible to repair the stock. Oil-soaked wood is ruined wood. It cannot be successfully glued, even with an epoxy compound. However, if the stock is free of oil and the broken pieces are available, it is often possible to restore the stock to a strong, useful life.

Clean breaks are the easiest to repair, but splintered breaks can be mended if there are no more than four or five major fractures. Attempts to repair severely splintered stocks are usually exercises in futility. Fortunately, stocks seldom break apart with many splinters.

Although repairs are easiest and best when all the broken wood is available, it is not unreasonable to repair stocks when a piece is missing.

Preparing Wood for Bonding

First, determine whether the broken pieces fit together reasonably well or if it will be necessary to splice in a piece of wood. If an additional piece of wood is required, there may be no special difficulties beyond trying to match the grain and color. This is especially true when the missing piece is a toe or a pistol-grip end. Simply find a piece of wood that closely matches in color and grain, and then cut it so the glued-on piece has its grain running in the same direction as the wood against which it will be glued. It's best to form a smooth, flat surface at the point of the break if replacement wood is to be added. Two flat, matching surfaces are much easier to join with a minimum of visible parting line.

Breaks requiring the addition of wood between two existing pieces need careful consideration. It is not practical, for example, to splice in

243

Broken or split stocks can often be repaired if the damage is not too severe. Here are two examples of typical breaks that can be repaired in your shop and extend the useful life of the stock.

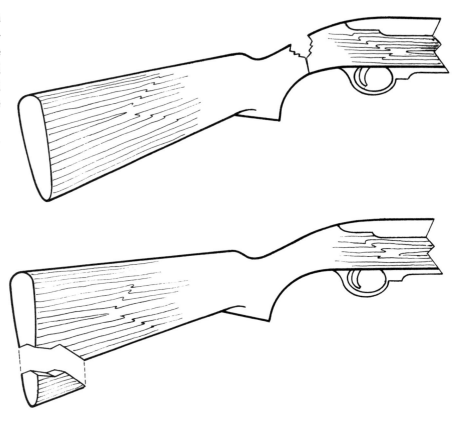

a new wrist in the pistol grip area between the remains of a fore-end and buttstock. To add wood between two existing pieces will require that the original pieces contact each other over at least 50 percent of the area to be repaired. Otherwise, it is unlikely that a strong repair can be made. Again, the sections of the original stock that will mate with replacement wood should be carefully worked into flats that will match similar flats on the new wood.

Make no attempt to have the replacement wood fit the contours and shape of the stock. Indeed, the added piece should be as large a block as possible to facilitate the later step of working it into the overall profile of the stock.

The replacement wood must be very carefully worked to match the mating surfaces of the repair. The quality of the job will be directly related to the fit of the replacement wood.

Next, make one or more grooves, depending on the size of the working area, in both the original stock and the matching repair block. These grooves will accept a good bit of epoxy which later will become internal supporting ribs, solidly bonding the stock repair. The depths and widths of the grooves should be about ⅛-inch. However, if you are uncertain about your ability to put such narrow grooves in both the original and repair wood and make them line up at least along 50 percent of their width, make the grooves wider—up to about ¼-inch.

If you just need to glue together two or more original stock pieces, first fit everything together. Determine what press-together or slide-together techniques will be required to have all the pieces mate as closely as possible to the original shape.

To repair a stock partially split at the pistol grip, insert a wooden wedge into the break, as shown. The two parts to be joined must bear against each other for at least half their surface. Clamp wedge in place.

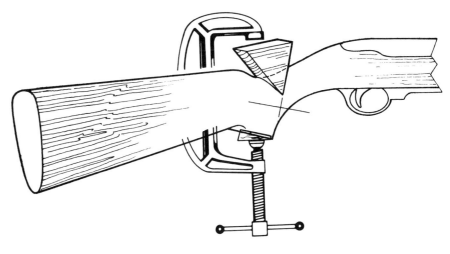

Clamping Requirements

You will need to hold all parts solidly together during the curing of the epoxy. This means one or more clamps will be required. You should determine the best clamping method for your repair before applying epoxy. Put everything together in a dry run and clamp up the work. Use pieces of soft wood to protect the original stock from damage due to clamping. You may wish to rasp a flat on any replacement wood to accept firm, even clamping pressure. The availability of suitable clamps will influence the worth of your repair. It's also important to find a way to position the clamps effectively, squeezing the repair surfaces together firmly.

Epoxy Bonding Procedure

When you are certain you know how best to hold the broken parts together and you have the proper clamps and know exactly how they should be positioned, prepare the epoxy. Mix an adequate amount to cover all the surfaces of the repair. Then place tape on your clamp jaws and cover the tape with the appropriate epoxy-release compound. Do this carefully, as you do not want to glue the clamps to the work. The same epoxy and release agents used for glass-bedding a rifle are ideal for stock repairs. Match the dying of the epoxy carefully to the color of the wood. A little too light will look better than a bit too dark.

Coat all surfaces of the repair with the epoxy, then assemble and clamp everything securely. If portions of the stock will need to be protected from the epoxy, (such as checkered areas or large finished areas), they should be covered with masking tape before mixing and applying the epoxy. Let the clamped repair begin to harden for about five hours.

After that initial hardening, carefully—without disturbing the clamps—remove any excess epoxy from the outside of the work. Then let the whole job continue to harden and cure for at least 72 hours.

Remove the clamps and, with a medium-coarse rasp, shape any added wood into the lines of the stock. Also, rasp away any excess epoxy. Do not work so fast as to rasp any of the original stock. If no replacement wood has been used, carefully remove any heavy excess of epoxy.

Pinning for Extra Strength

The repair is now about one-third done. Next, you must pin the stock to give it strength. Brownells brass stock-repair pins are strongly suggested. These are available in ³⁄₃₂-inch and ⅛-inch diameters. They are about 2½ inches long and are threaded to hold some anchoring epoxy. You will need to determine the angle or angles at which the pin or pins should be installed to provide maximum strength. Generally speaking, the pins should be placed at a right angle to the original break. Do not overdo the use of pins. One pin for every 1½ inches of length in the repair area is quite adequate.

If the repair involves a broken pistol grip or wrist, a good approach is to use two pins, placed to form an X through the repair area.

When you have decided on the number, locations, and angles of the pins, drill corresponding holes with a bit the same size as the repair pin. Then coat the repair pin with a bit of stock-

When epoxy hardens, shape new wood to match stock contour. Drill holes in the stock of a size to accept stock-repair pins.

Chuck pin in variable-speed drill, cover with epoxy, and drive it into hole.

bedding epoxy. Chuck the pin up into a variable-speed drill and run it into the pre-drilled hole at low speed. Allow 72 hours for complete curing and then cut off the pins flush with the repair.

Stock-repair pins are available from gunsmithing supply houses.

Contouring and Finishing

Now bring the repair surface into full and matching contours with the original stock. Do not remove excess amounts of original finish around the repair. However, you will need to feather the area to facilitate spot finishing. The brass repair pins are easily filed to match stock contours. You can put a drop of paint on each end before refinishing if you find the brass dots objectionable. Refinishing hints will be found in the chapter on building kit firearms.

If there are small chips, bits of missing wood, or tiny spots where epoxy did not fill in, you should correct these before refinishing. There are a number of ways to do so. You can mix up some additional epoxy to fill in voids. You can use a bit of shellac of matching color, working it into

This stock-repair kit includes shellac sticks, Fil-Stiks, and an electric hot knife for finishing.

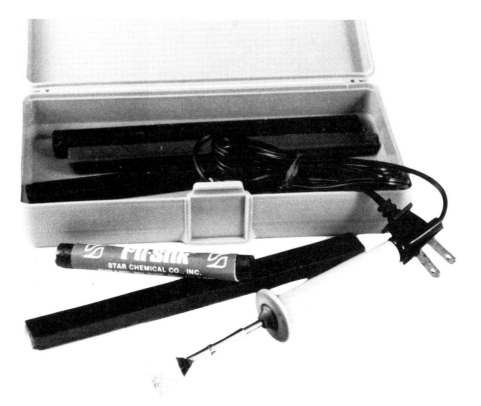

place with an electric hot knife. Or, if the spots are tiny enough, you can simply rub in a bit of Fil-Stik before refinishing. All the necessary items are available from woodworking outlets and gunsmith suppliers such as Brownells.

Restoration of Checkering

If the repaired area encompasses portions of checkering, obviously the checkering will need to be recut or extended across any replacement wood. Checkering is not a task for the inexperienced person, but while you're repairing a broken stock is an ideal time to begin to learn.

A carefully worked single-line cutter, following the original checkering as a guide, will work well. You may find the task easiest with a cutter that has a smooth edge (to follow existing checkering) and a separate single cutting edge. Beginning in an area of checkering and recutting some of the original lines, you can slowly progress until you are cutting new rows over the repaired area. If you go very slowly, working carefully outward over the repair, all should go reasonably well.

Remember that you should cut all the lines running in the same direction before cutting diagonal lines. Work new cuts carefully from existing lines and realize that these cuts must meet properly with existing cuts on the other side of the repair. You may do best by working from both sides of the repair gradually to insure alignment of the cuts. Scribe original cuts very, very shallowly until you are sure everything lines up, then go back and carefully cut your scribed lines deeper.

Gaining Experience

Stock repairs demand some improvisation. No two jobs will be exactly alike. Patience in fitting everything together, selecting matching color and grain for replacement wood, dying the epoxy, and careful use of repair pins and touch-up material will be essential. Every step is equally important. The mixing of the epoxy must be exact to afford the needed strength, and the placement of repair pins requires a certain insight into the need for strength.

I've found that the best stock repairs are made by those who have gained experience by doing a number of repair jobs. If there's an old, discarded stock lying about, you may just want to break it in half through the wrist and then repair it before attempting similar work on a favorite gun.

If the repair involves a split but not completely separated stock, give some thought to the need to get epoxy down into every area of the split. You may have to pry the split well apart to accomplish this. Indeed, in some instances it may be best to separate the stock at the split. It will require careful judgment to determine the best approach for a satisfactory repair.

I cannot overemphasize the need to work the repair through on a dry run. Alignment and clamping of pieces should not be first undertaken after applying the epoxy. A rehearsal is essential before the epoxy is mixed.

It is possible to use glue on some stock breaks. Where strength is not important, any of the good waterproof glues may prove satisfactory. Glues are generally easier and more convenient to use than a stock-bedding epoxy. But, in general, the use of an epoxy will prove to be the best and strongest method.

25

Building a Kit Rifle

The idea behind kit firearms is that the purchaser can save a great deal of money by supplying the necessary time and labor to fit, finish, and assemble the parts instead of buying a factory-finished gun. You can also derive considerable enjoyment from building your own firearm, but the truth is that very few purchasers of kit guns have the equipment or ability to properly finish the metal parts.

Cold bluing is all right for touch-up but seldom satisfactory when finishing an entire firearm. And the requirements for hot bluing, let alone proper polishing, are beyond most home-gunsmithing shops.

Kit guns (a lot of them, at any rate) have recently undergone a transformation that makes them attractive to many more people. I refer, of course, to the factory finishing of all metal parts. The purchaser can now just assemble the metal parts, fit them to the stock, and finish the outside of the stock. The inletting varies from 90 percent to 100 percent finished as the stock comes out of the kit box. In short, kit guns can now be assembled by almost anyone, and the metal is already blued.

Kits are available for such popular firearms as the Remington 700 (using an ADL-style stock) in calibers like .30-06 and .270. Kit guns are also

Thompson/Center New Englander kit rifle.

available for a wide range of muzzleloading firearms, and one manufacturer offers a kit gun for a single-shot shotgun.

For the purposes of this chapter, a Thompson/ Center New Englander kit was chosen. This kit is available for building a 12-gauge muzzleloading shotgun or a .50-caliber muzzleloading rifle. The two versions are nearly identical, except for the barrels and sights. The rifle model includes front and rear sights, while the shotgun has a single front bead.

Because all the metal parts are polished and blued, great care must be taken when fitting and assembling them, and while finishing the wood. Even so, properly transforming the kit into a finished rifle or shotgun is not quick or easy. A great deal of time and patience must be devoted to the project if it is to equal the quality of a factory-finished gun. Yet the slow, meticulous worker can produce a firearm that will actually be superior to the factory product.

Strategic Steps in the Kit-Building Approach

The proper approach to building a kit firearm is to be concerned with the interrelationships of the parts and work to make the overall firearm progress through various steps until the unit comes together in finished form. Avoid the temptation to bring any one section of the firearm to a completely finished state. Doing so will prevent you from working the rifle's overall form and lines into a well finished unit. Instead, the kit may wind up looking like an assembled jigsaw puzzle.

An obvious example of the right strategy is to perform all the coarser fitting and inletting jobs for the entire rifle before proceeding to the very exacting fitting and inletting which will bring wood and metal together in a professional manner. It has been my experience that working in this manner tends to slow me down and get me

thinking more about what I am doing rather than what I might be doing in a little while. And being repetitious in the type of work being done helps that work to go smoothly.

Tools and Preparations

To begin working on the Thompson/Center New Englander kit, some specific tools must be on hand. (To illustrate this chapter, I built the .50-caliber rifle, but the following information and instructions will apply to the New Englander shotgun, too.) Rough work tools will not be required, only finishing tools. A few fine rasps, assorted screwdrivers, several C-clamps, center punches, drill bits, a drill, some masking tape, and, of course, a selection of sandpaper will be needed.

To provide a non-marring surface on which to work, a softwood plank, perhaps 2 × 8-inch board approximately 24 inches long, can be used. Clamp the plank to the workbench to give about five inches of overhang. This will allow the

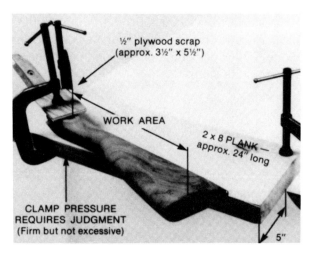

1. Working the buttstock. Turn the stock so the comb section clears the plank surface. This allows you to work the edges to a careful blend.

clamping of the rifle stock to the work surface. Always use a piece of wood between the clamp and stock. A piece of soft 3 × 5-inch plywood about ½-inch thick will serve very nicely. When clamping the stock to the work surface, do not use undue pressure or the stock will be damaged, even ruined. But do snug it up tight enough to prevent it from moving as you work on it.

Do not attempt to shortcut the job by trying to finish the stock while holding it by hand on top of a bench surface or, worse, by trying to work while holding it in your lap. If the finished stock is to have a look of quality, the work will need to proceed professionally and that means working on a well-clamped stock.

Butt Section of the Stock

The stock's steel buttplate is temporarily held in position with two Phillips-head screws. Leave

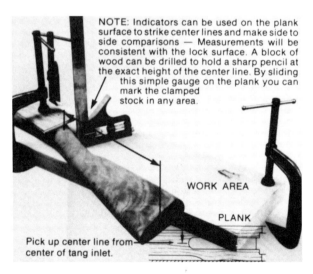

NOTE: Indicators can be used on the plank surface to strike center lines and make side to side comparisons — Measurements will be consistent with the lock surface. A block of wood can be drilled to hold a sharp pencil at the exact height of the center line. By sliding this simple gauge on the plank you can mark the clamped stock in any area.

WORK AREA

PLANK

Pick up center line from center of tang inlet.

2. When you've finished one side of the stock, turn it so the buttplate section clears the plank and work the other side.

these screws in place until the stock-finishing effort has been completed.

The fit of the wood around the buttplate will need minor touching up. Cover the buttplate edge with two thicknesses of masking tape and sandpaper the wood down carefully to the level of the tape. Use medium-grade sandpaper wrapped around a block of wood while the stock is clamped as shown in Figs. 1 and 2.

If you are very careful, after getting the wood down to the level of the masking tape wrapped around the buttplate edges, you can further improve the fit. Switch to a very fine grade of paper and work the wood so as to cut away the top layer of masking tape. (Do not attempt this until you have practiced the sanding technique on a scrap piece of metal. If you take away more than the top layer of tape you will damage the buttplate's finish.)

Be certain to follow the lines of the buttplate when sanding. The edges of the buttplate should be extended as imaginary lines well onto the buttstock. This will give a very professional appearance.

After working the butt area, use a fine-cut rasp to work the wrist area, removing any rough spots and bumps. Go gently to maintain the lines of the stock. Bring the entire wrist area to as smooth a finish as practical with the rasp, using long, overlapping strokes. This will prevent any hollows or dips from being inadvertently rasped into the stock. Proceed slowly, preserving the basic lines of the stock.

Now work the remaining area of the buttstock with medium-grade sandpaper, again wrapped around a block of wood. Bring all areas of the butt into a smooth and continuous surface. Be especially carefully working around the comb. You can improve upon the general lines, but do not attempt to bring a different character to the stock. Kit stocks have only enough wood on them to allow for finishing within the general framework of the factory shape.

Do not work on the immediate area of the tang, as this should not be done until the tang has been properly positioned. Also, stay away from the lock area at this time. Simply work up to a position a couple of inches from these areas.

Fore-End Section of the Stock

Clamp the stock as shown in Fig. 3 and install the brass escutcheons, one on each side of the fore-end. Press the escutcheons into place with the shouldered side inward. Using the appropriate screws (see assembly drawing), secure them so that escutcheons and screws seat correctly. The screws must follow the pre-drilled holes unerringly. After insuring that both escutcheons are seated properly, remove them until final stock finishing has been completed.

Work the fore-end wood carefully with medium sandpaper wrapped on a block of wood, and/or with fine rasps, to remove any bumps and

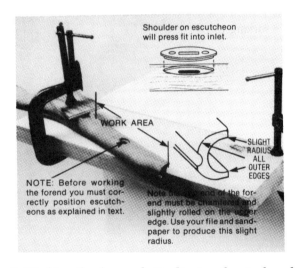

3. Working the fore-end. By flipping the stock and clamping it in the same manner, the opposite side of the fore-end can be worked.

to produce a flowing surface. Take great care not to remove any wood from the escutcheon's seat or from the barrel-channel edges. A slight radius (Fig. 3) must be put on the inside and outside edge of the forearm end.

Tang Section of the Stock

The tang must be in position at this point, so hook it over the barrel's hooked breech and place the unit into the stock. Using a soft leather or plastic mallet, tap the muzzle end of the barrel rearward to seat the tang fully against the breech wall of the stock.

Use only a large-faced plastic or leather mallet (larger than the barrel diameter) to prevent the mallet edge from slipping into the mouth of the bore and causing accuracy-destroying damage to the barrel's crown.

With the tang fully seated against the stock, securely lock the barrel and tang into position in the stock, using several turns of masking tape. Do this in the general area of the stock mortise for the escutcheons. Make sure the stock and barrel are secured tightly to prevent the tang from moving out of its positively seated position against the breech wall of the stock. Then clamp

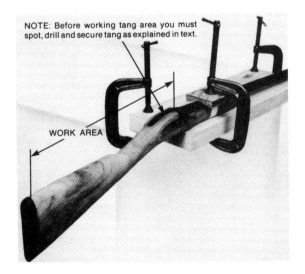

4. To work the comb and tang, lock the barrel and tang into position with several turns of masking tape. Then clamp the stock as shown. Drill holes for tang screws. Then sand and shape the wood.

the assembled unit as shown in Fig. 4.

You must now very carefully drill screw holes and install the tang screws. They must be put in precisely, so be sure that their heads will properly and fully seat. This means care must be taken to maintain the necessary angle when drilling the screw holes.

Taking care not to mar the finish of the tang, carefully center-punch both screw holes. Then using a ⅛-inch drill, make the holes for the tang screws. Refer to Figure 7 before starting this procedure. The holes should be drilled ¼-inch deeper than the length of the screws. Soaping the screws (by rubbing them on a bar of soap) will allow for easier in and out. Turn the screws in carefully, without applying undue force.

After the tang screws are seated, cover the entire tang with masking tape. Now work the wood around the tang, as you did the buttplate. Use care not to alter stock lines or mar the tang's or barrel's finish. Some long medium- or fine-cut rasps may be useful in smoothing this area. Long strokes will help remove the bumps while avoiding the digging of hollows.

Be particularly careful to follow the lines of the stock. It may be advisable *not* to use a block of wood for sanding in this area. Try both methods of sanding (sparingly) and adopt the method that best enables you to follow the stock lines. Be careful not to run the sandpaper up against the trigger guard.

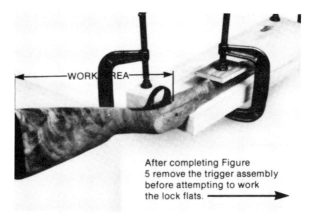

After completing Figure 5 remove the trigger assembly before attempting to work the lock flats. ⟶

5. Working the toe and trigger. Remove barrel and tang and clamp stock as shown. Spot, drill, and secure trigger assembly. Sand and shape wood.

Trigger Area of the Stock

Remove the barrel and tang from the wood, and clamp the stock as shown in Fig. 5. Place the trigger guard and trigger assembly into the stock mortise. Carefully center-punch both screw holes. Remember that the screws must enter the stock at the correct angle if they are to seat properly. Refer to Fig. 7 for a visual understanding of this procedure. Being careful to avoid finish damage, use a ³⁄₃₂-inch drill bit to make the trigger-guard screw holes. Soap the appropriate screws and secure the trigger guard. Then carefully and exactly mask off all of its surfaces with your tape.

Sanding and shaping the trigger area requires special care, as it is an awkward working surface.

Lock Area of the Stock

Remove the trigger guard. Remove the hammer from the lockplate and carefully position the lockplate in the stock, securing it with the lockplate screw (using the appropriate escutcheon from the opposite side of the stock). Then exactly cover the lockplate with masking tape. Next tape the stock to the work area, as shown in Fig. 6. Keep in mind that it will be extremely important to keep the lock area and the opposing side of the stock symmetrical with each other. It may help to lightly pencil a center line on the bottom of the stock, as shown in Fig. 2.

Work the wood around the lockplate down to the same level as the plate. Proceed as in previous efforts to make wood and metal blend. It will help greatly to use a flat block of wood,

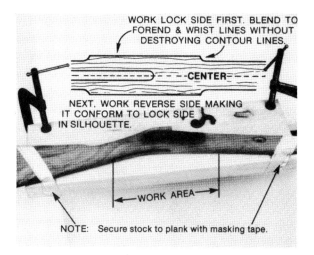

6. Working lock area. Remove trigger guard, remove hammer from lockplate and screw lockplate in stock. Then work the wood around lockplate.

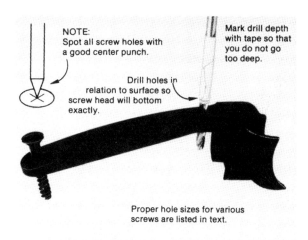

7. Method of spotting and drilling screw holes.

sandpapering merely to reduce the flat wood area to the appropriate height. Do not make any attempt to contour the lock area into the wrist or forearm at this time. When the flat of the lock area has been reduced to blend with the lock, remove the tape holding the stock to the work area. Then remove the lockplate, along with the retaining escutcheon and screw.

Retape the stock to the work surface with the lock side down, and proceed very carefully to work the left flat down to the same distance from the center line as the lock side of the stock. The best appearance will be achieved when the flat surface on this side of the stock approximates the flat surface on the lock side.

Factory-finished stocks seldom have sharp corners; it's just not practical to attempt sharp lines with mass-produced stocks. However, sharp lines can add a great deal to a finished stock. Therefore, consider preserving the sharp corners of the action and opposing-side flats.

You may also wish to add a little fluting at the comb area. A carefully applied round rasp can accomplish this. Use other sporting stocks from muzzleloaders and metallic-cartridge firearms to decide on the shaping and extent of such touches.

Finishing the Stock

Sand the ramrod and then install its cap and jag adaptor. Use a good grade of epoxy for this. Brownells Accra Glas works quite well.

With the rifle completely assembled, review the work. Check carefully to see that each screw is properly bottomed. If not, remove the screw, plug the hole with a suitable-sized dowel covered with a waterproof glue, and allow it to dry thoroughly. Then redrill the screw hole and seat the screw carefully.

Also check that the fit around the buttplate, tang, trigger guard, and lockplate is satisfactory. Make any minor corrections, being sure to tape any metal near areas needing rework.

If the overall flow of stock lines and fit at wood/metal joints is up to your best efforts, you are ready to begin the final finishing of the stock. Remove all the metal parts and set them aside.

Keep in mind when you begin sanding for the final time that the fit of metal parts to the stock will be impaired if too much wood is removed where wood and metal will meet.

Use a very fine grade of sandpaper for the final sanding and work only with the grain of the wood. After sanding, brush away any surface dust and moisten the outside surface of the stock with warm water. Just make the surface damp. It's best to apply the warm water with a damp cloth. Keep all moisture away from the barrel channel and stock mortises. This procedure will raise tiny "whiskers" on the surface of the stock. When the stock is completely dry, repeat the sanding with as fine a grade sandpaper as you can purchase. Re-moisten and re-sand.

Take great care to protect the raw surface of the wood during the final sanding operations. Prevent nicks and stains. These will detract greatly from the finished effort.

The stock is now ready for finishing. An oil finish is traditional with muzzleloading firearms. Such a finish will not produce excessive glare in the woods and can easily be repaired if minor nicks or scratches occur as time goes on. Several good stock finishes are available. A small quantity of wood filler (walnut-colored) will be needed. Many shooters have expressed satisfaction with Hoppe's Walnut Stock Filler and finish for the first coat and Hoppe's Boiled Linseed Oil for the final finish. Others have had excellent results with the Birchwood Casey Tru-Oil Stock Finish Kit, which contains small quantities of sandpaper, steel wool, stock filler, Tru-Oil Finish, Stock Sheen, burlap, and buffing cloths. (But for a professional job, more sandpaper and steel wool will be needed.)

Regardless of which finish you select, it is imperative that the wood be super-smooth and whisker-free before applying the first coat of stock filler.

A very generous supply of #260-grit sandpaper will be required for final sanding. I prefer to go to a #360-grit paper after sanding with the #260. If the second wetting of the stock raises a large number of whiskers, the wetting and de-whiskering with #260 paper should be repeated as many times as necessary. The last wetting should raise only an insignificant amount of whiskers.

After sanding, use a clean piece of 000 or 0000 steel wool to carefully wipe away any sanding dust. You are now ready to apply the stock filler, which fills in the tiny wood pores so that an absolutely smooth surface is available for the finish. Normally, the wood filler also adds a tone of walnut color to deepen the stock's hue.

Apply the filler according to the manufacturer's instructions. Always be sure the filler is well shaken before use, and wipe away any excess with a soft polishing cloth. Allow it to dry for a full 24 hours—longer if it's humid. Then, using #360-grit paper, lightly sand the stock's entire surface. *Lightly* is the key word. Remove all sanding dust with a soft, clean polishing cloth.

Now apply a thin coat of stock finish. Use enough to get complete coverage, but not so much as to cause wet spots or runs. When using oil finishes, apply the oil with the palm of the hand, rubbing until the stock surface becomes quite warm. You may wish to use a lint-free cloth to apply other types of finish.

Several thin coats are always preferable to one or two thick coats. Use a clean pad of 0000 steel wool to lightly rub down each coat of finish after it is completely dry. This may be 24 to 48 hours—or more—after finish application.

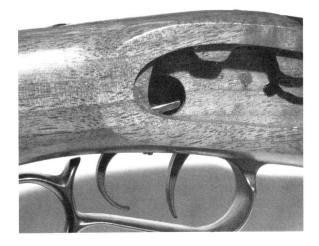

Properly completed stock will have all mortises, barrel channel, and other internal surfaces well protected with finish.

After applying the final coat, give the stock a good 72 hours to harden and dry before handling it. Do not rub the final coat with steel wool unless you wish to mute any reflective quality. Many shooters apply a good stock wax to help protect the wood and enhance its sheen.

Be sure to finish all wood surfaces, including stock mortises, barrel channel, butt, ramrod, etc. If raw wood is left unfinished, it will absorb moisture and, over a period of time, adversely affect your stock. You are now ready for final assembly of the firearm.

Use care when screwing the nipple in place so as to avoid damaging the threads.

Assembling Your Finished Kit Gun

Follow the manufacturer's instructions meticulously. The Thompson/Center New Englander rifle or shotgun kit demands that the sear lifter be correctly positioned in the trigger cut-out (see Fig. 6). Assemble the rifle carefully, insuring that each screw obtains a firm purchase in its hole. If you soaped the screws to help during repeated assembly and disassembly, remove all traces of soap with warm water and thoroughly dry them. Check the fit of all parts and verify that action and trigger function as intended.

When screwing in the nipple, be sure not to damage its threads or the corresponding threads in the breech. Also be certain the nipple is turned up snugly, using a proper-sized nipple wrench.

The finished gun should be an equal to a finished factory rifle. An inexperienced person may not quite reach this degree of proficiency on his first attempt, but after gaining some experience, a home gunsmith may well surpass the fit and finish of a mass-produced firearm.

Finished kit gun will always be a source of pride to a careful worker.

26

Drilling and Tapping for Sight Installation

There is no surer way to destroy any rifle, shotgun, or handgun than to drill and tap it for sight installation without benefit of an adequate drill jig, sharp drill bits and taps, and the knowledge of how to proceed.

Thus, this chapter is meant only for those who have (or will acquire) the necessary equipment.

That includes, at a minimum, the B-Square Pro-Scope Mount Jig, which comes complete with base block, bore-align arbor, two V-bushings, a #31 drill bushing, jig bars for both Mauser and Springfield receivers, cap screws, and wrench. With this tool you can drill Springfield, Enfield, and Japanese receivers with one jig bar and

B-Square Pro-Scope Mount Jig is the minimum essential for drilling and tapping military-style receivers for installing a scope mount.

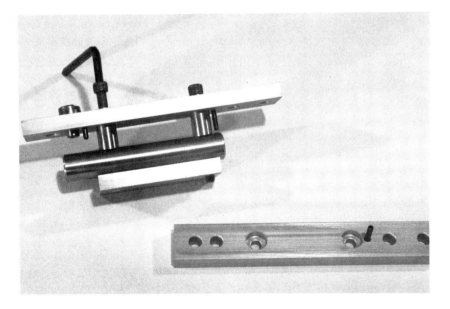

Mausers with the other. This unit, however, does not include the necessary tap guide. A B-Square Tru-Tapper is strongly suggested.

Setting Up the Jig and Receiver

The B-Square Pro-Scope Jig is a simple affair that uses a flat baseplate to provide a suitable flat work surface for the drill-press table. To use the jig, the bore-align arbor is inserted into the rifle's receiver (after removal of stock, trigger, bolt stop, or other encumbrances). Next, place both V-bushings, with the V contacting the arbor, over the holes in the arbor. Place the appropriate jig bar over the V-bushings so that the two recesses in the bar go over the bushings. Drop the Allen screws down through the jig bar, V-bushings, and bore-align arbor to hold everything in place. Finally, position the base block against the bottom of the receiver and turn the Allen screws loosely into it.

Note: The two holes in the jig bar with the narrowest spacing should be positioned at the rear of the receiver. These holes have a ½-inch spacing.

Before tightening the Allen screws, slide the whole assembly forward until the jig-bar stop pin contacts the rear of the front receiver ring. This is an important step and will properly locate the screw holes. Then tighten the Allen screws securely. The rifle's receiver is squared with the jig as a result of the receiver's bottom flat being securely held by the flat base block. It is important to note that this type of jig cannot assure correct alignment of the screw holes in relationship to the bore. In most cases, all holes will properly align. But if the barrel is not central and square with the receiver, difficulty in proper mount alignment with the bore can sometimes be encountered.

Next, place the correct drill bushing in the appropriate hole in the top of the jig bar, place the entire unit on the drill-press table, clamp it in alignment with the drill bit, and you are ready to drill holes. Be sure to set the drill-stop so you will not drill into the barrel with the forward hole on the front receiver ring. The three remaining holes can be drilled through the receiver. Blind holes (the front hole on the front receiver ring) present some special tapping problems, so drilling through the receiver is best whenever possible. Therefore, if you can drill the front receiver hole without a barrel in place, all the better.

Always be certain the holes in your chosen scope base (or bases) properly align with those in the jig bar. When installing Weaver blocks on a Springfield O3-A3, use the rear stop pin in the jig bar to properly locate the single rear receiver hole. To do this, simply slide the entire jig rearward (after drilling the forward holes) until the stop pin contacts the edge of the old rear sight's dovetail.

Always check mounts equipped with a recoil shoulder to insure that they properly fit the receiver. The forward jig-stop pin must contact the receiver at the same spot where the mount's recoil shoulder makes contact. Also be certain that the V-bushings do not contact the left side of the receiver (especially on small-ring models) as this will cause misalignment of the jig. If necessary, file or grind the V-blocks to insure proper clearance.

Drilling Recommendations

When drilling, use as short a drill bit as possible (screw-machine drill bits are ideal) to prevent the drill from wandering. It is also a good idea to use a new high-speed drill for each job. Do not use carbide drills. If the receiver is too hard to drill with a standard high-speed drill, it is too hard to be tapped. If you can drill successfully only with a carbide drill, you are sure to break off the tap when attempting to thread the hole. Avoid such grief and drill only those holes you can make with standard drills. If the receiver is too hard, have it spot-annealed by someone experienced in this procedure, to soften the area to be drilled.

Tapping Recommendations

After the holes are drilled, you need to carefully tap them. Use a new tap for each job. This is cheap insurance against breaking a tap. Broken taps can sometimes be removed successfully, but the risk of a ruined receiver or barrel is a real possibility whenever a tap breaks in a hole. So play it safe. Fluteless taps work best on very thin receiver sections. Fluted taps are used for all holes of normal or greater depth. Be sure to run the tap well through all drilled-through holes. Tapping should be done progressively. If the tap binds even a tad, back it out, clear away any chips in the hole and on the tap, relubricate the tap, and proceed. It is sometimes necessary to back out the tap several times before the hole is fully threaded. Always use tapping compound—not cutting oils—when tapping.

On blind holes, be careful not to run the standard tap too deeply—resulting in a broken tap. You will have to form the last three or four threads in a blind hole by using a bottoming tap. Again, be careful not to solidly bottom the tap.

Jig Recommendations for Demanding Jobs

The B-Square jig is adequate for occasional jobs, but if you are going to drill and tap receivers frequently, if you will need to drill and tap barrels for front and rear sights, or if you wish to eliminate the problems caused by an occasional barrel not properly aligned in the receiver, you need a unit such as the Forster Universal Sight Mounting Fixture. This unit will also allow you to drill holes on the side of a receiver—for side mounts and peep sights—with perfect bore alignment. And when needed, this fixture can be used to drill holes that, by requirement, do not align with the bore.

The Forster jig has remained virtually unchanged for a great many years because it has needed no change. And it is durable. Beginning in the mid-1950s I used one extensively for 12 years, and since then it has continued to see occasional use. Today the jig is as reliable as it was in the 1950s. It has been a near-foolproof aid for getting scope-mount bases or sights of any type installed right—the first time. Like any other specialized tool, it does, however, require some knowledge to use it properly. One cannot simply clamp a gun in it and start drilling.

For example, the Forster jig uses a raceway along its rear edge to position the over-arm in proper alignment. If drilling chips get into the raceway or if an accumulation of any grit is allowed to build up in it, the over-arm will not align properly and the drilled holes will not be where they are supposed to be. Ditto for the spacer bar. The best procedure is to clean the raceway carefully before each use and again clean out any chips that accumulate during use before moving the over-arm or space bar.

Usually the stock needs to be removed from the gun before placing it in the jig. In the case of firearms having separate fore-ends and buttstocks, only the fore-end must be removed. However, a buttstock left attached may make it awkward to position the drill fixture properly on the drill-press table. More than one gunsmith has had drill fixture and gun fall to the floor because of an imbalance caused by a buttstock hanging out in the air. The best procedure is to remove the buttstock and avoid grief.

It is necessary also to remove any magazine tube or other appendages that hang below the barrel in order to allow proper clamping of the barrel in the fixture's V-blocks. It is seldom nec-

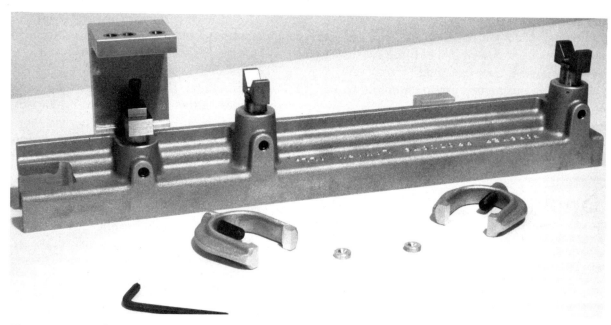

Forster Universal Sight Mounting Fixture is the answer to almost all drilling and tapping jobs.

Raceway of the drilling jig must be kept meticulously clean to insure positive alignment of the overarm and locator block.

essary to remove triggers, as the jig is appropriately relieved for these. Also, bolt stops, safeties, etc., can usually be left in place. Just be certain

that triggers, bolt stops, and the like do not come into contact with any portion of the jig, as misalignment of the barreled action could then occur.

Adjusting the Jig, Positioning the Work

When using the jig, the action-locking screw and bar should be removed from the action-supporting post. Then lay the barrel in the V-blocks with the action on the left end of the fixture (cut out for the trigger). The action should rest on the flat action-support post so the top of the action just contacts the undersurface of the drill bushings in the over-arm.

Basic adjustment requires the use of the rear V-block and the action-support bar to get proper elevations of the barreled action. Ideally, the rear V-block (closest to the action) should contact

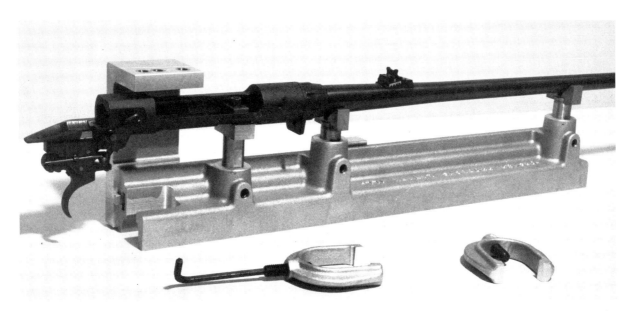

Properly installed barreled action. V-blocks are carefully adjusted for the correct height, the action properly leveled on the action support post, and the V-block and support-post clamps tightened securely.

the barrel on a cylindrical section. This is not always possible, but you can move the entire barreled action forward or rearward to accomplish this goal in most cases.

The front V-block must be elevated precisely to keep everything level. You measure the barrel diameter at both the rear and front V-blocks. You also need to measure the height of the rear V-block from its bottom flat edge to the machined top of the fixture. To arrive at the exact height needed for the front block, subtract the barrel diameter at the front V-block from the barrel diameter at the rear block. Then multiply the difference by 0.707. The resulting number should be added to the height of the rear block for a total measurement for the front V-block height.

When tightening the blocks, be certain to temporarily move the action-support block away to prevent any tipping of the barreled action. Then lightly lock the barrel into the V-blocks, using the supplied clamps. Be sure to use the supplied aluminum pads between the barrel and the clamp screws. Do not tighten the screws, as the barreled action must now be leveled with

Aluminum pads supplied with the Forster jig will prevent clamps from damaging the barrel finish.

respect to left and right orientation. Do this by carefully bringing the action-support bar against the receiver bottom (assuming it is flat). Rotate the receiver so it lies perfectly flat on the support post. Do not tighten the support-post screw.

Then install the action-locking block and screw and securely tighten. Tighten the action-bar support-post screw and then snug up the V-block clamps. It is important to be certain all the support-post screws are tightened against the flat milled on each post. If this is not done, serious misalignment can occur.

If the action does not have a flat bottom, it's necessary to use a level on some flat surface—side or top. Be certain the action is leveled within the jig. Use the machined surface on the back edge of the jig or the machined top surface of the over-arm (be sure it has been snugged up first) as a comparison.

Sometimes the rear V-clamp will interfere with the appropriate positioning of the over-arm. If so, remove it—but only after the action and barrel have been secured with the action-support bar clamp and the front clamp screw.

Next, carefully position the base or mount (with the over-arm moved out of the way) on the receiver. Carefully scribe the front receiver hole, using a pencil or steel scribe. If two-piece bases are used, be certain to locate the holes so that if,

at a later date, it becomes desirable to use a one-piece base the holes will be correctly positioned. To this end, it is wise to keep a one-piece base on hand and align the holes with it. Then the rear base of a two-piece unit can be positioned to drill the forth hole (not used with a one-piece base).

After scribing the front-hole position, situate the over-arm with the locating pin in its front hole, and the pin's center exactly in the middle of the scribed area. Then lock the over-arm into position, install the correct-size drill guide, and you are ready to drill the first hole.

Drilling and Tapping, Step by Step

Set the drill-press stop to drill almost through the receiver but not into the barrel. It is always a good idea to exactly position the locator block firmly against the over-arm and lock it in place. Then, if the over-arm must be moved for any

Drilling and tapping for a front ramp is an easy task with the Forster jig.

reason, it can be returned precisely to the same position by sliding it against the locator block.

Drill the first hole and then remove the drill guide, replacing it with the tap guide. Tap the hole. If the drill bushing just touches the receiver (when properly bottomed on the top of the over-arm) there will be almost no chance of the drill "walking" and mislocating the hole or breaking as a result of being flexed.

Always use a new drill and tap for each job. The grief that can come from dull cutting tools is easily avoided by using new ones on every job. With experience you may decide that a drill or tap can be used for two or three jobs, but go cautiously here. The amount saved in drills and taps over many decades will not pay for a single ruined receiver or barrel.

Often the second front receiver ring hole can be drilled simply by placing the drill bushing in the middle hole of the over-arm—but, do not assume this. It's best to move the over-arm out of the way and screw the mount to the receiver, using the one hole you have drilled and tapped. Then carefully scribe the second hole. Remove the base and carefully move the over-arm back into position, situating the locating pin in the

When the drilling or tapping bushings touch the receiver (or barrel), the chances of breaking the drill bit or tap are reduced to a minimum.

middle of the scribe. Remove the locating pin, install the drill guide bushing, and drill the second hole. Replace the drill-guide bushing with the tap-guide bushing and tap the hole.

Always use cutting oil when drilling and tap lubricant when threading the holes. Clean away all chips and lubricants between operations. Progress *slowly* with tapping. It may be necessary to back out the tap and clear away chips several times during the threading of a hole.

The drilling and tapping of the rear holes can be best accomplished if you drill through the receiver. Before doing so, be certain the drill will break through on a level area. If there is a step or sharp change in profile where the drill will come through, do *not* drill through as almost invariably a drill or tap will break when part of its diameter is free while the remainder bears against the work. There is no need to drill through the rear hole on the front receiver ring if the receiver is thick. On thin receivers, drill this hole through if it will not go into the barrel and if it will come through on a level area.

Be certain to position the first rear receiver-ring hole to accommodate a one-piece mount. Always use an actual base (now screwed to the front receiver holes) to locate this hole. Use the locating pin in the middle hole to accomplish this. Lock the over-arm in place and drill and tap as you did the front holes. Often the second hole for a two-piece base can be made by simply using the rear hole in the over-arm. But always double-check this, as described earlier. Erroneous assumptions lead to bad mistakes.

Note: Never drill or tap holes with the mount base(s) in place. Doing so may negate the positive alignment of each hole with the bore's axis.

Peep Sights and Side Mounts

Drilling for peep sights is done in a manner similar to drilling for scope bases, except that the

Drilling for peep-sight installation is easily accomplished with the Forster jig.

rifle is oriented with the appropriate side of the receiver in the up position. A level then must be used to insure that fixture and firearm are square. The action-support bar should be brought up against the action to support it during drilling. Obviously, though, the support-bar clamp is not used. All this holds equally true for the installation of side-mount scope bases.

On those rare occasions when the holes for a peep sight or side-mount scope base are not to be on the bore's axis, the over-arm is not used. In such cases, great care must be taken to prevent drill-bit "walk" and broken drill bits or taps.

Working Up Front

When drilling for a front-sight ramp or base, reverse the direction in which the gun is held in the jig, if possible, to place the action-support bar under the barrel at the point of drilling. Be sure the drill bushing contacts the barrel, and also be certain everything is level. Don't forget to allow for the variation in V-block heights, as previously explained.

If a barrel is to be drilled and tapped for any

combination of scope bases (receiver-mounted) and open rear and front sights (or barrel-mounted scope bases), I have sometimes found it best to do the entire job without re-orienting the gun in the jig. But if the front-sight ramp holes are more than an inch or two beyond the front V-block (barrel longer than 20 inches), it's best to re-orient the barreled action. Drilling a barrel that is not properly supported can cause it to flex away from the drill bit. This can result in a broken drill, a less than perpendicular-to-bore hole, or a broken tap. Obviously, a thin barrel requires closer support than a heavier one.

Drill-and-tap bushing sets for 3–56, 6–48, 8–40, or 10–32 thread sizes are available for the Forster jig, thus covering almost every possible firearm requirement.

Drilling and Tapping Cautions

Keep in mind that drilling can ruin a firearm if great care is not used. Double-check every single step. No attempt should be made to tap aluminum receivers, as invariably the steel screw will tear out the threads when properly tightened. And never drill and tap a hole that will not provide at least four full threads. Fewer turns and the screw may well pull out the threads when tightened.

Don't drill too deeply into any barrel. To create a too-thin barrel wall beneath the drilled hole is asking for serious problems. In general, there is no set rule for barrel thickness, as the required strength depends on the internal pressure generated at the point of the drilled hole when the gun is fired. This varies with cartridge, propellant speed, bullet weight, and distance from the bolt face. A good rule of thumb is never to drill more than half the barrel-wall thickness. And there is seldom need to go more than six

When drilling a barrel, never allow the drilled hole to go deeper than one-half thickness of the barrel wall.

threads deep, regardless of barrel-wall thickness. It is always advisable to have at least 0.020-inch barrel thickness.

Some exceptions do exist. For example, a front shotgun-bead hole can be drilled through the barrel (because of the low muzzle pressure). However, do not drill through barrels that are under 20 inches in length. But even then, a minimum of four screw turns will be necessary to keep the front bead from being blown out, and it must be fitted exactly flush on the inside barrel surface.

Always use a relatively small-handled tap holder when threading. This prevents over-torquing the tap and breaking it off in the hole.

Not enough can be said about the grief of trying to remove a broken tap. The best procedure is to make sure it doesn't happen. The use of a small handled tap will also help with the "feel" of the tap and your ability to keep everything in one piece.

Drilling and tapping a firearm for sights is one of the most common gunsmithing tasks. It can also be one of the most rewarding.

With experience, a firearm can be dis-assembled, set up in the jig, drilled, tapped, and bore-sighted in about 45 minutes. Such a job can bring sufficient monetary reward to make it all worthwhile—including the quick amortization of jig and drill press.

27

Fitting a Recoil Pad

A well-fitted recoil pad is something almost every shooter can use. Reduced recoil means reduced shooting fatigue and improved accuracy. For a shooter who finds recoil unpleasant or for anyone who finds that recoil induces flinching and thus causes poor accuracy, a recoil pad can be essential. A recoil pad can lengthen a too-short stock to comfortable proportions. And a recoil pad or a rubber buttplate is an excellent replacement for a cheap, fragile factory-installed plastic buttplate.

On the other hand, hardly anything can destroy the overall appearance and value of a good gun like a poorly fitted recoil pad. Stock heel and toe lines must flow uninterruptedly across the recoil pad. Changing angles at the pad juncture have the same effect as ink blots on a fine sketch. And unless wood and pad meet smoothly all the way around, the job is best left undone.

None of which is to say that pad installation is terribly difficult, but it does require a great deal of time, patience, care, and the need for a few basic essentials—most importantly a power sanding table.

There are two approaches to proper pad instal-

lation. The first is to exactly shape the pad, remote from the gunstock. This prevents marring the sometimes difficult-to-match stock fin-

A properly installed recoil pad can increase accuracy by eliminating fatigue caused by recoil.

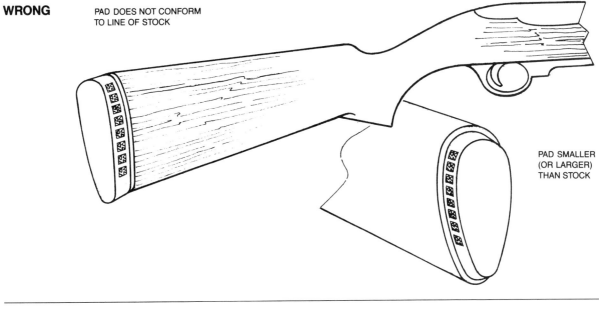

WRONG PAD DOES NOT CONFORM TO LINE OF STOCK

PAD SMALLER (OR LARGER) THAN STOCK

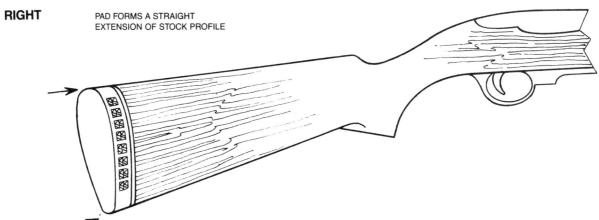

RIGHT PAD FORMS A STRAIGHT EXTENSION OF STOCK PROFILE

Improperly installed recoil pad will detract from a gun's value and appearance. Properly installed pad adds grace and beauty. Toe and heel lines must follow through into the pad and not change angles.

---

ish. This method is usually best for anyone with less than extensive experience.

The second method is to fit the recoil pad to the stock while it is attached thereto. This achieves the most perfect fit, but as a rule it should not be attempted on a valuable firearm without a lot of previous experience on guns of lesser worth. Of course, if the pad is being fitted to a stock that is to be completely refinished, or to a semi-finished stock yet to see its final shaping, this second method can be undertaken even by the amateur.

Method 1—Separate Shaping

The first method requires the use of a B-Square Recoil Pad Jig, a sanding table, suitable screwdriver with round shank, lubricant, and recoil pad which must be large enough to continue the lines of the stock heel and toe (see illustrations) but not so large as to require excessive material

B-Square Recoil Pad Jig is needed for separate-shaping method of installation.

Stock should be firmly masked at point of cut. This will prevent the wood from splintering when the stock is cut to size in a miter box.

removal. Cutting too deeply into a pad can uncover internal construction and thereby ruin it.

Begin by determining how much, if any, of the buttstock is to be removed to obtain the desired length of pull. Even if the stock is not to be shortened, any curvature of the butt must be removed. This is best done with a very fine-toothed and sharp saw in order to avoid the splintering that tends to occur at the bottom of the cut. Wrapping the stock with masking tape at the point of the cut will also help prevent splintering. If you splinter the stock at the bottom of the cut, it may well be ruined.

Always use a miter box to make the cut. Be certain the stock is positioned square and level before beginning. If it is your first attempt at cutting a stock, it is strongly advised that you make several practice cuts on a discarded stock. Cut slowly and carefully, without forcing the saw downward. Let the sharpness of the saw and its own weight supply the cutting action.

Most miter boxes will allow the cut to be made only by progressing from one side of the stock to the other. This maximizes the chance of splintering on the bottom side, due to the great surface

area. Some gunsmiths prefer to construct miter boxes that allow for cutting from the top (heel) of the stock to the bottom (toe). This confines any splintering to the relatively small toe area. However, elaborate systems of stock alignment and support must be developed for cuts of this type. The beginner is probably better off cutting in a standard miter box, from one side of the stock to the other. A sharp saw, properly used on a well-taped stock, will prevent problems.

After the cut, the flat must be sanded perfectly smooth, which also eliminates any very minor splinters. This is best done on a belt sander. Carefully bring the butt squarely onto the belt and sand until all traces of the saw cut and any minor edge splintering are removed. It requires great care and visual alignment to keep the sanding flat and perpendicular to the stock. If you sand at an angle, the job will look poor indeed. Again, practice on a discarded stock.

Next, to insure a perfect mating of recoil pad and stock, the back surface of the pad must also be sanded flat on a belt sander. Keep the pad square, and sand until all high spots disappear and the pad has a smooth, even surface.

With stock in miter box, use a sharp, fine-toothed saw to cut it slowly to proper length. Let the sharpness and weight of blade do the cutting, not the weight of your arm.

Sand the butt perfectly flat, preferably on a belt sander, and be certain to keep the work area from taking on an unwanted angle. Then sand the recoil pad until it too is perfectly flat.

Now you are ready to mount the pad to the stock. Begin by pushing a well-fitting Phillips screwdriver which has been properly lubricated (soap will work nicely) into the back side of the pad and out of the face side to mark the screw-hole locations. Then, using well-lubricated screws (again, soap works well), push the screws into the pad from the outside surface, and screw the pad to the buttstock.

It is important to locate the pad centrally on the stock. Be sure there is sufficient pad overhang to allow the heel and toe line to be maintained, or the job won't look right. But avoid excessive hangover on either end, especially with pads that have exposed vents or grooves. You don't want to wind up with a ½-inch overhang of solid rubber on the stock heel, while pad grooves come within ⅛-inch of the toe, or you actually have no solid toe at all.

Some shooters use (or try to use) the same stock holes for the recoil-pad screws that were used for the original buttplate screws. This is most often impossible if the pad is to be correctly aligned. It would be unusual to be able to use even one of the original screw holes. Instead,

drill the butt with the appropriate-size bit. Take care to insure that the holes are square and perpendicular to the buttstock. If they enter at an angle, it will be difficult to screw the buttplate down flush all around with the stock.

After securing the pad to the stock, carefully trace the stock's outline on the pad, using a sharp-pointed scribe. Get the outline as close to the stock as possible. If you do not, the pad will protrude around the wood when the job is finished. Remove the pad from the stock and mount it on the B-Square jig.

Lubricate the machine screws supplied with the jig. Then place the face of the pad against the jig's mount bar. Place a washer over the pad's top hole and insert the mounting screw, only loosely tightening it. Put in the bottom screw (don't forget the washer), and tighten both screws, but do not tighten so much as to distort the pad's shape.

Make certain the top (heel) end of the pad is located at the top end of the jig (double hole). If the bottom screw does not easily enter one of the jig bar's four bottom holes, relocate the top screw in the unused top hole.

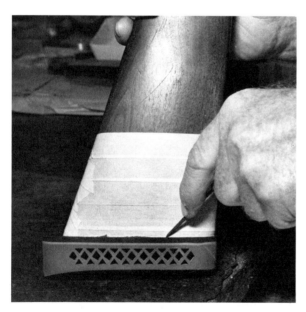

After mounting the pad to the stock, carefully scribe the butt's outline on the pad.

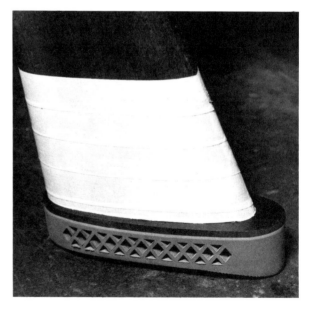

Be sure the pad is correctly oriented on the stock, with sufficient overhang at heel and toe.

Remove pad from stock and mount it on the B-Square jig. Use a square to obtain the correct toe angle for the jig, as shown in photo at top of page 272 of getting the correct heel angle; then sand toe area of stock.

Now loosen the screw holding the jig bar to the jig base. Position the jig base against the buttstock (heel to heel and toe to toe). Place one edge of a square along the bottom (toe) edge of the stock. Adjust the jig bar so the recoil pad's face aligns correctly with the other edge of the square. Tighten the jig-bar/base screw to lock the pad in alignment.

Place the jig base on the sander to position the pad's toe against the sander, and sand only the toe area to coincide perfectly with the line previously scribed. Be sure the screw holding the jig bar does not loosen, as this controls the proper angle of the stock toe and pad.

After the toe area has been sanded, loosen the bar/base screw on the jig and again place the jig base against the stock. This time use the square to align the heel of the stock and the face of the pad. When it is correctly positioned, lock the screw. Now sand the heel area of the pad. Once again be sure the screw holding the jig alignment does not loosen. If it does, use the square and stock to once again align the jig correctly.

After the heel has been sanded to coincide with the scribe lines, level the pad in the jig and sand the sides of the pad, *blending* it carefully into both heel and toe areas. When the sanding is done, install the pad on the stock. If you have been careful with the scribing of the stock outline on the pad and with the blending and sanding to the scribe line, you will have a good fit.

Method 2—Shaping an Attached Pad

The second method of pad installation provides an even better fit. It requires a very solid sanding belt (or disc), a steady hand, sharp eye, and a bit of masking tape. The procedure can easily result in a disfigured stock if a mistake is made, so practice on a discarded stock.

Obtain the correct heel angle with a square and then sand the heel. Be sure the screw holding the jig alignment does not loosen.

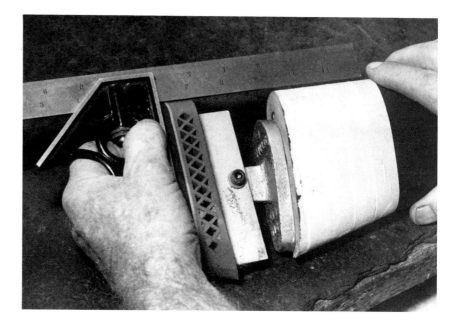

Begin by making the previously described stock cut to bring the pad-and-stock combination to the correct overall length. Leave an extra ⅛-inch to allow for sanding the stock and pad surfaces to a truly flat state. Remove the tape used for a cutting guide, then pierce the recoil pad screw holes as described earlier, and mount the pad firmly to the stock. Now carefully wrap the buttstock immediately in front of the recoil pad with two thicknesses of 3-inch-wide masking tape.

From this point on, successful installation depends more on art than mechanics. Rough-sand the pad on a hard disc or belt sander until you have brought it to within 1/16-inch of the taped stock. This can be done with a rough-grit sanding paper. Great care must be taken to insure that the heel and toe lines of the stock are continued into the pad. When the pad is about 1/16-inch from the tape, all the way around, switch to a finer-grit paper. A large-diameter sanding disc with a flexible (hard rubber) back is best at this point. Sand the pad until it is almost down to the masking tape. Now switch to a very fine-grade paper and sand, very, very carefully, to reduce the pad dimension to the same as the top layer of

An experienced workman can install a pad and then sand it on a belt or disc sander, bringing it down perfectly flush with the masking tape. Beginners should follow the preceding procedure.

masking tape. This is done by sanding through the top layer of tape without cutting into the bottom layer. Sound hard? Well, it does take skill, art, and patience, but the finished job will be as perfect a fit as possible without refinishing the stock.

After a pad installation has been completed, some shooters remove the pad and place a thin coat of glue on it and the stock, then screw the pad back on tightly. This helps keep the pad positioned, but if it ever needs to be removed some difficulty will be encountered.

Pad installation, with either method, is not for the faint of heart. A face mask and ample ventilation are always required. The mounds of rubber dust that pile up in the work area must be seen to be appreciated. The workman himself will be covered from head to toe with this same dust. But a properly installed pad is a gunsmithing effort that justifiably confers a lot of pride.

PART 5

THE FINAL STEPS

28

Ammunition and the Gunsmith

Functioning and accuracy problems are often gun-related. Misfires can be caused by a short firing pin, weak firing-pin spring, light hammer blow, excessive headspace, etc. Poor accuracy can be caused by improper barrel and receiver bedding, worn rifling, bore erosion and/or corrosion, a bad crown, loose sights, and so on.

But as often as not, problems are related to the quality of the ammunition used. It is important to be familiar with ammunition-induced difficulties and to know that not every box of centerfire ammunition purchased is capable of anything resembling good accuracy.

Ammo-induced misfires can be caused by primers seated too deeply, primers not seated deeply enough to properly stress the priming pellet, the wrong type of primer, cartridge cases with insufficient headspace, frost or ice on the shoulder of a case that affords minimal shoulder support (such as the .35 Remington), missing primer anvils, missing primer pellets, etc. Feeding problems in some semiautomatics may be caused by an incompatible bullet-nose shape or

This kind of accuracy is not easy to achieve. The right ammo is often a factor.

overall cartridge length. Difficult bolt closing on a reload can be caused by a case that exceeds the maximum case length (needs trimming), incorrect sizing (faulty die adjustment or die dimen-

277

sions), a rim that was bent when extracting a case from a sizing die (insufficient or poor sizing lubricant or wrong shell holder), or a too-long overall cartridge length for the bullet ogive. Poor extraction may be caused by ammunition that generates excessive chamber pressure. Poor ejection in a semiautomatic can be caused by ammo that generates insufficient chamber pressure.

With a semiauto or sometimes a pump, shotshells may not feed from the magazine due to too large a rim diameter (reloaded cases that have enlarged). In semiauto rifles and handguns, bullets must be securely held by neck tension. A firm crimp is also required except on straight, rimless cases. Sufficient neck tension and a good crimp prevent bullets from being driven deep into the case during feeding, which can cause excessive chamber pressure.

Indeed, the list of potential ammo-induced difficulties is very lengthy, but the most common problem caused by ammo is poor accuracy.

Shooting Groups to Evaluate Accuracy

Not every shooter knows how to evaluate accuracy. It is not possible to judge accuracy on the basis of a single group or even several three-shot groups. It takes a minimum of five five-shot groups to gain even a tentative notion of a firearm's potential. Five 10-shot groups will really begin to let the shooter know the capability of his gun.

The best way to test for accuracy is to hang two targets, one perfectly superimposed over the other, at 100 yards (shorter ranges will prove very little). Then fire the first five-shot group. If the gun is to be used for prairie-dog shooting or target matches, a 10-shot group should be used to reflect the intended use, which will see many shots fired with a warm or hot barrel. After the

first group has been fired, remove the top target and replace it with a new one for the next group. Be sure the new target is placed exactly over the one left in place. After each group has been fired, allow the barrel to cool down and repeat the test, shooting the new group on a fresh target, while leaving the original bottom target in place. After five groups have been fired, there will be five targets, each with one group on it, plus a sixth with all 25 (or 50) shots on it.

Examining each group will usually show at least a few targets with one or two so-called fliers on it. Examining the target containing all the shots fired will quickly reveal that those "fliers" really are part of the overall grouping capability of the firearm. It will be evident that five groups ranging between perhaps an inch and 1¾ inches (with good reloads) most often form a single group of perhaps 1¾ to two inches. The target with all the shots on it is, of course, the better indicator of the gun-and-ammo combination's actual capability.

This type of testing, using a backer target, will reveal that there really is no such thing as a flier shot. Individual "fliers" in the five-shot groups disappear in the combined group target. Each shot is part of the firearm-and-ammunition overall capability. Of course, the shooter must be up to the task. A poor shooter has no hope of realizing the potential of any firearm.

An even better way to evaluate accuracy potential is to shoot groups as described, but fire each group on a separate day. This will show the effects that lighting can have on accuracy, as well as the daily effects of the shooter's capability, the weather, etc.

What to Expect from Factory Loads

To the enthusiast, accuracy with factory ammunition is seldom impressive. Indeed, with the majority of factory centerfire rifle ammo, aggregate group sizes under three inches are seldom seen, and individual groups of two inches are good, 1¾ inches outstanding. Some individual lots of factory ammo perform admirably in certain firearms, but the next lot of the same type of ammo may be disappointing.

Some factory ammo does seem to do very well, lot after lot—most times, anyway. Such ammo includes Remington varmint-style loads using the Power-Lokt hollow-point bullets. These are available in .17 Remington, .222 Remington, .223 Remington, .222 Remington Magnum, .22-250 Remington, .243 Winchester, 6mm Remington, and .25-06 Remington. Another notable factory load is the Norma brand of 130-grain .270 Winchester ammo. Singularly best, on a consistent basis, is the Federal Premium 150-grain (Nosler Partition bullet) .270 Winchester load. Individual lots of Winchester 150-grain Power Point .30-06 have also proved to be quite good. With .22 rimfire ammo, the premium-priced CCI Green Tag and RWS R50 Long Rifle ammo are both outstanding.

When you encounter a particularly good lot of ammunition, take note of the lot number (printed on the inside flap, on the outside back of the box, or, in the case of plastic ammo boxes, a heat-embossed lot number may be used). Purchase all you can. Such ammo is not always easy to come by.

As factory ammo goes, there are only two loads I have encountered that will consistently shoot ¾-inch or better groups—and do it with 10-shot groups. They are the Sako brand .22 PPC (52-grain hollow-point boattail bullet) and the 6mm PPC (70-grain hollow-point boattail bullet). Any factory ammo that produces one to 1¼-inch groups with five shots can be considered outstanding. And any ammunition that will consistently produce such groups is entirely adequate for most accuracy testing of firearms.

But because such ammunition is comparatively rare, the shooter who wishes to test for accuracy often must reload. Much has been written about the need to develop, through extensive testing, a load that performs well in each rifle or handgun. In truth, extensive testing is

Some factory loads are extremely uniform. Most accurate big-game cartridge I've used is the Federal 270 Win. Premium with 150-grain (Nosler Partition bullet) .270 Winchester load.

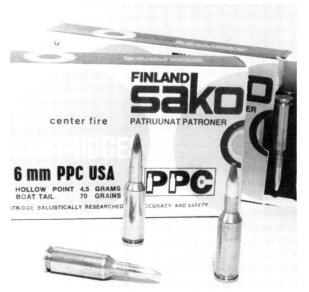

Perhaps the most accurate factory centerfire ammo in the world, the Sako 6mm PPC will consistently supply ½-inch 10-shot groups at 100 yards.

seldom needed. If it were, it would not be possible for factories or arsenals to manufacture large lots of match-grade ammunition that produce fine results in a great many firearms. And such match-grade ammo has been produced many times.

Ingredients of Accurate Handloads

The secret, if there really is one, to assembling top-accuracy ammo is, first, to be a proficient handloader, and second, to use proven components. This chapter cannot undertake to explain the myriad details required of a handloader. Such information is contained in volumes devoted solely to handloading. But I can list certain ingredients of match-grade ammo. It's not hard to do so, since for each cartridge-and-bullet-weight combination there are usually but one or two truly outstanding powders. If you do not find a listing for a particular cartridge in the tables, try one of the reloading handbooks that single out the better-performing loads.

Also included is a listing of factory ammunition that has been consistent in performance, with sufficient accuracy to be used for serious firearm-accuracy evaluation. Just keep in mind that ammunition can vary notably from one lot to another. It is possible that someday one of the listed factory loads may fail to perform as expected, or to encounter an unlisted factory load that performs outstandingly. Always there is the proven performance of good reloads to fall back on when good factory ammo is not available or affordable.

Also keep in mind that the conditions of reloading, the operator's methods, and the dimensions of the assembled ammo, as well as variations in components from lot to lot, can bring about substantial ballistic changes. Therefore, the listed loads may not be safe when assembled

A benchrest powder measure (this one from Sinclair) is an essential tool for loading accurate ammo.

by your methods, or with tolerances or component lots that differ from the test conditions.

It is essential to begin all reloading efforts at a powder charge a full 10 percent below the listed charge. Then, as pressure indications (learned from worthwhile reloading manuals) permit, increase the load in ½-grain increments. Never exceed the listed load, and discontinue the use of any component combination that shows any indications of excessive pressure before or at the maximum charge. No reload that results in difficult extraction after firing, enlarged case-head diameters, cratered primers, or any other problem indications should be used. Fire at least 10 rounds at each load increment before proceeding to the next.

SOME FACTORY LOADS THAT HAVE PRODUCED HIGH ACCURACY

Caliber	Brand	Bullet Weight in grs.	Bullet Type	Actual Velocity in fps	Velocity in fps	Test Bbl. Length (inches)	Test Rifle	Test Scope	Accuracy Average (1)
.22 LR	CCI	40	Green Tag	1138	1080	22	Kimber 82	6x Leupold	1″ (2)
.22 LR	RWS	39	R50 Match	1070	1080	22	Ruger 77/22	8x Leupold	¾″ (2)
.22 PPC	Sako	52	H.P.B.T.	3400	3400	24	Sako Varmint	12x Leupold	⁷⁄₁₀″
.222 Rem.	Rem.	50	Power Lokt H.P.	3140	2960	18½	Rem. Model 7	10x Zeiss	1⅛″
.223 Rem.	Federal	55	Amer. Eagle FMC	3240	3110	18½	Ruger Mini-14	4x Leupold	2″
6mm PPC	Sako	70	H.P.B.T.	3200	3140	24	Sako Varmint	12x Leupold	⅝″
.270 Win.	Norma	130	Soft Point	3060	3000	22	Rem. 700	3-9x Redfield	1¼″
.270 Win.	Federal	150	Nosler Part.	2850	2810	22	Win. 70 Feath.	4x Leupold	1″
7mm-08 Rem.	Rem.	140	Soft Point	2860	2675	18½	Rem. Model 7	1.5-5x Leupold	1¾″
.308 Win.	Rem.	150	Ptd. Core Lokt	2820	2770	22	Win. 70 Feath.	4x Leupold	1¾″
.30-06 Spfd.	Federal	125	Soft Point	3140	3100	22	Rem. 700	4x Redfield	1¼″
.380 Auto	Win.	85	Silvertip	1000	915	3¼	Walther PPK		2″ (3)
.38 Special	Win.	148	H.B. Wadcutter	710	740	6	S&W Model 19		2″ (4)
.357 Magnum	Win.	145	Silvertip	1290	1220	2½	S&W Model 19		3″ (4)

(1) Average accuracy for five five-shot groups at 100 yards except (2) five 10-shot groups at 50 yards and (3) five five-shot groups at 25 yards and (4) five five-shot groups at 50 yards.

RELOADS FOR MATCH-GRADE ACCURACY

Caliber	Weight (grs.)	Bullet Brand	Type	Powder Charge wgt. in grains	Vel. fps	Test Bbl. Length (inches)	Test Rifle	Test Scope	Accuracy Average (1)
.222 Rem.	50	Nosler	Match	23.0/Hodgdon H335	2920	18½	Rem. Model 7	6x Zeiss	¾″
.223 Rem.	55	Hornady	Cannelure	27.0/Hodgdon H335	3110	18½	Rem. Model 7	10x Zeiss	1″
.224 Wea. Mag.	50	Nosler	Match	30.0/Hodgdon H335	3450	24	Weatherby MKV	12x Leupold	1″
.22 PPC	52	Nosler	Match	24.5/Hodgdon H322	3120	24	Sako Varmint	12x Leupold	½″
.22-250 Rem.	55	Speer	Soft Pt.	38.0/Hodgdon H380	3500	24	Rem. 700	12x Leupold	¾″
6mm PPC	68	Berger or Watson	Custom	26.5/Hodgdon H322	3010	24	Sako Varmint	12x Leupold	¼″
.243 Win.	100	Nosler	Partition	40.0/IMR 4350	2820	18½	Rem. Model 7	6x Leupold	1¼″
.257 Roberts	100	Speer	H.P.	45.0/IMR 4350	3000	22	Ruger 77R	6x Leupold	1″
.270 Win.	90	Sierra	H.P.	55.0/IMR 4350	3000	22	Rem. 700	4x Leupold	1⅛″
.270 Win.	130	Speer	Spitzer	55.0/IMR 4350	3000	22	Win. 70 Feath.	4x Leupold	⅞″
.270 Win.	150	Speer	Spitzer	52.0/IMR 4350	2800	22	Win. 70 Feath.	3-9x Redfield	1″
7mm-08 Rem.	145	Speer	Spitzer	47.0/IMR 4350	2600	18½	Rem. Model 7	1.5-5x Leupold	1⅛″
.30-06 Spring.	125	Sierra	Spitzer	55.0/IMR 4064	3085	22	Rem. 700	4x Redfield	⅞″
.30-06 Spring.	150	Speer	Spitzer	52.0/IMR 4064	2900	22	Rem. 700	4x Redfield	⅞″
.300 H&H	180	Nosler	Partition	68.0/IMR 4350	2950	24	Rem. 700	4x Leupold	1⅛″
9mm Luger	100	Speer	H.P.	5.0/Herc. Bullseye	1265	4	S&W Model 59		2″ (2)
.38 Special	148	Speer	H.B. W.C.	3.0/Win. 231	750	6	S&W Model 29		2″ (2)

(1) Average accuracy of five five-shot groups at 100 yards except (2) average of five five-shot groups at 50 yards.

Maintaining Ammo Uniformity for Testing

Reloading match-grade ammo for accuracy testing demands special attention. Every single powder charge should be weighed exactly or thrown using a benchrest powder measure such as the one made by Fred Sinclair. Only match-grade primers should be used. I strongly favor the Federal 210M match-grade large rifle primer and the Federal 205M match-grade small rifle primer. CCI also sells match-grade primers, in large and small rifle sizes, and they perform admirably. When possible, use Federal match-grade cases. Unfortunately, these are available in only a limited caliber selection.

Primer seating should be done with meticulous care, each primer being seated from 0.003-inch to 0.008-inch below flush with the case head. Primer pockets should be carefully cleaned, and inside case necks should be brushed to remove any accumulated matter.

Cases should be exactly trimmed to identical lengths, and bullet seating must also be con-trolled to very small tolerances. When testing for functioning, always use full-length resize cases to insure that there will be no difficulty in feeding, chambering, and extraction. But for accuracy testing, neck-size just the first $\frac{1}{16}$-inch of the case. Naturally, neck-sizing only is not practical if the fired cases are used in any gun other than that in which they were originally fired. And, for safety, never use a case beyond the point where it requires a fifth trimming.

Ammunition for accuracy testing should be properly stored. A cool, dry place is needed, not a damp cellar or hot attic or the $-10°F$ garage. A temperature range of 45° to 75°F, with a humidity of 20 to 50 percent, is appropriate. Properly stored ammunition should have a rather long shelf life. But it is prudent not to load more ammunition than can be used over a span of two to three years.

It's most important to keep all ammo carefully segregated by lots. When you change a lot of powder, primer, bullet, or case, begin a new ammo lot. Lot numbers are on all worthwhile component packaging. Since lot variations can occur, loading and segregating by lot number will insure maximum uniformity. The best criterion to apply to match-grade reloads is to ask yourself this question about each round: "Is it the same as, truly identical to, the last round loaded?"

Reaming the primer pockets of cartridges is essential to achieve maximum accuracy.

Setting Up a Stable Shooting Bench and Gun Rest

Good ammo alone will not make for an effective accuracy test. It will be necessary to afford the rifle a very solid rest from a bench shooting position. Sandbags and leather or plastic sand-filled front and rear contoured bags are a minimum essential. With two 25-pound shot bags

Sandbags are inexpensive and provide a steady platform for benchrest shooting, but require adjustment.

(filled with sand) and a suitable set of front and rear contoured benchrest bags, such as supplied by Hoppe's, you have a rock-steady shooting rest.

The sandbag approach, while very inexpensive and effective, is not the most convenient way of solving the need for a very stable shooting platform. The sandbags seldom are the correct height to allow for proper alignment on a distant target. Thus, a lot of improvising, adjusting, and maneuvering will take place at the range to bring everything into proper alignment. An easier solution is to use one of the adjustable benchrests offered by several manufacturers.

CCL shooting stands are among the best benchrests one can use. These are manufactured by a Texas family devoted to shooting. When selecting a shooting stand, consider your specific needs. For example, the CCL Model 102 stand is fully adjustable for height and horizontal rotation of the fore-end rest. The buttstock (toe) rest is also fully adjustable, including the angle of the stock line. But it is designed solely for use with long guns.

The same firm offers a Model 200 stand which has an adjustable distance from the front fore-end support to the rear stock-toe support. This makes it handy for a wide variety of firearm lengths. And with an accessory front support, it converts quickly to a handgun rest.

A vise adapter for either of those CCL stands will convert the shooting rest into a very worthwhile work station. Such a stand can be one of the best investments a serious shooter/gunsmith can make. Shooting tiny groups from this well-padded rest is a snap.

If a benchrest table is not available, there are collapsible shooting rests that can be set up and used anywhere. One such rest is available inexpensively from Bill Cobb. Bill's rest will enable you to get very serious accuracy results and it doubles nicely as a hunting rest for long-range varminting or perhaps antelope or caribou hunting. I have shot many a one-inch group at 100 yards using one of these lightweight shooting rests.

Whatever shooting stand you select, be sure it has at least ½-inch felt padding at all the firearm contact points to prevent damage and to insure maximum accuracy.

Shooting from the Bench

When shooting from sandbags or a shooting stand, special techniques should be employed to insure best accuracy. It is important to adjust the rest and the firearm so the sight alignment can be properly maintained on target without any influence by the shooter.

Then place your shoulder as lightly against the butt as practical for the caliber being used. Shoulder pressure can cause gun movement in the stand. With .22 centerfires and most 6mm rifles, shoulder contact should barely exist. As caliber and recoil levels intensify, shoulder contact must be increased to prevent a painful impact of the butt. The use of a thick, highly recoil-absorbent shoulder pad will help to keep shoulder pressure against the gun to a minimum. Keep it as light and as uniform as you can. The gun should not be held in any other manner. Do not grasp the pistol grip with the trigger finger hand.

The trigger is released by placing the index finger on the trigger and the thumb on the back of the trigger guard. The trigger is then "pinched" between the index finger and thumb. This method is not practical for rifles with a recoil level of the .30-06 or greater. Generally, benchrest-shooting techniques are required for best accuracy results.

The B-Square benchrest, when fitted with a sandbag, is good for accuracy testing.

CCL offers several bench-rest shooting stands, each affording the most exacting shooting rest for obtaining maximum accuracy. With a vise adapter (*below*), the rest can be converted to a bench work station.

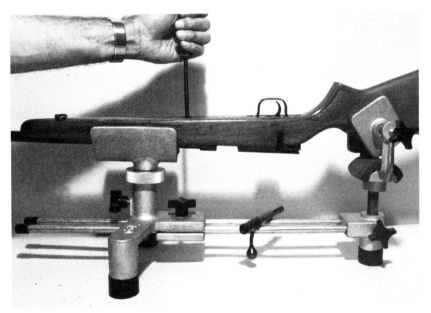

Caliber Identification

Caliber identification is often the task of any gunsmith or shooting enthusiast. Proper caliber identification for American firearms is seldom difficult, though sometimes confusing. For example, not everyone may recognize a barrel stamped 25 WCF, 32 WCF, 38 WCF, or 44 WCF as meaning .25-20 Winchester, .32-20 Winchester, .38-40 Winchester, or .44-40 Winchester. Or the fact that a barrel marked 25-35 Marlin or 30-30 Marlin is chambered for the .25-35 Winchester or .30-30 Winchester may not be obvious to inexperienced shooters. An accompanying table of cartridge-name variations will help to identify over two dozen American cartridges.

The metric cartridge designations on European firearms are not always easy to interpret. For example, the 8x57 Mauser (or 8mm Mauser) may well be marked 7.9x57 JS on the barrel. But similar markings such as 7.9x57JR or 7.9x57J could lead to serious problems if they were interpreted as designating the same 7.9x57JS cartridge. Another table in this chapter provides common European metric designations and equivalent American or English nomenclature for 30 cartridges. By referring to this table you may be able to identify quite a few puzzling European markings.

Additionally, a custom firearm clearly marked 22-250, 22 Varminter, or perhaps 25-06 may or may not be suitable for standard .22-250 or .25-06 Remington cartridges. Many custom chambers were cut with reamers made before the industry standardization of these cartridges—when they were still wildcats. Such chambers varied considerably from gunsmith to gunsmith, depending upon who made the reamers.

And some chamber markings may not necessarily mean you can safely use current ammo of the same designation. For example, a Winchester lever-action Model 73 rifle or an old Colt single-action revolver clearly stamped 44 WCF (.44-40 Winchester) would not be safe with current ammo. These guns were designed for ammunition loaded with black powder. Today's smokeless-powder ammunition produces pressures much too high to allow for use in guns designed for black powder.

The same warning applies to Damascus (twist) steel shotgun barrels. They were meant only for black powder. And they may no longer be safe even with black-powder loads if the laminated steel has suffered internal corrosion over these many decades.

It is not advisable, either, to shoot certain high-velocity rounds in guns chambered when only standard-velocity loads were in use. For instance, a Colt .32-20 revolver should be not used with .32-20 high-velocity ammo, nor should some of the very old .22 Long Rifle handguns and rifles be used with modern loads.

It is hoped that the accompanying tables will aid in proper caliber identification, but an entire book would be required to deal thoroughly with cartridge identification and proper cartridge use. In fact, a number of such volumes have been published, and you should add one or more to your reference shelf if you'll be handling old or uncommon calibers.

The use of the wrong ammo, or ammo of the wrong pressure level, can cause a burst gun and personal injury to the shooter and any bystanders. It is therefore essential to insure that the cartridges used in any firearm are appropriate. Assume nothing! When the slightest doubt exists, consult a professional who is well versed in caliber identification.

Finally, remember that many guns have been rechambered without being marked to indicate the correct cartridge. Indeed, I have examined barrels clearly marked for one cartridge and chambered for another—for example, a .300 Savage rechambered for another—.308 Winchester. Sometimes, too, barrels are rebored or relined with no reference to the new caliber—a .30-06 rebored to .35 Whelen or relined to .25-06, for instance. Always be certain; there's no other way to be safe.

Extreme caution is required in identifying many old cartridges which are not interchangeable with other, quite different cartridges having very similar names. For example, the .25-20 Single Shot and the .25-21 Stevens both are unique cartridges and not at all like the .25-20 Winchester. Nor does the .30-30 Wesson round, a much older cartridge, have any connection with the .30-30 Winchester. Others, such as the .32-40 Bullard, .38-40 Remington-Hepburn, and .38-56 Winchester have nothing in common with the sound-alike cartridges. Further confusion can occur as some old cartridges bear *identical* names, yet are considerably different in shape. These include the .40-90 Sharps (straight case) and .40-90 Sharp (bottleneck case); the .44-100 (Remington) and .44-100 (Ballard); the .45-75 (Winchester) and .45-75 (Sharps straight); the .44 Extra Long (Ballard) and the .44 Extra Long (Wesson); and the .44-90 (Remington Special), .44-90 (Sharps Necked), and .44-90 (Remington Straight). And how about the 303? Is it the .303 Savage round or the .303 British.

Rare cartridges such as the .45-150 (3½-inch)

AMERICAN CARTRIDGE IDENTIFICATION

Barrel Marked:	Correct Cartridge:	Barrel Marked:	Correct Cartridge:
5.56mm	.223 Remington	32 Colt New Police	.32 Smith & Wesson
244 Remington	6mm Remington	32ACP, 32CAP, 7.65mm (auto) 7.65 Browning	.32 Automatic
25ACP, 25CAP, 6.35mm (auto), 6.35mm Browning (auto)	.25 Automatic	8x57mm, 8x57mmJS, 7.92mm, 7.92x57mm, 7.92x57JSmm	8mm Mauser (not to be used in .318″-diameter barrels, which are chambered for the 8x57J cartridge)
25WCF, 25-20 Marlin, 25 Win., 25-20	.25-20 Winchester (also .25-20 Winchester High Velocity)[1]		
25-35 Marlin	.25-35 Winchester	32WSL, 32 Win.SL	.32 Winchester Self Loading (obsolete)
250 Savage	.250-3000 (Savage)	33WCF	.33 Winchester (obsolete)
7x57mm	7mm Mauser	35WSL, 35 Win.SL	.35 Winchester Self Loading (obsolete)
7mm Express Remington	.280 Remington	35WCF, 35 Win.	.35 Winchester (obsolete)
7.65mm Para., 7.65 Parabellum, 7.65 Luger	.30 Luger	351SL, 351 Win.SL, 351WSL	.351 Winchester Self Loading
30-30 Marlin, 30 Marlin, 30 Savage, 30 W.C.F.	.30-30 Winchester	38WCF, 38 Win., 38 Winchester, 38-40 Remington, 38-40 Marlin, 38-40	.38-40 Winchester (also .38-40 Winchester High Velocity)[1]
30 Krag,	.30-40 Krag		
30-06 Govt.	.30-06 Springfield	44WCF, 44 Win., 44 Winchester, 44-40 Remington, 44-40 Marlin, 44-40	.44-40 Winchester (also .44-40 Winchester High Velocity)[1]
7.62mm (NATO)	.308 Winchester		
30 Carbine	.30M1 Carbine	45 Govt., 45-70 Marlin, 45-70-405, 45-70-500	.45-70 Government
32WCF, 32 Win., 32 Winchester, 32 Marlin, 32-20	.32-20 Winchester (also .32-20 Winchester High Velocity)[1]		

[1]High Velocity cartridges in these calibers are no longer loaded, but old inventories may still be present on some dealers' shelves or among household contents.

Hepburn might be encountered, though it is listed almost nowhere and, indeed, an otherwise unimpeachable source at one time listed it as a figment of someone's imagination. That author purchased my almost mint-condition Remington Hepburn, so chambered, and undoubtedly regretted his earlier strong words, though he was delighted with his purchase.

Obviously, the fact that a given cartridge can be slipped into a chamber does not mean it's the right cartridge, and yet most problems have perhaps resulted from using the wrong cartridge simply because it would chamber.

Below is a list of cartridges that have been or can be dangerously misapplied—that is, loaded in the wrong firearm. A few of these make the shooter wonder how anyone could possibly close the bolt on the cartridge, but it has happened. Remember that, for the sake of safety, this listing should never be considered complete.

DANGEROUS OR MISMATCHED CARTRIDGES

Firearm Chambered for:	Wrong Cartridge for Firearm—DANGEROUS:	Firearm Chambered for:	Wrong Cartridge for Firearm—DANGEROUS:
.17 Remington	.221 Remington Fireball, .30M1 Carbine	.264 Winchester Magnum	.308 Winchester, .300 Savage, .303 British, .350 Remington Magnum, .375 Winchester
.17-223 Remington (wildcat)	.17 Remington, .221 Remington Fireball, .30M1 Carbine		
.223 Remington	.222 Remington	.270 Winchester	.30 Remington, .30-30 Winchester, .300 Savage, .32 Remington, .308 Winchester, 7x57mm Mauser, .375 Winchester
.222 Remington Magnum	.223 Remington		
.243 Winchester	.250-3000 Savage, .225 Winchester		
6mm Remington (.244 Rem.)	.250-3000 Savage, .225 Winchester	7x57mm Mauser	.300 Savage
.257 Roberts	.250-3000 Savage	7mm Remington Magnum	7mm Weatherby Magnum, .270 Winchester, .280 Remington, 7mm Remington Express, .35 Remington, .350 Remington Magnum
6.5mm Remington Magnum	.300 Savage		
.264 Winchester Magnum	.270 Winchester, .284 Winchester,		

Firearm Chambered for:	Wrong Cartridge for Firearm—DANGEROUS:	Firearm Chambered for:	Wrong Cartridge for Firearm—DANGEROUS:
.280 Remington	.270 Winchester, .30 Remington, .30-30 Winchester, .300 Savage, .308 Winchester, 7x57mm Mauser, .375 Winchester	.38-55 Winchester	.375 Winchester
		.375 Winchester	.38-55 Winchester, .41 Long Colt
		.22 Winchester Rim Fire	.22 BB Cap, .22 CB Cap, .22 Short, .22 Long, .22 Long Rifle
.284 Winchester	.300 Savage, 7x57mm Mauser		
.30-06 Springfield	.270 Winchester, 7x57mm Mauser, .30 Remington, .300 Savage, .308 Winchester, 8x57mm Mauser, .32 Remington, .35 Remington, .375 Winchester	.22 Winchester Magnum Rim Fire (22WMRF)	.22 BB Cap, .22 CB Cap, .22 Short, .22 Long, .22 Long Rifle
		.22 Winchester Auto	.22 CC Cap, .22 CB Cap, .22 Short, .22 Long, .22 Long Rifle
.300 H&H Magnum	.30-06 Springfield, 8x57mm Mauser, .30-40 Krag, .375 Winchester	5mm Remington Rim Fire Magnum	.22 CC Cap, .22 CB Cap, .22 Short, .22 Long, .22 Long Rifle, .22 Winchester Auto
.300 Weatherby Magnum	.338 Winchester Magnum		
.300 Winchester Magnum	8x57mm Mauser, .303 British, .350 Remington Magnum, .38-55 Winchester	.25 Stevens Long (obsolete)	5mm Remington Rim Fire Magnum (obsolete)
.303 British	.32 Winchester Special	.410 (shotgun)	.219 Zipper, .30-30 Winchester, .303 British, .32 Winchester Special, .32-40 Winchester, .35 Winchester, .38-40 Winchester, .44 S&W Special, .44-40 Winchester, .44 Remington Magnum
.303 Savage	.32 Winchester Special, .32-40 Winchester		
.308 Winchester	.300 Savage		
.338 Winchester	.375 Winchester		
.348 Winchester	.35 Remington		

Naturally, it is always dangerous to shoot any shotgun with a shell of a length longer than that for which it was chambered. A three-inch shell should not be used in a 2¾-inch chamber, even though it's of the same gauge. Shells 2¾ inches long should not be used in 2⁹⁄₁₆-inch chambers (beware, users of old 16-gauge guns).

Metric cartridges can bring on equal, if not greater, confusion for the American shooter. I've already mentioned one example—the 8x57mm Mauser, sometimes marked as 7.9x57JS, but never to be confused with 7.9x57J. Another example is the fact that early Mannlicher Schoenauer rifles clearly marked 6.5x53 M.S.

should be used with current ammo carrying the headstamp 6.5x54 M.S. Also remember that a 7x57mm Mauser cartridge should never be used when a 7x57R cartridge is required. The "R" in metric cartridge designation frequently means a rimmed cartridge. And metric designations include the same kind of confusing similarities that plague American nomenclature—for instance: 6.5x57 and 6.5x57R; or 6.5x58R (Sauer) and 6.5x58R (Krag-Jorgensen); or 9x56 and 9x57, and so on. As with U.S. rounds, different names sometimes refer to the same cartridge, or different names may be used in Europe and the U.S. Examples are shown in this list.

CORRESPONDING METRIC AND U.S. OR ENGLISH CARTRIDGES

Metric Cartridge Designation	U.S. or English Designation	Metric Cartridge Designation	U.S. or English Designation
5.6x35Rmm (not Vierling)	.22 Hornet	7.63x72mm	.300 Holland & Holland Magnum
5.7x43mm	.222 Remington	7.65x53mm	7.65 Argentine Mauser
5.56mm	.223 Remington	7.7x58 Arisaka	7.7 Japanese
5.6x52R	.22 Savage	7.9x57mm	8x57 Mauser
6.2x52mm	.243 Winchester	8x50R	8mm Lebel
6.5x50mm	6.5 Japanese	8.8mm	.358 Winchester
6.5x52mm Mannlicher Carcano	6.5 Italian	9.5x72mm	.375 Holland & Holland Magnum
6.5x52Rmm	.25-35 Winchester	10.4x38R Vetterli	.41 Swiss Rimfire
6.5x55mm	6.5 Swedish	10.75x73mm	.404 Rimless Nitro Express
6.9x64mm	.270 Winchester	11.15x58R	.43 Spanish
7.35 Carcano	7.35 Italian	11.15x60R	.43 Mauser
7.5x54 MAS	7.5 French	11.43x50R	.43 Egyptian
7.62x51Rmm	.30-30 Winchester	12.7x70 Schuler	.500 Jeffrey
7.62x51mm (NATO)	.308 Winchester	14.7mm	.577 Snider
7.62x54R	7.62 Russian		
7.62x63mm (U.S.)	.30-06 Springfield		

Caution: Beware of similarities in metric designations. Be sure, not sorry.

One of the methods often used to determine the correct cartridge for a firearm combines two steps. The first is to slug the bore, with a soft lead slug. This method employs a 100 percent pure soft lead ball, slightly oversized, which is very carefully driven into the muzzle. After it has been forced into the bore three or four inches, it is driven back out. The careful investigator will then be able to measure the lead slug and determine the bore's groove and land diameters, a big step in caliber identification.

In combination with the foregoing, a chamber cast is made, often using a Cerro-Safe nonshrinking alloy which is melted and then poured into the chamber (with the rifling lead properly plugged). When cooled, the chamber cast is removed and measured.

Both processes require a great deal of experience to prevent firearm damage. And thorough understanding of chamber and bore dimensions is essential. Simply comparing the chamber cast's dimension with a maximum cartridge drawing will never give identical numbers. As a rule, because of the experience and knowledge required, these methods are best undertaken only by qualified professionals. But knowing of such procedures, the reader may care to attempt them on an old and worthless (or nearly worthless) firearm in order to begin to develop the necessary skills. You will, of course, need reference cartridge drawings. Many of these are available from RCBS.

Cartridge identification can indeed be tricky, but with the information set forth in this chapter even the novice can begin to make correct investigations. As you gain experience, you'll want to broaden your knowledge by referring to books devoted exclusively to ammunition.

29

Testing The Repair

I've said it before, but it must be said again: Always be sure the gun is unloaded when doing repair tests except, of course, during actual test firing. Use dummy cartridges for all function testing.

Every repair, regardless of simplicity or complexity should be fully tested. If the repair was merely the replacement of a sight, then sighting-in the firearm again is test enough. A loose sight, one of inappropriate height, or any other such difficulty will become apparent during the shooting.

Function Testing

If the repair involved any of the feeding-cycle parts, extensive testing should be done. I repeatedly cycle dummy cartridges through the firearm—a full gun load of shells until 100 rounds have been so functioned. Then an actual firing test with 20 rounds is done to confirm that all is well. Such testing should be done after repairing any magazine follower, follower spring, cartridge guide, extractor or ejector. The effects of recoil on feeding parts should never be overlooked. Thus, actual firing is always essential.

Some repairs, such as firing pin and extractor replacements, demand that fired cartridges be

For function testing, first cycle dummy cartridges through your gun. If the gun functions properly, follow up by firing 20 live rounds.

carefully inspected for normal appearance—
depth and centered location of firing-pin indent,
no deforming of cartridge rim, etc. Any trigger
or safety repair requires the utmost in careful
attention and testing to insure that the integrity
of the firearm design has not been compromised.

Always test trigger repairs to make sure the
weight of pull remains constant over at least two
dozen dry firings. Use a scale or weights to do
this testing. Do not rely on interpreted finger
pressure. Check that when the gun is cocked and
ready, it will not disengage with a modest bump
or blow to the firearm. Test by using a rubber
mallet to strike the receiver and by bumping the
butt against an appropriately padded surface. A
gun that fires during these tests will, in all like-
lihood, fire if it is dropped when cocked. Such a
condition is unsafe!

Check all safety repairs or adjustments by
cocking the firearm and placing the safety switch

When firing pins, extractors, or ejectors have been
repaired or replaced, carefully inspect fired cartridges to be sure heads are normal.

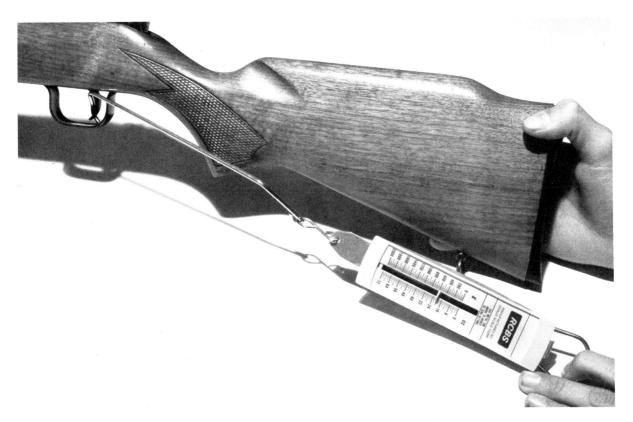

Trigger adjustments should be repeatedly tested for uniformity using a scale or weights.

Test safeties by applying maximum pressure to the trigger with two fingers.

Bumping the butt on a well-padded bench should not cause the trigger to release the sear.

peat the entire test several times. Take no short-cuts.

Complete or partial disassembly of any firearm, whether for repair or cleaning, always should be followed by a functioning test with dummy cartridges. If the trigger or safety parts were disassembled, a check of these is in order.

A stock repair always requires the actual test firing of an adequate number of rounds to insure accuracy (bedding repairs) and/or durability (break, split, or crack repairs).

Test Firing

The test firing of any gun that has had certain parts replaced— the firing pin, bolt, locking lug, bolt head, or other parts essential to the strength and integrity of the firearm—should never be from the shoulder. "Absence of body" is an industry phrase applied to certain ammunition testing and the proofing and test firing of any new firearm. Absence of body should also be applied to any firing test that involves the mentioned repairs or similar ones, or for the verification of cartridge identification.

in the safe position. Then apply all the pressure possible with right and left index fingers, trying to pull the trigger to fire the gun. If you can, the repair is unsatisfactory! If the gun does not fire, move the safety switch to the fire position. The gun should not fire as the switch is moved. Then return the switch to the "on" position, and re-

In other words, make certain no person is near enough to the firearm to be hurt in the event of a catastrophic failure. Parts and pieces blown away by high pressure gases can indeed do serious bodily harm, or worse. For the appropriate test firings, tie the firearm to an old tire, or, better still, mount it in a suitable shooting jack and fire it from a remote position, using a lanyard wrapped around trigger and trigger guard as shown in an accompanying illustration. Stand protected from any explosion hazard when firing the gun.

Of course, be certain that recoil will not move the gun and/or shooting jack so as to cause damage to either. It is particularly important to insure that recoil will not move the firearm in the shooting jack, as this can cause extensive damage. The butt should bear firmly against some portion of the stand, and provisions should be made to prevent muzzle jump from twisting the gun out of the stand. Furthermore, recoil needs to be absorbed by a heavy recoil-spring mechanism or stock cracks will result.

Do not use a shooting rest or stand designed for benchrest shooting or repair work for your test firing. Such stands do not support the gun properly, and damage will result.

Additional Checks and Safety Precautions

Always use the appropriate headspace gauges after any chamber work or after repair or replacement of barrel, bolt, or locking parts. After drilling or tapping any barrel, double check to insure that the drilled holes do not penetrate more than half of the barrel-wall thickness. If you have tapped a shotgun barrel for screw-in chokes, be certain a choke tube is tightly in place before test firing.

Before firing, make sure there are no heavy deposits of oil or grease in the barrel and no

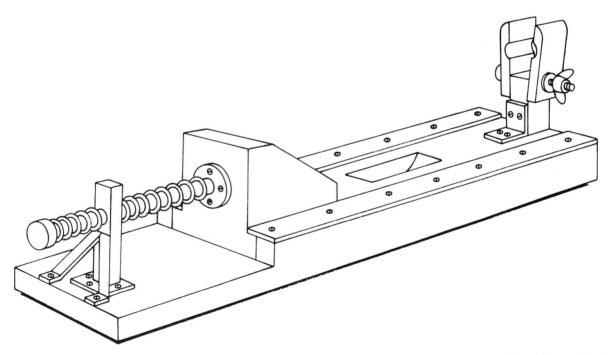

A good shooting jack for test firing. When the jack is firmly anchored, the heavy spring will absorb recoil and prevent stock cracks.

patches or brushes were left in the bore. Barrels are easily burst due to excessive oil, grease, or a patch left behind.

Make sure all disassembled parts were replaced and properly assembled. When replacing stocks, always avoid excessive tightening of screws to prevent stock cracks. Be sure any sight-mounting screws used on the receiver do not protrude through the receiver. Be certain the collimator spud has been removed from the gun after bore-sighting. After a glass-bedding job, double check everything to be sure no epoxy has migrated to where it is not supposed to be.

In short, check and double check everything possible. Strange and not so strange things can happen. For example, driving a new rear open sight into a barrel just might cause a front ramp screw to loosen. Or the drilling and tapping of a receiver might cause a few tiny metal particles to get into trigger or safety mechanisms, making them unsafe. Replacement or tightening of a front action screw could cause the screw to infringe deeply into the receiver's bolt-locking lug recess, making it difficult or impossible to operate the bolt. A trigger job may make some safety-switch work necessary. And the reverse is equally true. And so it goes.

Whatever the job, one sign of a true gunsmith is knowing what to check, besides the actual work done, after job completion. Take the time to think through the most important part of any repair: the completed work inspection. It will pay huge dividends.

30

Sensible Alternatives in Gunsmithing

Some time ago, a very wise person said, "If it isn't broken, don't fix it." These words have been repeated countless times. Tinkering when there is no need can lead to a real requirement for more than tinkering. A gun often needs less fixing than at first may be supposed. A poor trigger pull can sometimes mean a replacement trigger is needed, but perhaps, the trigger merely needs some adjusting. The current Savage 110 rifle trigger is as good as any replacement trigger I have used—if that 110 trigger is adjusted precisely, as described earlier in this work.

A smart gunsmith figures out how much gunsmithing is required to reach a goal. Suppose a friend brings you his favorite scope-sighted .30-06 and says he would like to have back-up iron sights installed. The first reaction might be to drill and tap the barrel for a dovetail rear-sight base and a screw-on front ramp. This means disassembling the rifle and requires a Forster drill jig to make and thread four barrel holes. If something goes wrong, there is a risk of ruining the barrel.

A knowledgeable person would consider the use of scope rings that have sights on top. Such rings with sights are offered in several configurations by firms like Millet and Williams. The Millet rings require only the use of a Redfield Jr.-style mount base. If the gun already has a Redfield, Burris, or Millet base on it, all you need is to change scope rings. Ditto for Williams rings if the gun is equipped with a Williams base. And if the base on the rifle is not compatible, it's a lot easier to change a scope base than to drill and tap four barrel holes.

The short space between scope-ring open sights means they will be less accurate than barrel-mounted open sights, but open sights on a scoped rifle will probably never get used anyway. They are there simply for that one-in-5,000 emergency—and then the ring sights will get the job done. Even the non-adjustable ones can work effectively under such circumstances if the rifleman knows where his gun shoots when they are used.

As another example, why drill and tap a grooved-receiver .22 for a peep sight when Williams makes peeps that instantly slip into the receiver groove. At worst, you will have to install

297

a higher front bead to properly align the new peep. At best, you will avoid stripping threads in an aluminum receiver or having to inlet a stock to clear a side-mounted peep.

If someone decides he would like to have a ramp front sight instead of a plain old post, don't start drilling and tapping right away. You can purchase a Williams Shorty ramp that attaches to the barrel by means of a dovetail adapter. Any gun that has a ⅜-inch dovetail can be quickly and almost effortlessly fitted with one of these ramps. Such easy gunsmithing is smart gunsmithing.

If there's a need for a quality scope to be mounted on a .22, drilling and tapping may still be unnecessary since one-inch scope rings are available to fit dovetailed .22 rifle receivers.

If the only thing wrong with a rifle's bedding is the fit of the receiver's recoil shoulder in the stock mortise, try glass-bedding only the recoil shoulder in its mortise. More may look and sound great, but may not add a bit to the rifle's performance. If simply bedding the recoil shoulder doesn't give the desired results, the remainder of the action can always be bedded later.

A smart gunsmith also tries to avoid gimmick ideas. For example, if the customer wants to inlet a compass into his rifle's stock because he always loses his compass, suggest that he get a lanyard so he can hang the compass from a belt loop. The compass won't be lost and neither will the gun's full resale value. If he persists, at least he won't be able to accuse you of not telling him about "gunsmithing" that detracts from firearm value.

Suppose the decision has been made to bore, ream, and tap a shotgun barrel for screw-in chokes because the owner has no use for its modified choke and wants only a cylinder bore. It might make a heap of sense simply to cut 2½ inches or so off his present barrel, reinstall the front bead and thus have a cylinder bore without spending so much time and money. Naturally,

this will work only on a plain barrel, as vent ribs are not designed to be cut.

If you've decided to start milling, cutting, and fitting some battery-powered sight to a revolver in order to make it useful for nighttime raccoon hunting and/or nighttime police duty, there are easier ways that don't include electrical contact switches and so on. How about using the Meprolight sights? They'll work on any S & W revolver (and there are models for other handguns and long guns) as long as the gun has a ramp front sight with a plastic insert. These Israeli imports (by Hesco) work day or night, require no maintenance, and have no switches, bells, or gongs. Self-powered by a tiny quantity of radioactive tritium gas (less than 31 millicuries), they show up bright in the dark and as a white-outline rear sight and white-dot front sight in daylight. Total installation takes about 20 minutes.

You simply break out the original plastic ramp inset and clean out all traces of plastic. The replacement front sight fits into the original dovetail and is glued into place with Loc-Tite 610 glue. The original rear blade is removed by cranking its screw clockwise until the screw bolt snaps. Then the sight blade is pressed away until the bolt-retaining nut shows from the opposite side of the sight. Unscrew it and the broken bolt and you are ready to drop in the glow-in-the-dark Meprolight sight.

Why install a recoil pad on every long gun owned if a slip-on or pin-on pad will do? Not every shooter needs a recoil pad when hunting, yet for sighting in and plinking a pad sure is nice.

There are equally effective alternatives to many other repair efforts. Why wrestle to compress a coil spring, slip it onto a shaft, and then put everything into place in the gun when someone is selling an inexpensive, easy-to-use tool that gets the job done right every time? Browse through a good gunsmithing catalog (the Brownells catalog is a great example) to come up with dozens of ideas for doing a job easier, faster, and right.

Appendix

This appendix provides a number of quick references—drill sizes, metric conversions, energy/velocity formulas, etc. It also lists sources of supplies, tools, parts, and accessories. No such listing can be truly complete, but every effort has been made to include all those sources mentioned in the text plus many more. In the following pages you will find:

Alpha Drill Sizes
Numerical Drill Sizes
Standard Drill Size for Tap Size
Screwdriver Bit Limits
Metric Conversions & Foot-Pound/Velocity Calculations

DIRECTORY OF SOURCES FOR:
Cartridge Drawings
Cleaning Chemicals & Equipment
Cold Bluing Kits
Gun-Repair Vises & Stands
Gunsmithing Accessories, Supplies, Tools
Gunsmithing Schools
Headspace Gauges
Parts (General)
   Savage Parts
   Reloading (accuracy tools & equipment)
   Scopes & Mounts
   Shooting Stands & Rests
   Sights
   Special Tools, Jigs, Fixtures
   Stock Finishes & Finishing Kits
   Triggers

ALPHA DRILL SIZES

Drill Letter	Dia. in inches	Drill Letter	Dia. in inches	Drill Letter	Dia. in inches
Z	0.413	Q	0.332	H	0.266
Y	0.404	P	0.323	G	0.261
X	0.397	O	0.316	F	0.257
W	0.386	N	0.302	E	0.250
V	0.377	M	0.295	D	0.246
U	0.368	L	0.290	C	0.242
T	0.358	K	0.281	B	0.238
S	0.348	J	0.277	A	0.234
R	0.339	I	0.272		

NUMERICAL DRILL SIZES

Drill Number	Dia. in inches	Drill Number	Dia. in inches	Drill Number	Dia. in inches
1	0.228	28	0.141	54	0.055
2	0.221	29	0.136	55	0.052
3	0.213	30	0.129	56	0.047
4	0.209	31	0.120	57	0.043
5	0.206	32	0.116	58	0.042
6	0.204	33	0.113	59	0.041
7	0.201	34	0.111	60	0.040
8	0.199	35	0.110	61	0.039
9	0.196	36	0.107	62	0.038
10	0.194	37	0.104	63	0.037
11	0.191	38	0.101	64	0.036
12	0.189	39	0.100	65	0.035
13	0.185	40	0.098	66	0.033
14	0.182	41	0.096	67	0.032
15	0.180	42	0.094	68	0.031
16	0.177	43	0.089	69	0.029
17	0.173	44	0.086	70	0.028
18	0.172	45	0.082	71	0.026
19	0.166	46	0.081	72	0.025
20	0.161	47	0.079	73	0.024
21	0.159	48	0.076	74	0.023
22	0.157	49	0.073	75	0.021
23	0.154	50	0.070	76	0.020
24	0.152	51	0.067	77	0.018
25	0.150	52	0.064	78	0.016
26	0.147	53	0.060	79	0.015
27	0.144			80	0.014

STANDARD DRILL SIZE FOR TAP SIZE

Tap	Drill
10–32	#21
8–40	#28
6–48	#31
3–56	#45

SCREWDRIVER BIT LIMITS*

Blade Width (fractions of 1 inch)	Blade Thickness (fractions of 1 inch)	Working Torque (inch-pounds)	Breaking Torque (inch-pounds)
1/8	1/40	15	17
5/32	1/32	31	35
3/16	1/40	31	35
3/16	1/25	45	50
15/64	1/25	67	75
1/4	1/40	67	75
1/4	1/25	94	105
3/8	1/40	99	110
21/64	1/32	103	115
21/64	1/25	135	150
3/8	1/25	144	160
3/8	1/20	180	200

Assumes chrome-nickel-molybdenum steel with hardness of Rc52 to Rc55.

Metric Conversions and Foot-Pound/Velocity Calculations

To convert millimeters to inches:
   Multiply mm $\times$ 0.3937 = inches
To convert inches to millimeters:
   Multiply inches $\times$ 25.40 = mm
To convert meters per second to feet per second:
   Multiply mps $\times$ 3.281 = f.p.s.
To convert feet per second to meters per second
   Multiply f.p.s. $\times$ 0.3048 = mps
To convert foot-pounds to kilogram-meters
   Multiply ft.lbs. $\times$ 0.1383 = kilogram-meters
To convert kilogram-meters to foot-pounds:
   Multiply kilogram-meters $\times$ 7.233 = ft. lbs.

To convert pounds per square inch to kilograms per square centimeter:
   Multiply p.s.i. $\times$ 0.07032 = ksc
To convert kilograms per square centimeter to pounds per square inch:
   Multiply ksc $\times$ 14.23 = p.s.i.
To obtain foot-pounds (kinetic) of energy at a specific velocity:
   Square the velocity, multiply by the bullet weight in grains, and divide by 450,240

$$\frac{V^2W}{450,240} = \text{ft. lbs. (kinetic energy)}$$

DIRECTORY OF SOURCES

Cartridge Drawings

RCBS Operations
  (popular calibers)
P.O. Box 1919
Oroville, CA 95965
(916) 533-5191

Cleaning Chemicals and Equipment

Birchwood Laboratories, Inc.
  (Birchwood Casey)
7900 Fuller Rd.
Eden Prairie, MN 55344
(612) 937-7934

Blacksmith Corp.
  (Artic Friction Free)
Box 424
Southport, CT 06490
(800) 531-2665

Cortland/Precision
  (Parker Hale Rods)
3736 Kellogg Rd.
P.O. Box 5588
Cortland, NY 13045-5588
(800) 847-6787

J. Dewey Mfg. Co. Inc
  (Rods & Patches)
186 Skyview Dr.
Southbury, CT 06488
(203) 264-3064

Jet-Aer Corp.
  (G96 Products)
100 Sixth Ave.
Paterson, NJ 07524
(201) 278-8300

Venco Industries
  (Shooter's Choice)
16770 Hill Top Park Pl.
Chagrin Falls, OH 44022
(216) 543-8808

Marble Arms Corp.
420 Industrial Park
P.O. Box 111
Gladstone, MI 49837
(906) 428-3710

Outers
Rt. 2
Onalaska, WI 54650
(608) 783-1515

Penguin Industries Inc.
  (Hoppe's Products)
Airport Industrial Mall
Coatesville, PA 19320
(215) 384-6000

Reardon Products
  (Dry Lube)
323 N. Main St.
Roanoke, IL 61270
(815) 772-3153

Rig Products
87 Coney Island Dr.
Sparks, NV 89431-6317
(702) 331-5666

RTI Research Ltd.
  (Accubore bore cleaner)
P.O. Box 48300
Vancouver, B.C.
V7X 1A1 Canada

WD-40 Company
P.O. Box 80607
San Diego, CA 92138-9021
(619) 275-1400

Yankee Hill Machine
  (Kleen Bore #10)
20 Ladd Ave.
Northampton, MA 01060
(413) 586-7240

Cold Bluing Kits

Birchwood Laboratories
  (Birchwood Casey)
7900 Fuller Rd.
Eden Prairie, MN 55344
612-937-7933

High Tech Specialty Lube
  (Jenolite Kits)
815 Kipling Ave.
Toronto, ON
M8Z 5G8 Canada
(416) 236-3534

Jet-Aer Corp.
  (G96 Products)
100 Sixth Ave.
Paterson, NJ 07524
(201) 278-8300

Penguin Industries
  (Hoppe's Products)
Airport Industrial Mall
Coatesville, PA 19320
(215) 384-6000

Gun-Repair Vises & Stands

Decker Shooting Products
1729 Laguna Ave.
Schofield, WI 54476
(715) 359-5873

CCL
P.O. Box 162
Harper, TX 78631
(512) 864-4254

Gunsmithing Accessories, Supplies, Tools

Alex Inc.
   (broken shell extractor)
P.O. Box 3034
Bozeman, MT 59715
(406) 282-7396

Brownells
   (super complete catalog)
Rt. 2, Box 1
Montezuma, IA 50171
(515) 623-5401

B-Square Co.
P.O. Box 11281
Fort Worth, TX 76109
(817) 923-0964

The Chapman Mfg. Company
   (screwdrivers)
P.O. Box 250
Durham, CT 06422
(203) 349-9228

Clymer Manufacturing
   (chamber reamers)
1645 W. Hamlin Rd.
Rochester Hills,
   MI 48063-5207
(313) 853-5555

Constantine's
   (woodworking tools)
2050 Eastchester Rd.
Bronx, NY 10461
(800) 223-8087

Forster Products
82 E. Lanark Ave.
Lanark, IL 61046
(815) 493-6360

Gaydash Industries
   (Versa-Vise)
1347 Middlebury Rd.
Kent, OH 44240
(216) 673-7054

Grace Metal Products Inc.
P.O. Box 67
Elk Rapids, MI 49629
(616) 264-8133

Henricksen Tool Co. Inc.
   (chamber reamers)
P.O. Box 668
Phoenix, OR 97535
(503) 535-2309

Hesco
   (Meprolight sight)
Rt. 4, Greenville Rd.
La Grange, GA 30240
(404) 884-4057

Michaels of Oregon
P.O. Box 13010
Portland, OR 97213
(503) 255-6890

Pachmayr Ltd.
   (recoil pads)
1987 S. Mountain Ave.
Monrovia, CA 91016
(818) 357-7771

Redfield
   (collimator)
5800 E. Jewell Ave.
Denver, CO 80224
(303) 757-6411

Superior Products
   (E-Z Way Case Remover)
P.O. Box 541
Rockford, MI 49341

Texas Platers Supply
2453 W. Five-Mile Pkwy.
Dallas, TX 75233
(214) 330-7168

Trexler Industries
   (Kwik Klip for Rem. 700)
Mag-Con Inc.
P.O. Box 2047A
Allentown, PA 18001
(215) 433-2400

Williams Gun Sight Co.
   (front sight pusher)
P.O. Box 329
Davison, MI 48423
(313) 742-2120

Woodcraft
   (woodworking tools)
P.O. Box 4000
Woburn, MA 01888
(800) 225-1153

Gunsmithing Schools

Lassen Community College
Gunsmithing School
   Coordinator
P.O. Box 3000
Susanville, CA 96130

Rochester Institute of
   Technology
College of Fine and
   Applied Arts
P.O. Box 9887
Rochester, NY 14623

Trinidad State Junior College
Chairman, Applied Science
Trinidad, CO 81082

North American
   School of Firearms
   (Correspondence Course)
Education Service Center
Oak St. & Pawnee Ave.
Scranton, PA 18515
(717) 342-7701

Headspace Gauges

Brownells
Rt. 2, Box 1
Montezuma, IA 50171
(515) 623-5401

Forster Products
82 E. Lanark Ave.
Lanark, Il 61046
(815) 493-6360

Henricksen Tool Co. Inc.
P.O. Box 668
Phoenix, OR 97535
(503) 535-2309

Parts

Browning
Rt. 1
Morgan, UT 84050-9749
(801) 543-3200

Colt Industries
P.O. Box 1868
Hartford, CT 06102
(203) 236-6311

Gun Parts Corp.
   (formerly Numrich)
West Hurley, NY 12491
(914) 679-2417

Interarms Co.
   (Walther)
10 Prince St.
Alexandria, VA 22313
(703) 548-1400

Kimber of Oregon
9039 S.E. Jannsen Rd.
Clackamas, OR 97015
(800) 547-8910

Marlin Firearms Company
100 Kenna Dr.
North Haven, CT 06472
(203) 239-5621

O. F. Mossberg & Sons Inc.
7 Grasso Ave.
North Haven, CT 06473
(203) 288-6491

Navy Arms Co.
689 Bergen Blvd.
Ridgefield, NJ 07657
(201) 945-2500

Precision
   (Parker Hale parts)
P.O. Box 5588
Cortland, NY 13045-5588
(800) 847-6787

Remington Arms Co.
Arms Service Dept.
Ilion, NY 13357
(315) 894-9961

Smith & Wesson
2100 Roosevelt Ave.
Springfield, MA 01101
(413) 781-8300

Springfield Armory, Inc.
420 W. Main St.
Geneseo, IL 61254
(309) 944-5631

Stoefer Industries
55 Ruta Ct.
South Hackensack, NJ 07606
(201) 440-2700

Sturm Ruger
1 Lacey Pl.
Southport, CT 06490
(203) 259-7843

Thompson Center
P.O. Box 5002
Rochester, NH 03867
(603) 322-2394

U.S. Repeating Arms Co.
   (Winchester firearms)
P.O. Box 30-300
New Haven, CT. 06511
(203) 789-5000

Reloading

RCBS Operations
P.O. Box 1919
Oroville, CA 95965
(916) 533-5191

Sinclair International
   (catalog, $2)
718 Broadway
New Haven, IN 46774
(219) 493-1858

Savage Parts

Savage Services Corp.
330 Lockhouse Rd.
Westfield, MA 01085

Badger Shooters Supply
Owen, WI 54460

Ellett Brothers Inc.
Columbia Ave.
Chapin SC 29036

Jack First Inc.
  (also obsolete parts)
44633 N. Sierra Hwy.
Lancaster, CA 93535

Freeland Scope Stands
3737 14th Ave.
Rock Island, IL 61201

Gunpar Ltd.
Box 809 Hwy. 28 N.
Lakefield, ON
KOL 2HO Canada

Simmons Gun Specialties
700 S. Rogers Rd.
Olathe, KS 66061

Walker Arms Co. Inc.
Rt. 2, Box 73
Selma, AL 36701

Scopes & Mounts

B-Square Co.
  (mounts only)
P.O. Box 11281
Fort Worth, TX 76109
(817) 923-0964

Burris Co. Inc.
Box 1747
Greely, CO 80632
(303) 356-1670

Conetrol Scope Mounts
Hwy. 123 S.
Seguin, TX 78155

Leupold & Stevens, Inc.
P.O. Box 688
Beaverton, OR 97075
(503) 646-9171

Millet Industries
  (mounts)
16131 Gothard St.
Huntington Beach, CA 92647
(714) 842-5575

Redfield
5700 East Jewell Ave.
Denver, CO 80224
(303) 757-6411

Williams Gun Sight
P.O. Box 329
Davison, MI 48423
(313) 742-2120

Shooting Stands & Rests

Bill Cobb
3377 Woodland Dr.
Murrysville, PA 15668
(412) 327-6057

CCL Mfg.
P.O. Box 6
Harper, TX 78631
(512) 864-4349

Penguin Industries
  (Hoppe's Products)
Airport Industrial Mall
Coatesville, PA 19320
(215) 384-6000

Sights

Lyman Products
West St. & Rt. 146
Middlefield, CT 06455
(203) 349-3421

Marbles Arms Corp.
P.O. Box 111
Gladstone, MI 49837
(906) 428-3710

Micro Sight Co.
242 Harbor Blvd.
Belmont, CA 94002
(415) 591-0769

Millet Industries
16131 Gothard St.
Huntington Beach, CA 92647
(714) 842-5575

Williams Gun Sight
P.O. Box 329
Davison, MI 48423
(313) 742-2120

Special Tools, Jigs, Fixtures

B-Square Co.
P.O. Box 11281
Fort Worth, TX 76109
(817) 923-0964

Brownells
Rt. 2, Box 1
Montezuma, IA 50171
(515) 623-5401

Forster Products
82 E. Lanark Ave.
Lanark, IL 61046
(815) 493-6360

Foredom Co.
    (flexible shaft grinders)
Bethel, CT 06801
(203) 792-8622

Millet Industries
    (handgun sight tools)
16131 Gothard St.
Huntington Beach, CA 02647
(714) 842-5575

Trulock Tool
    (choke tube install. kit)
P.O. Box 74
Whigham, GA 31797
912-762-4678

Stock Finishes &
Finishing Kits

Birchwood Laboratories Inc.
    (Birchwood Casey)
7900 Fuller Rd.
Eden Prairie, MN 55344
(612) 937-7934

Jet-Aer
    (G69 Products)
100 Sixth Ave.
Paterson, NJ 07524
(201) 278-8300

Penguin Industries
    (Hoppe's Products)
Airport Industrial Mall
Coatesville, PA 19320
(215) 384-6000

Triggers

Dayton-Traister Co.
4778 N. Monkey Hill Rd.
Oak Harbor, WA 98277
(206) 675-3421

Hastings
    (Rem. 1100 & 870)
P.O. Box 224
Clay Center, KS 67432
(913) 632-3169

Timney Mfg. Co.
3106 W. Thomas Rd.
Phoenix, AZ 85017
(602) 269-6937

Index